W9-BCC-443

The Psychiatrists

By the same author:

THE LABOR GOVERNMENT AND BRITISH INDUSTRY, 1945–51

THE JEW IN A GENTILE WORLD
(anthology)

JAMES FORRESTAL:
A Study of Personality, Politics, and Policy

POWER, CORRUPTION, AND RECTITUDE
(with H. D. Lasswell)

THE PSYCHIATRISTS

BY

Arnold A. Rogow

G. P. Putnam's Sons
New York

Library of Congress Catalog Card Number: 74-96210

PRINTED IN THE UNITED STATES OF AMERICA

To

GORDON N. RAY, PRESIDENT,

and the

John Simon Guggenheim Memorial Foundation

Contents

Preface

THIS book began as a study of the values of psychiatrists and psychoanalysts and the role of these values in psychotherapy. Of the many possible definitions of the term "values," the one chosen was "a conception, explicit or implicit, distinctive of an individual or characteristic of a group, of the desirable which influences the selection from available modes, means, and ends of action. It is thus not just a preference, a desire, but a formulation of the desirable, the 'ought' and 'should' standards which influence action." [1] My initial interest, in other words, was in what psychiatrists and psychoanalysts regarded as " 'ought' and 'should' standards" for themselves, their patients, their society, and the world. In searching through the available literature on the subject, I could find few studies that were not subjective, impressionistic, or based on a small number of interviews and questionnaires. It struck me as noteworthy, however, that all of the studies supported the hypothesis that values in the sense defined above can and do influence psychotherapy. As one study put it, "values do get communicated. The apparent relationship between value change and therapeutic change suggests that this may be a condition of successful treatment." [2]

As the study progressed through the early stages, it became clear that the question of values could not be considered apart from the nature, problems, and goals of psychiatry itself. Evidently the values of psychiatrists and psychoanalysts, and the use made of these values in therapy, reflected differences in personality, training, practice, and general outlook, not excluding views about morals, social issues, and politics. In its final form, therefore, the study took on the dimensions of a comprehensive inquiry into the scope, influence, and future of psychiatry in the United States; in essence, I was striving for a full-face and profile portrait of the American psychiatrist/psychoanalyst circa the late 1960's.

Since my own training involves political science rather than psychiatry, perhaps I should briefly explain my interest in the psychiatrist and his world. To begin with, I conceive of political science as a discipline embracing every institution that shapes values in society, because *ultimately politics in a democracy reflects values much more than it shapes them*. What Americans want, or think they want, from life ultimately determines what the executive and legislative branches—and even the courts—do in the policy-making field. We also have reason to believe, thanks to an increasing volume of research by psychologists, sociologists, and some political scientists, that the political process in a crucial sense begins in the home; that is, the business of becoming involved in politics is affected by the experiences and behavioral patterns that define childhood, adolescence, marriage, adulthood, and aging. The values that emerge from these experiences are central in shaping political views in the end, and it is the aggregation of these views that shapes the nation and, to a large extent, the international community.

Psychiatrists and psychoanalysts are important in this process because many of their patients are persons with important jobs in business, government, and the professions, education, the arts, literature, and sciences—and their wives and children. Since psychiatrists, and especially psychoanalysts, so often deal with people who are themselves influential, psychiatrists and psychoanalysts are strategically placed for shaping values at all levels of society. And this is quite apart from the fact that they are called upon increasingly to render presumably expert judgment on a large variety of economic, social, political, and world problems. Perhaps it is not too much to say that where the public once turned to the minister, or the captain of industry, or the historian, or the scientist, it is now turning more and more to the psychiatrist. But to this and related developments we shall return in due course.

On the assumption that psychiatrists and psychoanalysts are

influential figures in the life of the nation, in May, 1966, I distributed a detailed pretested questionnaire to a sample of members of the American Psychiatric Association and the American Psychoanalytic Association. The questionnaire was mailed to every thirtieth name in the directories of the Associations; the total number of questionnaires mailed was 490. About 30 of these could not be delivered because of the intended recipient's death or incorrect address. Of the remaining 460, 184 questionnaires were returned filled out (although not completely filled out in all cases), for a percentile return of 40.0. Members of the American Psychiatric Association accounted for 149 questionnaires; members of the American Psychoanalytic Association for 35.

While a response of 40 percent is regarded as above average for a mailed questionnaire requiring for completion at least one hour of work, the timing of the questionnaire was not auspicious. Two years earlier, a national magazine much given to shock-effect journalism had sent questionnaires to all psychiatrists in the country inquiring about the mental health of Senator Barry Goldwater, Republican Presidential candidate in 1964. The resulting uproar within and without psychiatric circles did not favor cooperation with any future effort to determine the profession's position on various issues, including politics. Fortunately, I was aided by a sympathetic news story about the study in the April, 1966, issue of *Psychiatric News,* official newspaper of the American Psychiatric Association, and by a column I wrote, "Roaming the Behavioral Sciences," which appeared in *Psychiatric News* in October, 1966.

The questionnaires were returned unsigned, to guarantee anonymity, except in those cases where respondents were also willing to be interviewed. Those who expressed such willingness totaled 71, distributed over twenty-five states and the District of Columbia. Eventually 38 interviews were conducted, all but one of them tape-recorded, averaging one hour each. I have informally questioned a number of past and present patients in therapy or analysis, but these are not the patients of the clinicians involved in the study. The book, then, is based on the questionnaires, the interviews, and the literature of psychiatry and psychoanalysis, as indicated by footnotes and references.

In distinguishing psychiatrists from psychoanalysts, a distinction made necessary by significant differences in training, theory, method, and approach to patients, I have relied on criteria devised by the two major professional associations. Hence, *for purposes of the present study,* psychiatrists and psychoanalysts are medical doctors who have had specialized training in the treatment of mental and behavioral disorders. A psychiatrist is a member of the American Psychiatric Association who, following graduation from medical school, has completed an approved residency in psychiatry, usually in a department of psychiatry, hospital, or clinic. A psychoanalyst, on the other hand, is a psychiatrist who has been accepted for membership in the American Psychoanalytic Association under standards established by the Association for the practice of psychoanalysis. In general, he is someone who has had a personal and/or training analysis and has taken specialized work in the theories and methods of psychoanalysis.

To avoid misunderstanding, I should like to make clear that not all psychiatrists with medical degrees belong to the American Psychiatric Association, and not all psychoanalysts with medical degrees belong to the American Psychoanalytic Association. A number of outstanding analysts have been trained in institutes not accredited by the American Psychoanalytic Association, such as the William Alanson White Institute of Psychiatry, the American Institute of Psychoanalysis, the Psychoanalytic Institute of the New York Medical College, and the psychoanalytic training facility of Tulane University. For the most part, analysts trained in these institutes are ineligible for membership in the American Psychoanalytic Association, and while many of them receive prominent mention in the following chapters, they are not included among the analysts who received questionnaires. The questionnaire, or study, group, however, does include analysts who belong to organizations not recognized by the American Psychoanalytic Association, of which the American Academy of Psychoanalysis is the most prominent; such dual membership is possible when an analyst has been trained in one of the Association's accredited institutes. The views of the various analytic "schools" or circles, therefore, are well represented, despite confinement of the questionnaire to Association members.

Psychiatrists in private practice usually see patients once or twice a week and are mainly interested in the contemporary day-to-day situation. They endeavor to relieve anxieties, clarify issues, promote insight, and increase confidence; as a rule, they try to be supportive in dealing with their patients' problems. Psychoanalysts, by contrast, may see patients in analysis three, four, or even five times each week, although this aspect is becoming less important as more and more analysts experiment with short-term analyses, fewer and shorter sessions per week, analyses the terminal dates of which are fixed in advance, and other innovations. Analysts also emphasize different material than the psychiatrists—for example, dreams, stream of consciousness and free association, childhood memories, sexual fantasies, and so forth. Usually in psychoanalysis the patient lies on a couch with the analyst seated behind him or to one side.

These distinctions do not mean that psychoanalysts do only psychoanalysis and psychiatrists do only psychotherapy. Many analysts have some patients in therapy, and many psychiatrists do some analysis. Further, there are psychoanalysts and psychotherapists who are not medical doctors but PhD's in psychology, sociology, or even philosophy and political science. Some psychotherapists have social work degrees—usually they hold a Master's degree—and an undetermined number of therapists have only a Bachelor's degree, or no degree at all. But this does not imply that the practice of psychoanalysis and psychiatry should be confined to medical doctors. There have been many distinguished clinicians who have not had medical training, notably, Bruno Bettelheim, Erik H. Erikson, Anna Freud, Erich Fromm, Ernst Kris, Rollo May, Theodor Reik, and Carl R. Rogers, among others.* Freud himself did not regard a medical degree as essential, and what he referred to as "the question of lay analysis" is still under discussion in psychoanalytic circles.

Clearly, I can make no claim that 184 psychoanalysts and psychiatrists, all of them doctors and members of the two leading professional associations, are representative of the entire psychiatric universe. The sample was not chosen by a procedure that produces a representative cross section, and it was further limited by the self-selection process inherent in the voluntary return of questionnaires. It is possible, however, that a larger sample would not have given significantly different results. In an effort to determine whether those who mailed back their questionnaires differed

* For identifications of leading psychiatrists and psychoanalysts, with special reference to those mentioned in the book, see Appendix I. A glossary of psychiatric and psychoanalytic terms appears as Appendix II.

in important ways from those who failed to return questionnaires, I sent a brief inquiry, also in questionnaire form, to the non-returnees. This further request for information produced 77 replies, the content of which suggests that there are more similarities than differences between the 184 respondents and those who did not return questionnaires. Detailed comparisons may be found in Chapter III.

But the most serious problem in a study of this sort arises from the simple fact that we do not have any reliable description of the "typical" psychoanalyst or "average" psychiatrist. Hence, there is no way of knowing to what degree the 184 respondents qualify or do not qualify as spokesmen for American psychiatry and psychoanalysis. Surveys now in progress, including studies sponsored or conducted by the National Institute of Mental Health (NIMH), no doubt will ultimately supply much-needed information about the mental health professions.

In the meantime, there is something to be said for the approximate, the tentative, and the suggestive, even if, ultimately, such formulations must give way to more definitive interpretations. Until then, those who are made restless, anxious, or critical by these qualifications would do well to recall that absolute facts, like absolute love, absolute virtue, and absolute truth, are difficult to come by and may be irrelevant to life's major concerns. As Justice Holmes once remarked, following a statement that he "hated" facts, "I always say the chief end of man is to form general propositions—adding that no general proposition is worth a damn." [3] While it is hoped that some of the propositions that follow are "worth a damn," there is no guarantee that Holmes was wrong, either with reference to the present study or any other study characterized, as such studies must be, by a limited understanding of man's behavior in a complex world.

I

The Crisis in American Psychiatry

IN reflecting on the role of psychiatrists in the United States, one is tempted to recall Winston Churchill's comment about the debt owed by the British to the pilots of the Royal Air Force in the early years of the Second World War. In a tribute to their steadfastness and heroism during the Battle of the Blitz of 1940–41, Churchill declared, with his customary eloquence, that "never have so many owed so much to so few."

A cynical veteran of the psychoanalytic couch—that is, someone who has been seeing an analyst three or four times a week for several years at a cost of many thousands of dollars—could be forgiven for suggesting that the remark was descriptive only of the financial relationship between psychiatrists and their patients. The present context of the quotation, however, is set by the fact that never before has the mental health of so many Americans been so dependent upon the ministrations of a relatively small number of psychiatrists and psychoanalysts. Approximately 20,000 psychiatrists, assisted by psychologists, social workers, nurses, and other technicians, are directly or indirectly responsible for the one-half million Americans who are confined to mental hospitals, with perhaps another half million in general hospitals and private clinics; one out of every two hospital beds is occupied by a mentally disturbed patient. In their role as part-time doctors and consultants to corporations, government, the armed forces, universities, labor unions, neighborhood mental health centers, and other agencies, the nation's psychiatrists also deal with a significant portion of the estimated 10 percent of Americans who are suffering from some form of mental illness. Approximately 1,000,000 persons visit psychiatrists each year, and while many receive some form of psychotherapy for a total of only a few hours, an impressive number spend an hour or more each week with their doctors over a period of many months or even years. About 11,000 Americans are undergoing psychoanalysis at any given time. Finally, psychiatrists and psychoanalysts are being called upon with increasing frequency to render public pronouncements on issues ranging from Vietnam to Haight-Ashbury.

Psychiatrists have long been consulted in criminal cases to aid in determinations of sanity, but it was not until the Presidential election of 1964 that they were asked to pass judgment on the sanity of one of the leading candidates for our highest political office—and more than 2,000 of them did render an opinion on the mental state of Barry Goldwater. Still other psychiatrists write regular columns for newspapers and magazines, such as *McCall's* and *Cosmopolitan*,[1] or appear frequently on television, as "experts" on the nation's sex life, race relations, and foreign policy. It is as if the public demanded of each psychiatrist that, like Francis Bacon, he take the whole world for his province.

But if, on the one hand, the psychiatrist is for many Americans a surrogate father, mother, rabbi, priest, minister, political leader, policy maker, and psychological soul brother, on the other hand, he is viewed by many of the same Americans with considerable suspicion and even hostility. Is psychiatry, they wonder, really a medical science, or is it a sham specialty or quackery that probably does more harm than good? Is the psychoanalyst a legitimate practitioner of mental theory, or is he the modern equivalent of the primitive witch doctor with his colleagues, the psychiatrists and psychiatric social workers, cast as sorcerer's apprentices? Was Freud himself truly that genius "who divined the famed riddle [of the Sphinx] and was a man most mighty," * or was he merely the first of the eminent "headshrinkers," the term itself redolent

* On Freud's fiftieth birthday in 1906, his Viennese colleagues presented him with a medallion, on one side of which was his profile and on the other the line quoted from Sophocles's *Oedipus Tyrannus*. According to Ernest Jones, "When Freud read the inscription he became pale and agitated" because as a student at the University of Vienna he had had the fantasy of seeing his bust among those of former famous professors with the identical inscription from Sophocles. In 1955 his bust with the inscription finally did find a place among the others. Ernest Jones, *The Life and Work of Sigmund Freud,* II (New York: Basic Books, 1955), 13–14.

of the dark and mysterious rites practiced by aboriginal peoples lost in the past?

Among intellectuals especially, many of whom have been in analysis or have been influenced by Freudian formulations, it has become increasingly the fashion in recent years to regard psychoanalysis as something of a fraud. Indeed, the evidence is overwhelming that psychoanalysis has long ceased to serve as the opiate of the intelligentsia. Thus, in the popular satire *America Hurrah: 3 Views of the U.S.A.,* by Jean-Claude van Itallie, which deals irreverently with television, employment agencies, motel life, and much else, there is one reference to psychoanalysis. One of the actors says:

> Hostile, blah
> Mother, blah
> Penis, blah
> Money, blah

Presumably, these four themes are what psychoanalysis is about. And in another setting, occasioned by the 1966 publication of *Thomas Woodrow Wilson,* by Freud and William Bullitt, a psychoanalytical study of the twenty-eighth President,[2] the novelist Vladmir Nabokov was gleeful that the book was receiving almost unanimously adverse reviews. Writing to the British magazine *Encounter* from his home in Switzerland, Nabokov commented: "I welcome Freud's *Woodrow Wilson* not only because of its comic appeal, which is great, but because that surely must be the last rusty nail in the Viennese Quack's coffin." [3]

It is a rare week when psychoanalysis is not referred to in one of the intellectual weeklies as, for example, "the high rhetoric of gossip," [4] or, in a reference to Thomas Mann's *The Magic Mountain,* as a type of "suffering which occasionally takes the form of being talked to death." [5] In a review of a book on the follies of medical history and "the pathetic credulity of multitudes in the face of the particular medical fad of the moment," the view is put forward, "Doubtless the psychiatrist's couch, mass produced on the American scale, will come in for a patronising smile in a generation or two. . . ." [6] Meanwhile, there is the "dreariness of a psychoanalytic approach to the arts," [7] and the lament that the intellectual capital of psychoanalysis has been depleted, evidenced by the fact that contemporary psychoanalysts cannot approach Freud either as thinkers or as writers.[8]

Although psychiatrists and analysts are no longer invariably depicted in cartoons as bald, bearded, owlish-looking, and speaking in a central European accent, the newer images are not always flattering. In a number of plays and movies, notably *The Girl in the Freudian Slip* and *The President's Analyst,* the psychiatrist is seen as the seducer, or would-be seducer, of attractive female patients and other pretty women—it is not unusual for the patient to be suffering from nymphomania—and, in addition, as a pimp and drug pusher (*The Line of Least Existence*). The psychiatrist-as-sexual-deviant makes an appearance in *What the Butler Saw,* and in *Lord Love a Duck* the female psychiatrist is shown as far more obsessed by sex than her patient. *The Impossible Years* portrays the psychiatrist as unable to cope with his own teen-age children, although he has written a book about adolescents and how to deal with them.

Nor is the psychiatrist in fiction, with a few exceptions, a more engaging figure. In Lawrence Durrell's *Tunc* (1968), a psychoanalyst, sexually aroused by a female patient's account of her amorous adventures, engages in masturbation. The psychiatrist in George Bishop's *The Psychiatrist* (1968) caresses his female patients in accordance with the principles of "affective touch therapy" and is also involved in a relationship with his daughter that has marked sexual overtones. In Leah Jacobs' *The Psychiatrist's Wife* (1966), the psychiatrist is engaged in an effort to make his wife psychotic, and Dariel Telfer's *The Caretakers* (1959), set in England, like almost all novels about mental hospitals since M. J. Ward's best-selling *The Snake Pit* of 1946, seeks to demonstrate that psychopathology in such hospitals is not confined to the patients. Without question, the most affirmative fictional portrait of a psychiatrist in recent years is Millen Brand's *Savage Sleep* (1968), but his book is less a novel than an idealized account of the life and career of psychiatrist John N. Rosen, advocate of psychoanalytic psychotherapy for schizophrenics.[9]

Nor are criticisms confined to intellectuals and literary figures. Many judges and lawyers complain about the interventions of psychiatrists in criminal cases, arguing that prosecution and defense lawyers rarely have trouble locating psychiatrists who will testify for and against the competence of the accused to stand trial. Perhaps the most dramatic recent example of the uses and abuses of psychiatric testimony occurred during the trial of Sirhan B. Sirhan, the assassin of Robert F. Kennedy. Several psychiatrists and clinical psychologists testifying for the defense agreed that Sirhan was too mentally disturbed to premeditate the murder of Kennedy; at least two of them referred to Sirhan as "a schizophrenic of the paranoid type." But those who appeared for the prosecution denied that the defendant was psychotic. According to psychiatrist Seymour Pollock, Sirhan had "no significant paranoid features, no significant deviations," although he was "tense, somewhat insecure, somewhat vulnerable, superstitious, fearful and withdrawn from close personal relationships." [10] Because of this and other examples of imprecise and conflicting psychiatric testimony in trials, it is to be expected that in many instances judges and jurors are more confused than enlightened by psychiatric judgments in criminal cases.*

Workers in the mental health field, including some psychiatrists, have taken issue with commitment procedures and the role of psychiatrists within mental institutions; and in universities, professors and students raise questions about the use made of psychiatric judgments in admissions, disciplinary actions, and job recommendations. And above all, there are those critics whose experience of psychiatry has been personal and direct: the thousands of patients and former patients who have spent large amounts of money in a futile quest for mental well-being and serenity. Almost everyone, whether patient or nonpatient, seems to know about the failures of analysis and therapy in the circle of friends and among the famous. Thus, it is almost common knowledge in literary

---

* Hence Karl Menninger's plea to the courts in his book *The Crime of Punishment* that "all psychiatrists be excluded from the courtroom! Put us all out and make us stay out. After you have tried the case, let us doctors and assistants examine him and confer together outside the courtroom and make a report to you which will express our view of the offender—his potentialities, his liabilities, and the possible remedies." The situation is further confused by recent modifications of the so-called McNaghten Rule, based on a British case in 1843, which holds that the legal test of sanity is knowing the difference between right and wrong. In California a death sentence can be averted if the defense can prove "diminished responsibility" on the part of the accused at the time the crime was committed. In 1967, New York declared in a penal law revision that "a person is not criminally responsible for conduct if at the time of such conduct, as a result of mental disease or defect, he lacks substantial capacity to know or appreciate either the nature and consequences of such conduct; or that such conduct was wrong." Quoted in the New York *Times,* March 10, 1969. Menninger's views are elaborated in a long interview in *Psychology Today,* February, 1969, 56–63.

circles that Zelda Fitzgerald, wife of the novelist, despite the renown of her analyst, Adolf Meyer, ended her days in a mental institution, and it appears that A. A. Brill, translator of Freud, was hardly more successful in treating the father of Frank Conroy.[11] Even the great Jung in 1913 was capable of telling Montagu Norman, head of the Bank of England from 1920 to 1944, that his illness was not manic-depression, which it probably was, but a "general paralysis of the insane, an incurable by-product of syphilis. . . ." [12] Virginia Woolf, also a victim of manic-depression and, finally, a suicide in the River Ouse, perhaps was beyond the help of any psychiatrist, but it is noteworthy that the last "famous Harley Street specialist" she and her husband consulted, "as he shook Virginia's hand, said to her: 'Equanimity, equanimity, practise equanimity, Mrs. Woolf.' " [13]

No wonder that psychiatrists are subjected to both serious and frivolous criticism, ridiculed, attacked, lampooned, burlesqued, mocked, and even given several pages in *Mad* magazine's "Psychoanalysis Primer" of which "Lesson 9" is devoted to Freud:

> Years ago, all Psychiatrists believed
> That Sigmund Freud was right.
> Freud theorized that the basis for all Neurosis
> Was sex.
> Everything with Freud was Sex, Sex, Sex.
> Today, we know that Freud was wrong.
> But we also know that Freud
> Must have been great fun at parties.
>
> Today, many Psychiatrists believe
> That Sex is only *part* of the problem.
> How small a part?
> How big a part?
> That all depends on how well you're making out!
> Today, "Love" rather than Sex is the theme.
> Today, people want to *Feel Loved.*
> Today, people want to *Express Love.*
> Doesn't that make you yearn
> For the good old days? *

* *Mad,* July, 1967, 35. Other "Lessons" deal with "Choosing a Psychiatrist," "Types of Patients," "The Psychiatric Consultation," and "Group Therapy," among other topics, in a generally good-natured manner. Jokes and cartoons making fun of psychiatry abound, of course. Many of them concern the theme that in psychiatry

If criticism of psychiatry were confined to persons outside the profession, it perhaps could be explained in terms of the inevitable disappointment of grandiose expectations, and in fact, there is much evidence that psychiatry has been oversold in America as both therapy and panacea. Analysts and their sympathizers might suggest that the critics were mainly disgruntled patients who had been inadequately analyzed themselves, or those whose transference problems had not been successfully resolved, and indeed there are tendencies within certain psychoanalytic circles to regard critics within and without the profession as disturbed types. Unfortunately for these efforts to account for criticism, psychoanalysts and psychiatrists themselves have become increasingly skeptical about the goals, methods, and achievements of their professions. Never before has there been so much collective soul-searching and self-examination, so much questioning of theory and technique, so much discussion of principles, problems, and policies. Indeed, it is not exaggerating too much to say that psychiatry and psychoanalysis in the United States are undergoing an identity crisis, to borrow a term from Erik Erikson, that is, a crisis of doubt and uncertainty about the present status and future direction of the profession.

The identity crisis is particularly acute in psychoanalysis, where, in some discussions at least, the possibility is mentioned that psychoanalysis as such may not have a future. Despite "pretentious affirmations to the contrary," writes O. H. Mowrer, "the fact is that psychoanalysis, on which modern psychiatry is largely based, is in a state of virtual collapse and imminent demise." [14] According to another influential critic, there has been no important progress in psychoanalytic theory since 1930 or even before. "Ego psychology not withstanding," notes psychoanalyst Abram Kardiner, "the Freudian frame of reference has yielded no new information, only exegesis," and is in grave danger of becoming irrelevant to other behavioral sciences. "Is it of value to us to know," asks Kardiner, "that the Sioux child has a sense of

any behavior can be "analyzed" to the point of absurdity, as in the joke about the young lady who obtained a job as a receptionist for an analyst, only to quit after a few weeks. Asked why she had quit, she explained that in dealing with an analyst one can never win. "If I came to work late, it was because I was hostile. If I came early, I was anxious. If I arrived on time, I was compulsive." The point of the story, suggesting that in the psychiatric transaction it is the therapist and not the patient who wins every time, is a popular one.

guilt about the aggressive reactions provoked by his weaning trauma, and then lives it out in a religious ritual of the Sun Dance? This is a sample of the kind of information yielded by reductionist methods. If this is all psychoanalysis can say to social science, we cannot blame the latter for ignoring it." [15] There can be little question, observes Theodore Lidz, that while psychoanalysis, which replaced psychobiology, "brought such notable advances, we find that its leadership has faltered and now virtually halted. There have been few significant advances in recent years." [16]

The failure to advance, in the view of some analysts, is due in part to the "parochial behavior of the various training institutes." [17] The tendency of their members, writes Roy R. Grinker, Sr., is "to consider abandoned concepts as integral parts of their field instead of viewing them in historical perspective. The outstanding evidence for this view is the pedagogical attitude in the psychoanalytic Institutes where chronological ordering of Freud's writings seems more important than emphasis on shifting concepts." [18] Elsewhere Grinker laments: "Psychoanalysis, for which many have sacrificed so much, has not become the therapeutic answer; it seems to be mired in a theoretical rut vigilantly guarded by the orthodox and, except for relatively few examples, prevented from commingling with science." [19]

The problem with new ideas and approaches, comments an analyst from the study group,*

> is that they make us anxious, make us wonder whether we were on the right track before. And there's also the American scene when psychoanalysis was introduced in this country. At that time there was very little research, boredom with the existing classifications, and no proven methods of doing therapy. So people went overboard for psychoanalysis, and at first there was a gratifying pioneering spirit. But gradually what was loose and relaxed became rigidified. More and more centralized authority went to the American Psychoanalytic Association, which made rules and regulations each institute had to follow. You had to accept what your teachers taught you—or you weren't fitted to be an analyst.

---

* Psychiatrists and analysts identified as members of the study group and/or not named are among those who filled out questionnaires and were interviewed.

> The early atmosphere—that we're on to something new, we've got something different, people don't like the emphasis on sexuality but we gather strength from the fact we know what we're doing, and so forth—became bastardized into "we're isolated, we have lots of enemies, we won't accept other attitudes, we don't even like people to come to our meetings and discuss things." But it's changing. . . .

Echoing Grinker, Lawrence S. Kubie comments that even deviant theories eventually rigidify and become change-resistant. Declaring that he has "yet to find a heterodox analyst of any so-called 'school,' " Kubie observes that "each deviant tends to create his own orthodoxy and ultimately to become his own Messiah, whether this be Freudian, Jungian, Rankian, Horneyian, Kleinian, Sullivanian, or the Rado-Kardiner-Levy axis at Columbia. Each group tends all too rapidly to become formula-ridden and hide-bound. Each develops a tendency to outlaw the data and the theories from other schools, and to view them with angry rejection and suspicion." Freud himself, Kubie continues, was an exception in that he was continually criticizing, altering, and changing his own theories, but only a partial exception because "we cannot say that Freud welcomed the heterodoxies of others with equal hospitality." [20]

Other criticisms stress the methodological inadequacies in psychoanalysis, and certainly there can be no challenging of the view that little is known about factors that lead to success and failure in treating patients or what makes and does not make an effective analyst. Frequently, it is pointed out as a major weakness how much theory rests on a single case history, or at most a few case histories, which may or may not have been adequately explored; there is no practical way by which the findings of one analyst in a given case can be tested by another since, unlike conditions in the sciences, the precise circumstances of the analyst, his patient, their transactions, and the time-space continuum of their relationship cannot be exactly replicated by any other analyst.[21] The selection of disease models or examples in psychoanalysis, which may reflect the preferences and problems of the analyst rather than any sample population for the particular problem dealt with, is often the basis for far-reaching generalizations that may not deserve support. As one observer has remarked:

> Freud used hysteria as the model for his therapeutic method, depression as the basis for his later theoretical conjectures. Adler's clinical demonstrations are rivalrous, ineffective, immature character types. Jung's examples were restricted to a weary, worldly, successful, middle-aged group. Rank focused upon the conflicted, frustrated, rebellious artist aspirant. Fromm's model is the man in a white collar searching for his individuality. And Sullivan's example of choice is the young catatonic schizophrenic.[22]

It also has been remarked that some of Freud's most influential theories do not derive from patients he had in analysis. His *Analysis of a Phobia in a Five-Year-Old Boy,* better known as the Case of Little Hans, was based on conversations with Little Hans' father, who conducted his son's analysis; Freud apparently saw the boy only once. Freud's concept of the relationship between paranoia and repressed homosexuality, a concept still supported by orthodox psychoanalysts, originated from his reading in 1910 of the memoirs of a German judge, Daniel Paul Schreber, whom he never met.[23]

Still others are critical of psychoanalysis because of its confinement to those relatively few Americans whose income, occupations, and education afford them the time and money for analysis. Available information suggests that the average complete psychoanalysis totals between 700 and 800 hours at a cost of $25 to $35 per hour. Taking the lowest figures, a completed analysis will cost at least $17,500 over a period of three or four years. Little need to labor the point that, as one critic has put it, "Psychoanalysis, quite obviously, is for the few, and it offers little hope to the masses," [24] whether or not it is also true, in the words of another, that the gravity center of psychiatry as a whole is "cream puff psychiatry" or the "private practice of psychotherapy in plush downtown offices with financially secure individuals suffering mainly from boredom or the stresses and strains of frantic pleasure-seeking." [25]

Finally, the question has been raised whether psychoanalysis even for analysts provides the needed answers and solutions, whether, in fact, psychoanalysis works for the analysts themselves. What is the point of it all, asks psychoanalyst Allen Wheelis in "To Be a God": ". . . work a little harder, make more money, children off to college, freedom then and the world tour, back and more work, weddings and thrown bouquets, and then the coronary. Is this the way to live?" [26]

Similar if not identical questions and criticisms have been leveled at psychiatry as well. An increasing number of practitioners have begun to entertain the view that most mental illness is the result of biochemical or neurophysiological disturbances, from which it follows that the "50-minute hour," if efficacious at all, is efficacious only for those suffering from mild and relatively minor neuroses. Even these problems, some believe, will yield in time to improved forms of tranquilizers and other drugs, thus consigning therapy to the museum of medical antiquities.[27] Other critics, doubting that psychotherapy should be the preferred treatment in any circumstance, argue that most neurotics appear to recover spontaneously whether they are treated or not,[28] and still others, known as behavior therapists, feel that the future is in the direction of treating neuroses as habits acquired by learning or conditioning that can be got rid of by processes of un-learning and un-conditioning.[29] A large number of psychiatrists note the lack of scientific method in treatment and research, a lack reflected in the extreme faultiness of psychiatric screening techniques. Thus, in one study of such techniques with reference to more than 100,000 men constituting the entire population at all induction centers in the United States, the proportions rejected on psychiatric grounds varied from 0.5 percent at one induction station to 50.6 percent at another, although the test scores had much the same frequency distribution.[30]

Psychiatric predictions of unsatisfactory military performance have also been extremely unreliable. During World War II and the Korean War, for example, predictions made on large numbers of soldiers were 90 percent correct with reference to satisfactory service, but only 25 percent correct for unsatisfactory service. Although it is possible, as was claimed by psychiatrists who evaluated the results, that the unexpected satisfactory performances derived from such situational circumstances as leadership and good unit morale, the implications of such a finding for psychotherapy have not been thoroughly explored.[31] In more recent studies of psychiatric screening of Peace Corps volunteers, it was found that the performances of the Peace Corps workers "bore no relations to the predictions of a team of psychiatrists who had rated them before they left [for Ghana]." [32] Another study of Peace Corps volunteers disclosed that when psychiatrists predicted serious interference with effective functioning, they were "impressively accurate" where they had found substantial amounts of illness. When they did not find substantial amounts of illness, however, and "made judgments purely on the basis of ego strengths, the quality of object relationships, the motivational system, and the cognitive capabilities of the volunteers, their predictions about effective functioning were barely better than chance."[33] *

Still others are critical of psychiatry's conceptual as well as terminological confusion. A 1959 handbook, since reprinted many times, is titled *Psychoanalysis and Psychotherapy: 36 Systems,* and since it was first published, as someone remarked, at least ten additional "systems" have made an appearance, with more on the way.[34]

In recent years the training of psychiatrists has received much critical discussion from varying points of view, with some critics favoring closer ties to general medicine,[35] others stressing the need to expose psychiatric residents to the methodologies of science,[36] and still others emphasizing the importance of the social sciences in psychiatric curriculum. A small but influential number of psychiatrists are experimenting with computers in the belief that certain kinds of patient data can be fed into computers, thus making it possible for them to diagnose and to some extent treat many types of mental illness currently handled by clinicians.[37]

Some of the most serious charges leveled at psychiatry involve allegations of conservatism, conformity, parochialism, and "brainwashing" disguised as objective therapy and mental health. Bruno M. Bettelheim, for example, has suggested that "psychiatrists are a rather conservative group who avoid not only radical

---

* According to Admiral Hyman G. Rickover, who has long been critical of the social sciences, psychiatry, and the Department of Defense, psychiatric study of West Point cadets who failed in their first year at West Point has been no more successful than the screening of Peace Corps candidates. The study as reported by Rickover suggested that cadets who identified with the male role and who had greater "acceptance, support, and love from their mothers did well," whereas "those who were not close to their fathers and who didn't admire them and whose mothers were overprotective and domineering could not take the rigors of West Point. On the basis of this study, I doubt that Alexander the Great, Hannibal, Julius Caesar, Napoleon, George Washington, John Paul Jones, Stephen Decatur, U. S. Grant, or David Farragut could have made the grade at West Point." Quoted in *Psychiatric News,* September, 1968. Of course, those mentioned by Rickover neither confirm nor deny the study of first-year cadets at West Point.

solutions, but even a radical analysis of the problem." [38] Frank Riessman and S. M. Miller have accused psychiatrists of retreating from "broad social change and passionate political involvement" in favor of "professional parochialism," prestige considerations, and infatuation with method.[39] Robert Coles warns against "the carefully well adjusted and certified . . . Organization Men in psychiatry. . . . We try to hide behind our couches, hide ourselves from our patients. In doing so we prolong the very isolation often responsible for our patients' troubles. . . ." [40] Coles and others have commented on "man's ability to brutalize people by labeling them 'sick,' " the theme of a number of novels about mental hospitals, including Valeriĭ Tarsis' *Ward 7* and Ken Kesey's *One Flew Over the Cuckoo's Nest*.[41]

Ethical problems, dilemmas, and mistakes frequently plague individual psychiatrists and the professional organizations. In 1964 and 1968, despite the opposition of the American Psychiatric Association, approximately 2,000 psychiatrists were willing to pass judgment on the mental health of Senator Barry Goldwater and President Johnson, for the benefit of a magazine exposé. Although Defense Department regulations prohibit the release of medical information without the consent of the person concerned, detailed reports alleging that New Orleans District Attorney James C. Garrison and Alabama Governor George Wallace had been discharged from the Army because of psychoneurosis were "leaked" to newspapers in 1967 and 1968. Following the marriage of Jacqueline Kennedy and Aristotle Onassis in 1968, three psychiatrists, in a newspaper article headed "Three Psychiatric Experts Tell . . . Why Jackie Married Onassis . . . and How It Will Affect Her Children," were quoted as saying, in part, that "Jackie is emotionally immature; her sexual needs are not as strong as many women her age, and she wanted a father figure for herself rather than a husband and lover." * Nor was respect for psychiatrists increased when it became apparent that a clinical psychologist appearing for the defense in the Sirhan trial had used

* The article, published in the *National Enquirer,* drew an angry response from C. H. Hardin Branch, chairman of the APA's Ethics Committee. Branch, in an editorial in *Psychiatric News,* castigated the unnamed "Psychiatric Experts," two of whom were APA members, but noted sadly: "It is impossible for the ethics committee to deal appropriately with matters of this sort. . . . I know of no way in which scientific objectivity, common sense, good manners, and good taste can be legislated." *Psychiatric News,* January, 1969.

language in his testimony characterized by "a series of striking similarities" with that of a case study in a book by a New York psychiatrist. Unfortunately for the good name of American psychiatry, most of the public does not distinguish between psychiatrists and psychologists, especially when the latter practice psychotherapy and in other respects resemble their medical counterparts.[42]

Of all critics of psychiatry in recent years, Thomas S. Szasz is undoubtedly the best-known, and he has also aroused the most controversy. A member of the American Psychoanalytic Association since 1952, Szasz has attacked psychoanalysis and psychiatry at their roots by arguing, in a number of books and articles, that mental illness, with the exception of certain organic diseases, is itself a myth, and that therefore psychiatry is far more related to moral philosophy and social theory than to medicine. According to Szasz:

> Clearly, psychiatry is much more related to problems of ethics than is medicine. I used the word "psychiatry" here to refer to the contemporary discipline concerned with problems in living. . . . Accordingly, the psychiatrist's socio-ethical orientations will influence his ideas on what is wrong with the patient, on what deserves comment or interpretation, in what directions change might be desirable, and so forth. . . . Can anyone really believe that a psychotherapist's ideas on religion, politics, and related issues play no role in his practical work? If, on the other hand, they do matter, what are we to infer from it? Does it not seem reasonable that perhaps we ought to have different psychiatric therapies —each recognized for the ethical positions which it embodies— for, say, Catholics and Jews, religious persons and atheists, democrats and Communists, white supremacists and Negroes, and so on? [43]

Szasz has also criticized his fellow psychiatrists for their role in courts and university health services,[44] and he has argued that the influence of the psychiatrist as "moral legislator and social engineer" is to deprive man of his liberty by taking from him his "moral burdens" and choices, that is, his "liberty and hence his very humanity." [45] Moreover, unlike other *enfants terribles* within the profession, Szasz has given wide circulation to his views by publishing them in a large number of popular periodicals, including the *New York Times Magazine, National Review,* and *Harper's.**

Like other professionals, psychiatrists are loath to have allegedly soiled laundry exposed to public view, and they are inclined to defend themselves in ways that are not much different from those utilized by politicians, captains of industry, labor leaders, and other occasional targets of censure. Thus, there has been less discussion of the issues raised by Szasz than of the fact that "Szasz's opinions are now distributed along with Robert Welch's *Life of John Birch* by the Defenders of American Liberties, headed by a former McCarthy committee counsel, Robert Morris. The anti-mental health movement, with a potential membership of 26½ million Goldwater voters, finds confirmation of its views in Thomas Szasz." [46] With reference to Coles, writes one counter-critic, "one wonders whether the psychiatric critic of psychiatry like Dr. Coles is really a religious or political reformer who has confused the microcosm with the macrocosm," and, as regards Wheelis, " 'To Be a God' is more psychopathological than just a literary essay in quiet desperation." [47]

* In his writings that deal with the role of psychiatrists in political or quasi-political trials, Szasz has expressed opinions that are widely shared in the profession. Thus, a number of those critical of the use of psychiatrists in the Ezra Pound case, a *cause célèbre* with Szasz, have pointed out that the four psychiatrists who declared Pound mentally incompetent to stand trial for treason either did not make an exhaustive investigation of his condition or wrongly chose not to make public what they had found. Their *entire* report was as follows:

> The defendant, now 60 years of age and in generally good physical condition, was a precocious student, specializing in literature. He has been a voluntary expatriate for nearly 40 years, living in England and France, and for the past 21 years in Italy, making an uncertain living by writing poetry and criticism. His poetry and literary criticism have achieved considerable recognition, but of recent years his preoccupation with monetary theories and economics had apparently obstructed his literary productivity. He has long been recognized as eccentric, querulous, and egocentric.
>
> At the present time he exhibits extremely poor judgment as to his situation, its seriousness and the manner in which the charges are to be met. He insists that his broadcasts were not treasonable, but that all of his radio activities have stemmed from his self appointed mission to "save the Constitution." He is abnormally grandiose, is expansive and exuberant in manner, exhibiting pressure of speech, discursiveness, and distractibility.
>
> In our opinion, with advancing years his personality, for many years abnormal, has undergone further distortion to the extent that he is now suffering from a paranoid state which renders him mentally unfit to advise properly with counsel or to participate intelligently and reasonably in his own defense. He is, in other words, insane and mentally unfit for trial, and is in need of care in a mental hospital.

Quoted in Fredric Wertham, "The Road to Rapallo: A Psychiatric Study," *American Journal of Psychotherapy,* 3, 4 (October, 1949), 595.

Whatever the merits or demerits of these criticisms of the critics, there can be little doubt that the current mood of American psychiatry and psychoanalysis is chastened and introspective, even if, at times, that mood is also angry and resentful. When it is further asserted, particularly by way of statistics rather than flat statements, that psychiatry and especially psychoanalysis are being deserted by the brighter medical students, or that the rates of suicide, alcoholism, divorce, and disturbed offspring are higher in psychiatry than in other professions, or that the proportion of those cured of serious mental illness is no greater today than in the eighteenth century, the professional insecurity and anxiety even of those who are most secure and least anxious in their personal lives is apt to increase sharply. Many psychiatrists, including those who are most given to professional self-examination, find it ironic that in the seventh decade of the century, when so much has been achieved by their profession, so much more should be demanded and that, in some respects, attitudes toward psychiatry, especially psychoanalysis, of the public and of other doctors have changed very little since the early days of Freud. While no major critic is echoing the dean of the University of Toronto who in 1910 accused Freud of advocating "free love, removal of all restraints, and a relapse into savagery," neither is anyone repeating William James in telling analysts that the "future of psychology belongs to your work." [48]

What, then, *is* the future of psychiatry and psychoanalysis? In the direction of scientific method and more effective use of computers? Toward social and community psychiatry and more relevance to the problems of war, race, poverty? Closer ties with general medicine and increasing interest in biochemistry and neurophysiology? And within the practice area, do the signs point toward more or less use of behavior-control drugs, more or less private practice, more or less group psychotherapy, more or less experimentation with newer therapies based on drama, music, poetry, "sensory awakening," "sensitivity training," and the role of psychedelic chemical agents such as LSD? If these questions are difficult and admit to no certain answers, they are no more difficult than questions facing other professions, groups, and classes who have reached a critical crossroads in history. For psychiatrists, as for all others who are searching for bearings amid the confusions of the age, the essential question in its simplest terms is: Which way is up?

II

Profile of a Profession

PSYCHIATRY, unlike psychoanalysis, did not begin in the twentieth century, but its influence and eminence are of relatively recent origin. If we view 1844, the founding year of what later became the American Psychiatric Association, as the official birthdate of American psychiatry,* it is possible to suggest that psychiatry did not come of age until World War II, when, quite apart from its usefulness in the war, psychiatry became an accepted part of the American scene and even achieved a certain fashionableness. Since this development owes so much to the impact upon psychiatry of Freudian psychoanalysis—one is tempted to credit Freud with both the birth of psychoanalysis and the rebirth of psychiatry—it is conceivable that psychiatry without psychoanalysis would have taken quite a different direction, perhaps back toward the mental hospital from which it emerged more than a century ago, or toward an easier synthesis with other behavioral sciences. For it is clear that the broad acceptance of psychiatry relates not only to a rising incidence of mental distress but to the prestige of psychoanalysis, the principles of which transformed the nature of psychiatric training, practice, and research. Whatever the future holds, the growth patterns of psy-

* There were, of course, psychiatrists in America before 1844. The physician and signer of the Declaration of Independence Benjamin Rush (1746–1813) is commonly regarded as the founding father of American psychiatry, and his portrait appears on the official seal of the APA. Rush was an enthusiast for such dubious practices as bleeding and purging—it is possible that his heavy reliance on the former dispatched George Washington before his time—but in treating the mentally ill he anticipated some of the theories and techniques associated with the behavior therapists, especially their emphasis on curing neurosis through "reciprocal inhibition." For a perceptive study of Rush and his times by a biographer who is himself a psychoanalyst, see Carl Binger, *Revolutionary Doctor: Benjamin Rush, 1746–1813* (New York: Norton, 1966).

chiatry and psychoanalysis have been remarkably similar, and they face somewhat similar problems with respect to orientation and direction.

During the first one hundred years, most psychiatrists were employed in or attached to mental hospitals (this is still the case in Great Britain and many foreign countries), and their total number remained small. Founded in 1844 by 13 physicians who were mental hospital superintendents, what was then called the Association of Medical Superintendents of American Institutions for the Insane had fewer than 200 members as late as 1890. Perhaps a change of name in 1892 to American Medico-Psychological Association aided growth in accordance with the modern notion that what matters is the "image"; at any rate, by 1910 membership reached almost 500, and in the next decade it doubled to approximately 1,000. It is of interest that the words "psychiatry" and "psychiatric," although in professional use, were rejected for organization title purposes, apparently because of ambiguities in meaning, and it was not until 1921 that the American Medico-Psychological Association became the American Psychiatric Association (APA).*

By 1930, membership in the APA had reached 1,346; by 1940, ten years later, it had almost doubled again, reaching a total of 2,423. From 1940 to 1950, expansion was extremely rapid, with the annual growth rate—that is, rate of membership increase—averaging an unprecedented 9.2 percent each year. In the decade ending in 1950, membership more than doubled, reaching a total of 5,856, and ten years later the membership figure had grown to 11,637, although the annual growth rate had decreased to 7.1 percent. In 1969, there were approximately 17,000 members, representing 74 percent of the estimated 23,000 psychiatrists in the United States.† NIMH projected membership for the APA is between 18,300 and 20,600 members and between 5,300 and 6,100 residents (physicians in training to be psychiatrists) by 1975. Perhaps the combined total of members, nonmember psychiatrists, and residents will approximate 26,700 by 1975.[1]

Whereas the proportion of physicians in the population has

* The British equivalent of the APA continues as the Royal Medico-Psychological Association, affiliated with the Royal College of Physicians and Surgeons. Efforts are under way to establish independent status for British psychiatrists and an organizational structure similar to that of the APA.

† In 1968, about 6,500 psychiatrists did not belong to the APA.

American Psychiatric Association Organization Chart

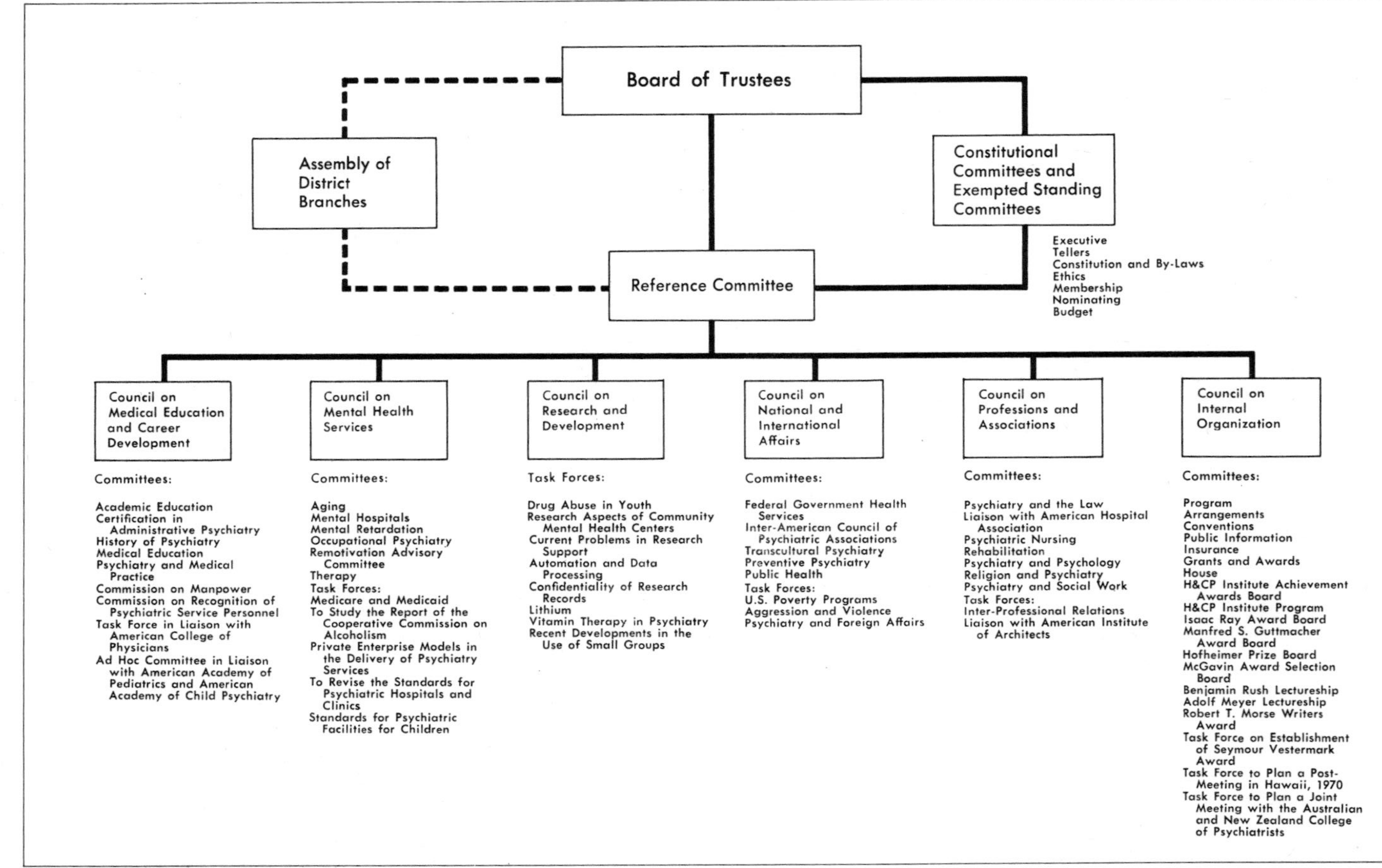

Table 2. Growth Characteristics of APA Membership*

Year	*APA members per million population*	*Percentage APA members in physician population*
1930	10.9	0.9 (1931)
1940	18.3	1.4
1950	38.5	2.6 (1949)
1960	64.4	4.8

* John Romano, "Twenty-five Years of University Department Chairmanship," *American Journal of Psychiatry Supplement*, June, 1966 pp. 13–14.

been declining for some years, the proportion of psychiatrists both within the population and within the medical profession has been increasing since 1930. As Table 2 shows, the growth of psychiatry in terms of APA membership has more than kept pace with population increase.

At the present time, psychiatrists constitute 5 percent of all physicians in private practice (in New York City the figure reaches 12 percent).[2]

Like many organizations, the APA has different categories of membership. All members other than certain classes of fellows must be physicians who have had psychiatric training or experience. About 50 percent of members are General Members—that is, psychiatrists who have had at least three years of acceptable training or experience in psychiatry. Associate Members are physicians who have not completed their residencies and are not in training but who have had at least one year of full-time training or experience in psychiatry. Members in Training are psychiatric residents who have completed one year of training (such membership is limited to five years). Fellows are those who have been General Members for at least five years and who have made a significant contribution to psychiatry, and Distinguished Fellows are physicians or other scientists who, while not members of the APA, have made distinguished contributions to psychiatry or related sciences. Honorary Fellows are nonphysicians who have rendered "signal service" in the promotion of mental health and psychiatry.*

* In 1969 there were 19 Distinguished Fellows and 29 Honorary Fellows, the latter including Judges David L. Bazelon and John Biggs, Jr., Senator Lister Hill, Urban Coalition head John W. Gardner, and Anna Freud.

Annual meetings of the APA, usually held in May and lasting four and a half days, attract a large proportion of the membership and their wives (or husbands). The 1967 annual meeting, for example, drew some 6,360 APA members and their families to Detroit for a variety of activities including the presentation of 261 papers, therapeutic workshops, closed-circuit television programs usually presented early in the morning and late at night and available in hotel rooms, breakfast seminars, and evening panels. The convocation of the meeting was presided over by the Right Reverend Richard S. Emrich, Episcopal Bishop of Detroit. There was a presentation by the American Conservatory Theater of Samuel Beckett's *Endgame* and Edward Albee's *The American Dream*, followed by a discussion, an art show of works by APA members, and a "jam session" featuring APA musicians. The annual banquet saw the return engagement of Guy Lombardo and His Royal Canadians ("Dancing from 9 P.M. to 1 A.M."). Tours "For Members and Guests" were scheduled to the Department of Psychiatry of the University of Michigan, the Research Division of the Lafayette Institute, General Motors, and the Ford Motor Company's Rouge Plant. "For the Ladies" there were tours to the Ford Rouge Plant (but on a different day than the tour set for "Members and Guests"), Henry Ford Museum, Greenfield Village, Detroit's Institute of Arts, and Windsor, Canada. In view of this schedule, and the fact that three-day meetings of both the American Psychoanalytic Association and the American Academy of Psychoanalysis immediately preceded the APA convention, it is not to be wondered that there was a first-aid station in the exhibit area with "resident physicians from the city hospital . . . on duty at all times."

Psychiatrists also belong to and attend meetings of other psychiatric organizations. The World Federation for Mental Health (WFMH) has among its members more than two dozen American organizations in the mental health area, including such specialized associations as the Academy of Religion and Mental Health, American Society for Adlerian Psychology, and the American Society for Clinical Hypnosis. Not listed among WFMH members are the American Ontoanalytic Association (for existential psychiatry), the Society for Biological Psychiatry, and the Association for Research in Nervous and Mental Disease. It is not unusual for psychiatrists to belong to one or more organizations in addition to the APA, not including the World Psychiatric Association, to which they are affiliated as APA members.*

Of these supplementary organizations the most important are the American Orthopsychiatric Association (AOA) and the Group for the Advancement of Psychiatry (GAP). Founded in 1924 by nine psychiatrists, among whom the best-known was Karl Menninger, AOA promotes a multi disciplinary approach to problems of mental illness which, if not treated, can become acute (the term *orthopsychiatry* should be broadly understood to mean preventive psychiatry). By 1967 its membership had reached 2,700, made up of 983 psychiatrists, 648 psychologists, 891 social workers, and 199 social scientists, educators, lawyers, nurses, and pediatricians. The *American Journal of Orthopsychiatry*, official publication of the AOA, is published five times each year and reaches 8,000 subscribers in all parts of the world.

Like AOA, the Group for the Advancement of Psychiatry, founded in 1946, originated as a "Young Turk" effort to broaden the horizons of American psychiatry, at least as those horizons were viewed by the leadership of the APA. Karl Menninger, together with his brother William and thirteen other psychiatrists, was again influential, although with GAP the initial focus was the inadequacies and shortcomings of psychiatric treatment that were demonstrated on both the military and civilian fronts during World War II. Primarily a research organization, GAP, whose membership has never exceeded 200, operates through twenty-one working committees specializing in such fields as public education, government agencies, international relations, aging, and college students, in addition to more conventional psychiatric research areas. GAP's more than sixty published reports in these fields—it does not sponsor a journal—have been influential in many public policy areas, including civil rights, sexual behavior on college campuses, and nuclear disarmament.[3]

As may be expected, the geographical distribution of both

* The World Psychiatric Association, mainly an association of member societies, had 67 organization members in 1968, to which between 40,000 and 50,000 psychiatrists belonged. In 1964 it established a category of individual members. The U.S.S.R., with 21,000 members in its All Union Society of Psychiatrists (9,000 psychiatrists and 12,000 neurologists), has the largest national psychiatric organization, and Japan, with 3,000 psychiatrists, is not unimportant. All of Black Africa, at the other extreme, contains 16 psychiatrists; Nigeria, for example, has a total of two.

psychiatrists and psychoanalysts is grossly uneven. There are psychiatrists in each of the fifty states, although the ten most populous states account for about two-thirds of the total. More than half of all psychiatrists live in New York, California, Illinois, Massachusetts, and Pennsylvania, although these states have less than a third of the population. Almost 4,000 psychiatrists live and work in New York State, 3,000 of whom are located in the five boroughs of New York City (approximately one-third of New York City's psychiatrists are in full-time private practice, the remainder being engaged in part-time private practice or attached to hospitals, clinics, and medical schools).[4] Many of the estimated 600 Negro psychiatrists in the United States, or less than 3 percent of the total psychiatric population, reside in New York City.*

At the end of 1966 it was estimated that almost 50 percent of the nation's psychiatrists were engaged in private practice as their major professional activity, and almost a quarter were full-time hospital staff members.[5] Most of the latter are employed in public mental hospitals; a study released in 1966 reported that 149 of an estimated 165 to 170 private mental hospitals had 533 full-time psychiatrists on their attending staffs.[6] Psychiatry departments of 78 medical schools in 1965–66 employed 1,443 full-time faculty members, but perhaps a third of these are nonpsychiatric physicians and behavioral scientists (physiologists, sociologists, psychologists, etc.).[7] Almost 2,000 psychiatrists work for the federal government, more than half of the total in the Veterans Administration.[8] The remaining number of psychiatrists are in administration or full-time research.

The counterpart of the APA in the psychoanalytic world is the American Psychoanalytic Association (APsaA). From a membership of 92 in 1932, the APsaA included 192 analysts by 1940, and twenty years later, in 1960, membership totaled approximately 1,000. There were an estimated 1,289 members at the end of 1968, or roughly one analyst for every 13 psychiatrists who were members of the APA. The ratio of analysts to population was one for every 167,000 persons.

---

* According to psychiatrists Chester M. Pierce and Alvin F. Poussaint, "perhaps 300 are members" of the APA. *Medical Tribune,* May 29, 1969. It is also of interest that in 1962 there were approximately 3,800 Negro physicians, constituting a ratio of 20 per 100,000 population. The ratio of white physicians, by contrast, was 132 per 100,000 population. Current estimates suggest that Negro physicians account for 2.2 percent of the total number of physicians.

Unlike the APA, the American Psychoanalytic Association has only Members or Honorary Members,* although some of the local societies have created additional membership categories, including Accredited Members, Guest Members, Affiliate Members, Non-Therapeutic Affiliate Members, Non-Therapist Members, Corresponding Associate Members, Corresponding Non-Therapeutic Affiliate Members, Special Members, Research Affiliate Members, and Life Members. In 1968–69, there were six Honorary Members of the national body of whom the best-known was Anna Freud. Miss Freud was also an Honorary Member of the Boston, Cleveland, Detroit, New York, San Francisco, Topeka, and Western New England psychoanalytic societies, and the Philadelphia Association for Psychoanalysis. Erik H. Erikson, although not a physician, was a Member of the American Psychoanalytic Association and Western New England Psychoanalytic Society and an Honorary Member of the Pittsburgh and San Francisco societies.

In 1968–69 there were no psychoanalysts in sixteen states,† and only one in each of six states.** In effect, psychoanalytic subculture in the United States is concentrated in six population centers, but even among these the distribution is far from even. As Table 3 shows, Beverly Hills has more analysts than Los Angeles, and New York City almost one quarter of all analysts in the United States; in fact, since there are more analysts in New York than in any European country,‡ New York has fair claim to being the world capital of psychoanalysis.

The six population centers, with their 742 psychoanalysts, account for almost 58 percent of the American Psychoanalytic Association membership.

Organized psychoanalysis in America began in 1911 with the founding of the New York Psychoanalytic Society and the Ameri-

* In May, 1967, the Executive Council recommended to Association members that the category of "Special Members" be established for those with nonmedical training as well as for supervisory analysts.

† Alaska, Arkansas, Idaho, Iowa, Kentucky, Maine, Mississippi, Montana, Nebraska, Nevada, New Hampshire, North Dakota, South Carolina, South Dakota, Utah, and Wyoming.

** Alabama, Delaware, Indiana, New Mexico, Rhode Island, and West Virginia. The four states with two analysts are: Arizona, Minnesota, Oklahoma, and Oregon.

‡ In 1965 there were 106 members and 179 associate members of the British Psycho-Analytic Society and the Institute of Psycho-Analysis. In terms of psychoanalytic population Britain ranks second to the United States.

Table 3. Geographical Distribution of American Psychoanalytic Association Members, 1968–69*

New York City		314
Beverly Hills	67	
Los Angeles	57	124
Washington D.C.	63	
Bethesda, Maryland	16	92
Chevy Chase, Maryland	13	
Chicago		75
Philadelphia		72
Boston	42	
Cambridge	23	65

* Based on the roster of the American Psychoanalytic Association, 1968–69.

can Psychoanalytic Association.[9] The origins of the latter, however, have been somewhat obscured by conflicting accounts of the histories of the International, American, and New York associations and societies. In 1933 the American Psychoanalytic Association established its present organizational form as a federation of societies and institutes, the number of which, by 1968–69, reached a total of 29 societies and 20 training institutions.

For psychoanalysis, as for psychiatry, the period of rapid growth was between 1940 and 1960, when membership in the American Psychoanalytic Association increased more than five times. Six new societies were founded between 1940 and 1950, a decade termed "the roaring forties" by one historian of psychoanalysis, and an additional ten were created between 1950 and 1960, the "precipitate fifties." [10] While some of this growth reflected the influx of European refugees fleeing from Naziism,* the major factor was the prestige in psychiatry of psychoanalytic training, a prestige that has been declining in recent years. From 1958 to 1960, for example, there were roughly twice as many applications for membership in the American Psychoanalytic Association as

* Foreign-born analysts in the United States, many of whom have been important figures in the psychoanalytic movement, include Erik H. Erikson, Erich Fromm, Heinz Hartmann, and Theodor Reik, and, among those deceased, Alfred Adler, Franz Alexander, Frieda Fromm-Reichmann, Karen Horney, Ernst Kris, Otto Rank, and Wilhelm Reich. The list of refugee Jewish analysts is sufficiently impressive to justify the statement that the history of psychoanalysis in America, like that of atomic physics, would have been very different had it not been for Adolf Hitler.

in the years 1964–66; and late in December, 1967, it was reported that the 20 applications that had just been decided upon "was the smallest total in many years." [11] Many analysts believe that psychoanalytic training no longer attracts the top students in the medical schools, the quality of which, in terms of student recruitment, apparently has been declining for a member of years.* According to one report in 1967, while psychoanalytic training is improving, "fewer candidates are applying than ever before [and] the quality of the applicant is less than desirable." [12] While there has been no decline in the number of medical students choosing psychiatry as a career, there is some evidence that psychiatry courses in medical schools are held in low regard by students, and this may be a further factor predisposing the better students to select other specializations.†

---

* One study of medical schools dates the decline to 1955, when aptitude scores and other measures of ability among medical school applicants began to demonstrate a marked downward trend. The study hypothesizes that "the increased recruitment of students into basic sciences, mathematics and engineering, along with the considerably enhanced income prospects in many of these fields, may have lured away prospective medical applicants with particularly strong quantitative and scientific interests and abilities." If this decline continues, the study observes, "to the point where the lowest echelon of accepted applicants becomes a group that is incapable of applying scientific advancement and methodology in the treatment of human illness, there will be cause for real alarm." Eric Klinger and Helen Hofer Gee, "The Study of Applicants, 1957–58," *Journal of Medical Education,* 34 (April, 1959), 432–35, quoted in Bertram D. Lewin and Helen Ross, *Psychoanalytic Education in the United States* (New York: Norton, 1960), 59. It is also of interest that the student dropout rate in medical schools is approximately 11 percent or about twice as high as it was in 1952. Robert L. Robinson in *Psychiatric News,* April, 1967.

† In 1964 about 0.4 percent of medical students were choosing psychiatry as a career. Nevertheless, one 1967 survey conducted by Pietro Castelnuovo-Tedesco, based on responses of 110 graduates of 41 American and Canadian medical schools, indicated that psychiatry "is regarded as one of the most poorly taught, poorly remembered, generally inadequate courses offered in medical school." Asked to name the "worst taught subject," 27 percent of the students picked surgery, followed by 20 percent who selected psychiatry; 43 percent felt that the teaching of psychiatry had been either poor or indifferent.

One explanation of the students' "anti-psychiatry bias" was that they relate to psychiatry as "spectators" rather than as participants in a learning process. The typical student, it was suggested, attends lectures and watches senior staff members demonstrate techniques in interviewing, yet his opportunity to learn by doing is limited." Dr. Pietro Castelnuovo-Tedesco, *Archives of General Psychiatry,* June, 1967, quoted in *Psychiatric News,* August, 1967. Asked by *Psychiatric News* to comment on Dr. Castelnuovo-Tedesco's findings, thirty heads of psychiatry departments challenged the accuracy of the survey, but some noted the possibility that the students' attitudes reflect the generally low standing of psychiatry departments relative to other departments in medical schools. Most respondents drew attention

A further factor in the decline of the psychoanalytic movement in the United States is the confusion of theories and doctrines reflected in ideological warfare, hairsplitting theoretical controversies, and splintering into rival factions that has characterized psychoanalysis almost from the beginning. Thus, by 1967, organizations in addition to the American Psychoanalytic Association included the American Academy of Psychoanalysis, established in 1956 by Franz Alexander, Roy R. Grinker, Sr., Frieda Fromm-Reichmann, and others as a less orthodox and more eclectic association than the American Psychoanalytic Association; the Association for the Advancement of Psychoanalysis, founded by Karen Horney in 1941 and largely devoted to expounding her own concepts and approach*; the Association for Psychoanalytic Medicine, formed in 1945 by Viola Bernard, Carl Binger, Abram Kardiner, John A. P. Millet, Sandor Rado, and others, in order to foster a greater interest in science and medicine; and the William Alanson White Institute, created in 1942–43 by a group of analysts who believed that psychologists, sociologists, and other nonmedical personnel could be trained as psychoanalysts.† There

---

to the "inherent difficulty of integrating behavioral science theory with biological science fact in a medical context." *Psychiatric News,* November, 1967.

In a further comment in *Psychiatric News* of January, 1968, Dr. Castelnuovo-Tedesco reported that "40 percent felt that they had not learned as much psychiatry as they would need to practice medicine in their specialty; 31 percent reported that the teaching of psychiatry had been based primarily on lectures and had included little direct contact with patients; 25 percent had never treated a patient with psychotherapy; the majority of those who had treated patients psychotherapeutically had not had the experience of either beginning or completing the patient's treatment; and 36 percent thought that in their future practices they would not use psychotherapy at all or only in 'emergencies.' Despite this, the majority were positively disposed toward psychotherapy. 63 percent were of the opinion that psychotherapy is an effective form of treatment, 74 percent said they like to try to understand the patient's troubles, and 73 percent thought that most patients could benefit from brief psychotherapy."

* The history of the Association for the Advancement of Psychoanalysis, and its training affiliate, the Institute for Psychoanalysis, illustrates the parthenogenetic tendencies of the psychoanalytic movement. According to Millet, Harry Stack Sullivan and Erich Fromm originally supported Horney and her associates Clara Thompson and William Silverberg, but withdrew a year or so later together with Thompson because of Horney's opposition to training nonmedical personnel. In 1944, when Horney refused an invitation to merge her association with the Psychiatric Department of New York Medical College, a number of her colleagues, including Silverberg and Judd Marmor, resigned from the association and proceeded to form "the first medical-school-affiliated psychoanalytic training institute in the New York Medical College, Flower-Fifth Avenue Center." Millet, *op. cit.,* p. 571.

† Because of this issue, the Institute was denied membership in the American Psychoanalytic Association. The issue of training for nonmedical personnel has

are also small societies of analysts based on the teachings of Alfred Adler, C. G. Jung, Otto Rank, Wilhelm Reich, and Theodor Reik, among others.

Factionalism, arising from doctrinal and/or personality conflicts, is also reflected in the existence of two or more societies or institutes within a geographical area. In the normal course, a training institute for a given geographical area is created when a number of training analysts from established institutes move to the area and create an educational program for candidates in training. Thus, the Seattle Psychoanalytic Institute had its beginnings in 1946 when Douglas Orr, the only accredited analyst in Seattle at that time, was appointed a training analyst by the San Francisco Psychoanalytic Institute, of which he was a charter member. Not long after, Orr was joined by another analyst from New York who, like Orr, was appointed a training analyst by San Francisco. The first candidates began their own personal analyses in 1947, and in due course there were other analysts and candidates on the scene. In 1957 the Seattle Psychoanalytic Society was organized with a membership of thirteen, and in 1966 the Seattle Institute was accorded full institute status.

The history of societies and institutes, however, is not always so uneventful. New York City, for example, has two societies that are recognized by the American Psychoanalytic Association, excluding the Association for Psychoanalytic Medicine and societies in Long Island, Westchester, and New Jersey. The Los Angeles Psychoanalytic Society, originally the sole organization in the area, now shares psychoanalysis in that part of the county with the Southern California Psychoanalytic Society, the offices of which are only a few blocks away; both organizations, almost needless to say, are located in Beverly Hills. Philadelphia also has two psychoanalytic organizations, while Michigan has three, all headquartered in Detroit. The division of the Washington-Baltimore Psychoanalytic Society into what is now the Washington Psychoanalytic Society and the Baltimore Psychoanalytic Society has been attributed to a "power struggle" rather than to any doctrinal difference.[13]

In 1968 personal as well as doctrinal factors played a role in the

---

also caused difficulty in the relations between the International Psycho-Analytic Association, founded by Freud and his associates in 1910, and the American body. Freud himself was unable to persuade the Americans that medical training was not a prerequisite to competence in psychoanalysis.

decision of seven of the nine training analysts at the Case Western Reserve Institute to organize their own Cleveland Psychoanalytic Institute, a decision subsequently approved by the APsaA after at least two official "investigations" into the cicumstances. Similarly, the creation in 1950 of the Los Angeles Society for Psychoanalytic Medicine, subsequently the Southern California Psychoanalytic Society, was viewed with suspicion by the Los Angeles Psychoanalytic Society and the parent APsaA itself. In the recollection of one analyst,

> The Southern California bunch were originally the black sheep, without question. The Los Angeles group was regarded as the true repository of analytic fidelity and the others as mavericks—nice guys and all that, but still mavericks. So they were investigated, once, twice, maybe even a third time, and given a rough going-over, so much so that they protested very strongly to New York. But they were investigated anyhow, and what happened? They got a glowing report—excellent curriculum, good morale, and so on and so forth. It's the LA group that begins to have trouble with divisions, factions, what not, so they begin to spend more time arguing and fighting than on productive work. I understand that they're overturning the old timers, and that some of the younger people are moving toward Melanie Klein. Maybe they'll end by substituting a new dogma for the old one. In any case, the Southern California group is now very favorably regarded.

In 1968–69 there was talk of a merger of the two societies. In other instances as well, personality and power conflicts have been more significant than theoretical issues as such, although the later are sometimes exploited as rationalizations for separatist actions. As a consequence, not all of the orthodox Freudian analysts are in one organization in, say, Los Angeles or New York, and all of the nonorthodox or antiorthodox analysts in the other. The psychoanalytic societies in Chicago and San Francisco are regarded as extremely conservative organizations in analytic terms, but each of them has among its members a number of eclectic nonconformists.

There are also societies and training centers affiliated with the American Academy of Psychoanalysis, which, with a membership of more than 600,* has become the most important rival organi-

* Of these, approximately 80 are "Scientific Associates"—that is, physicians who are not analysts, and social scientists as well as other professionals who lack medical degrees.

zation to the American Psychoanalytic Association. Relations between the Association and the Academy, never easy, have occasionally been acrimonious. When the Academy was first organized, the Association tried to persuade the American Psychiatric Association to deny it any place on the program at APA annual meetings. The most recent controversy involves the claim of the Association that it alone is qualified to accredit candidates for psychoanalytic training, a claim denied by the Academy president in 1967, Dr. Harold I. Lief. The controversy arose in connection with a decision of the Veterans Administration that psychiatrists seeking psychoanalytic training were eligible for financial assistance under the Veterans' Assistance Act. The Association's position is that only psychiatrists trained in its approved institutes are qualified psychoanalysts; it does not recognize institutes affiliated with the Academy. The Academy's position, on the other hand, favors a "constructive coexistence" under which analysts trained in either Association or Academy institutes should be permitted to join both organizations if they so desire. Under present arrangements, many analysts trained in Association-approved institutes are members of the Academy and the Association, but Academy-trained analysts are not admitted to the Association.*

Theoretical and doctrinal differences between the two organizations are reflected not only in their admission requirements but in their semiannual meeting programs. Thus, the 1968 fall meeting of the American Psychoanalytic Association, held at New York's Waldorf Astoria Hotel, included papers on "The Psychoanalytic Treatment of Character Disorders: With Special Consideration on the Genetic and Dynamic Aspects of Acting Out Behavior," and "Orality and the Primitive Ego"; there were also papers dealing with dreams, masochism in women, bisexuality and depression, "Xerostomia: The Dry Mouth Syndrome," and other topics. The programs of Association meetings in recent years suggest that the themes discussed changed relatively little from meeting to meeting,

* The issue of accreditation was discussed in an exchange of letters between officers of both organizations in *Psychiatric News,* February, May, and June, 1967. The Veterans Administration prudently declined to take sides in the controversy, declaring that courses and related work approved for training were those accredited "by the approving agency of the appropriate State" or by a nationally recognized accrediting agency or association. The list of such agencies, it assured the Academy, "does not designate any agency as the nationally recognized accrediting agency in the field of psychoanalysis . . . no agency has been so designated." Quoted in the Academy's *Newsletter,* 11, 2 (October, 1967).

although new topics do occasionally appear on the agenda; for example, relationships between psychoanalysis and science, or the role of analysts in community health programs.

The Academy, on the other hand, is likely to devote entire meetings to such innovations as ego psychology (the theme of its 1966 fall meeting) or ethology and psychoanalysis (May meeting, 1967). The 1967 fall meeting was devoted to "Psychoanalysis and Dissent" and featured papers ranging from "The Dissent of Norman Thomas" to "Psychodynamics and Therapy of Civil Rights Activists." The May, 1969, meeting was given over to "Disorders of the Work Function." In 1967 the Academy's Frieda Fromm-Reichmann award for a distinguished contribution to the knowledge of the etiology, nature, or therapy of schizophrenia was presented not to an analyst but to novelist Hannah Green for her novel *I Never Promised You a Rose Garden.** Another facet of Academy interests is reflected in its relationship to the American Association for the Advancement of Science (AAAS). Every other year the Academy sponsors a joint meeting with AAAS, held during the annual convention of the latter, in accordance with its belief that psychoanalysis must draw closer to the sciences, especially the behavioral sciences, or continue to lose status as a discipline that has something important to say about man's nature.†

Whatever the final resolution of the controversies within and between psychoanalytic organizations, there can be little doubt that the training of psychiatrists and psychoanalysts has been broadened in recent years to include some exposure to science and nonpsychiatric behavioral theory. The interest in areas formerly regarded as irrelevant to professional concerns is reflected in a sharp increase in journal articles addressed to psychiatric training, one emphasis of which is on the need to provide residents with courses in the behavioral and social sciences. Another reflection is in the frequency of panel discussions at annual meetings devoted to curriculum changes in psychiatry departments and psychoanalytic institutes. In effect, the profession is engaged in a continuing self-examination of its theories and methods, a self-examination

* New York: Holt, Rinehart and Winston, 1964. Apparently Dr. Fromm-Reichmann, who died in 1956, had planned to collaborate with Miss Green in writing a book about schizophrenia.

† In 1967 the Association for the first time cosponsored a meeting with the AAAS. The meeting on December 27, 1967, was devoted to "Psychoanalytic Studies in Child Development: Biological and Social Deprivation in Early Childhood."

which has already significantly influenced psychiatric training in many if not most of the nation's medical schools.

As noted earlier, such training necessarily begins in a medical school; neither the American Psychiatric Association nor the American Psychoanalytic Association, with few exceptions, admits nonphysicians to active membership. For most psychiatrists the time elapsed between entering medical school and certification in adult and/or child psychiatry will be a minimum of five years. If a psychiatrist then decides to become a psychoanalyst—that is, if he applies and is admitted to a training institute—an additional three years or more of training will be required, including a preparatory analysis of at least 300 hours.* It has been estimated that the cost of psychiatric training is between $20,000 and $35,000, a considerable portion of which is financed by Public Health Service and state grants and stipends.[14] In 1960 cost estimates for psychoanalytic training ranged from $20,000 to $28,000.[15]

There are considerable diversities in the character and duration of training programs for both psychiatrists and psychoanalysts. In many medical schools a student may complete his psychiatric training in five years or even less, but the training period will normally be longer if he specializes in child as well as adult psychiatry, or if he seeks advanced training as a research psychiatrist. Graduates of medical schools and physicians who decide to become psychiatrists after having practiced in other specialties ordinarily will serve three-year residencies to qualify in child and adolescent psychiatry,† and two-years residencies to qualify in adult psychiatry; in some medical schools the two residencies can be combined in a four-year program leading to certification in both adult and child psychiatry. While most psychiatry departments encourage residents to seek certification through an exami-

* In a study of the length of such analyses based on the years 1946–57, the mean number of hours ranged from 473 (Philadelphia Psychoanalytic Society) to 963 (Cleveland Psychoanalytic Society). The national mean was 609 hours. Bertram D. Lewin and Helen Ross, *Psychoanalytic Education in the United States* (New York: Norton, 1960), 174–75. A study of twenty-two training analysts appointed between 1966 and 1968 showed an average of 899 hours of training analysis for each, compared with 696 in 1958. *Journal of the American Psychoanalytic Association,* 16, 2 (April, 1968), 340.

† For those entering psychiatry after medical school, a common requirement for admission to training is a one-year internship in a field other than psychiatry, in addition to a medical degree from an approved medical school. The list of those who have become psychiatrists after some years in other careers includes all medical specialties and, in addition, lawyers, professors, veterinarians, and rabbis.

nation given by the American Board of Psychiatry and Neurology, only a little more than a third of psychiatrists hold such certification, the great majority in psychiatry alone. Fewer than 3 percent are certified in child psychiatry.

Because of the extreme emotional demands made on psychiatrists, it is suggested from time to time that psychiatrists should undergo at least a partial psychoanalysis as part of their training, and most psychiatrists who have done so indicate they have benefited in terms of both their personal and their professional lives. As one of them puts it, following a personal analysis of almost four years, "the results were good for all of my relationships, and certainly for my practice. I used to practice with a lot more tension and anxiety than I do now. Since a lot of psychiatrists are fairly disturbed people, it would be a good thing if they subjected themselves to some form of psychoanalytic treatment."

The American Psychiatric Association, however, has never required or even recommended psychoanalysis as a part of residency training. At a 1952 Conference on Psychiatric Education there was "virtually unanimous agreement" that it was "not necessary to be psychoanalyzed in order to develop competence as a psychiatrist . . . ." Arguing that "for most individuals" a short period of psychotherapy is sufficient, Franklin G. Ebaugh in 1957 declared "the fact is that necessary awareness of one's own personality patterns, areas of threat, anxiety and hostility, tendencies to 'project,' and 'blind spots' resulting from defense structures can be obtained in other ways" than undergoing psychoanalysis.[16]

Courses involving sociology and psychology, on the other hand, are becoming increasingly numerous in medical schools and especially in psychiatry departments. Many departments now have professorships filled by behavioral scientists, and in some instances their courses are required rather than elective. While much of the teaching in sociology is medical sociology, or concerned with techniques of research, a growing proportion is designed to acquaint the psychiatric resident with the economic, social, ethnic, and even political facts of life as these affect the distribution of mental illness in society. Psychologists, mainly clinical psychologists, are often responsible for teaching methods of personality assessment, such as the Rorschach and thematic apperception tests, but they may also deal with relevant aspects of social dynamics. The teaching staff in psychiatry may include additionally communications experts, persons trained in human engineering, statisticians, legal scholars, biochemists, neurophysiologists, ethologists, and anthropologists.

The central core of the curriculum, however, usually consists of a didactic program focused on the principles and techniques of psychotherapy and somato-therapy (shock treatment and drug therapy). Residents generally are involved with patients from the start of training and in addition take courses and seminars concerned with the psychopathology of neuroses and psychoses, clinical neurology, personality development, personality assessment, child psychiatry, psychopharmacology, research problems, and other topics. Much attention is given to interviewing techniques and the skills involved in probing a patient's history and accurately diagnosing his problems; teaching methods often include observation of patients and therapists through one-way mirrors (the side facing the patient and therapist is the mirror side), closed-circuit television, and tape recordings. In some psychiatry departments one or two residents interview a patient under supervision and then discuss what occurred with the faculty and other residents. Depending on staff interests, residents may also take work in hypnosis, group psychotherapy, family therapy, law and psychiatry, the psychology of sleeping and dreaming, and community or social psychiatry. Psychoanalytic theories are subsumed under various labels in the didactic program or taught in special courses and seminars.*

Rather different training is provided psychiatrists who desire to become psychoanalysts under rules established by the American Psychoanalytic Association. In addition to a medical degree and psychiatric training the candidate for training must convince the training institute that his qualities of character and personality combine to insure his suitability for analytic training. Usually the initial determination of his suitability is made through one or more interviews with faculty members of the institute, supple-

* Psychoanalysis, like psychiatry, tends to play a relatively minor role in medical school administration. Hence, few deans of medical schools have been psychiatrists or psychoanalysts. Psychoanalysts who were medical deans in 1969 included Frederick C. Redlich at Yale, Douglas Bond at Western Reserve, and LeRoy P. Levitt at the University of Chicago. Robert H. Felix, dean of the St. Louis University Medical School and former APA president, is an honorary member of the Washington (D.C.) Psychoanalytic Society.

mented by letters of recommendation and, in certain cases, examinations and other evidence of competence.

Once admitted for training, the candidate must undergo the preparatory analysis previously noted "four or more times a week" and also carry through a program of assigned reading, lectures, and supervised clinical experience, all of which is designed to provide him with a thorough knowledge of Freud's theories and other relevant psychoanalytic contributions.[17] He is further required to analyze under supervision at least two adult cases, devoting to each a minimum of 150 hours of analysis and "carrying at least one of them through the terminal phase of analysis." It is expected that material from these analyses will be presented by him "in no less than three extended presentations" at clinical conferences, of which he is required to attend at least fifty during his training. At each stage of training his progress is determined by the institute's educational committee. While some part of this determination is based on oral or written examinations, "of greatest importance is the estimation of the quality of the student's work in his supervised clinical experience and in the presentation of cases in clinical conferences. This constitutes a check upon the preparatory analysis as well, and can be expected to show either its adequacy or the need for further personal analysis." [18] If the candidate successfully completes the training program, he is given a written statement to that effect by the institute, and he may then apply for membership in the American Psychoanalytic Association. It is to be noted that such membership is not automatic; in certain cases the Association has not admitted graduates of institutes to membership.

In view of the time, cost, and rigorous training required to become a psychiatrist, and the even greater burdens imposed on those seeking to become psychoanalysts, it is not surprising that those who survive the course differ from other physicians in important ways. Even as medical students they are less interested than other students in the physical aspects of medicine, and as undergraduates they are more likely to have majored in the social sciences and humanities.[19] On tests they are apt to reveal a preference for teaching and research careers rather than clinical practice,* and they also score higher than other medical students on

* "The bulk of today's [psychiatry] students display the characteristics of scientists who wish to do research, combined with some teaching and treating some

measures of introspection and autonomy.[20] Apparently they attach a lower preference to economic rewards and a higher one to aesthetic values.[21] They score higher than other doctors on measures of verbal proficiency,[22] and lower on tests of authoritarianism.[23] Of all medical specialists they are the least likely to have been influenced by their parents in choosing a medical career, and the most likely to have been influenced by teachers.[24] They are more likely than other physicians to have been born in large cities,[25] and, as will be seen in Chapter V, they are alone in the medical world in consistently voting Democratic in Presidential elections.*

Conscious motivations in becoming a psychiatrist include a desire to help those who are mentally distressed and an interest in the problems of mental illness. In one study of male psychiatrists it was found that the "earliest known factors initiating movement toward a career in psychiatry are primitive identifications and objects from preoedipal and oedipal years. Of these, involvement with mother and the mothering functions seem most common." [26] A study of aptitude for psychoanalysis, again confined to males, found the aptitude "core" to reside in the analyst's "psychologically accessible latent femininity and his correlated passivity." [27] There is some evidence that the relative absence of aggressive personality components is more marked in the case of psychiatrists than in other medical professions, and there is reason to believe that psychiatrists who are mainly psychotherapists are less aggressive than those who emphasize drugs and shock treatment.

But there is also evidence that many physicians who become psychiatrists do so, at least in part, because of personal troubles for which, hopefully, their psychiatric training and practice will offer a solution. Indeed, the possibility that "some who take up psychiatry probably do so for morbid reasons" has been advanced as an explanation for the disproportionate number of suicides among psychiatrists, even taking account of the fact that "Doctors

---

patients 'scientifically.' They resemble graduate students in the natural sciences far more than they do clinicians." Daniel H. Funkenstein, "Editor's Notebook," *American Journal of Psychiatry,* 124, 2 (August, 1967), 227.

* In 1969 it was reported that a "large proportion" of medical students who are not affiliated with any religion choose psychiatry as a specialty. According to the study, which was based on a survey of 2,630 medical students at eight medical schools, general practice was favored by Protestant students, internal medicine by Jews, and surgery by Catholics. *Psychiatric News,* April, 1969.

of Medicine are more prone to suicide than men in other occupations." * Clearly, for some who go into psychiatry the ancient admonition "Physician, heal thyself!" is a literal commandment pointing to one type of career rather than another. The role of personal problems in psychiatric careers is also important in the treatment of patients. Insight into such problems, assuming the problems are not incapacitating, lends itself to empathy, understanding, and a more meaningful relationship with patients than would be possible in the case of a psychiatrist whose own life had been relatively untroubled.

Even those who are reasonably free of personal troubles when they embark on training are not likely to emerge unscathed from the hazards of residency or the early years of practice. First-year residents may have difficulty establishing their identity as physicians since they are dealing with problems very different from those they encountered in medical school. Feelings of incompetence and inadequacy are easily aroused in their attempts to treat psychotic or seriously disturbed patients, and it is to be noted that the initial experience of most residents is with such patients rather than with those minimally ill. To the extent that his patients come from the less educated and poorer sections of society, as most of them do in the state hospitals and Veterans Administration facilities, the resident may experience major communication difficulties, patients' hostilities, and other therapeutic blocks that activate his own insecurities or anxieties. For residents and experienced psychiatrists the failure of patients to improve or, worse still, the suicide of a patient can markedly increase doubts regarding proficiency and, not infrequently, precipitate a depression.

Nor are the stresses of training and the early years of practice necessarily less severe for the families of psychiatrists. While there is no clear evidence that the divorce rate among psychiatrists is unusually high, the impression of some authorities on training

---

* Quoted from the *British Medical Journal* in Walter Freeman, "Psychiatrists Who Kill Themselves: A Study in Suicide," *American Journal of Psychiatry,* 124, 6 (December, 1967), 846–47. Based on obituary notices in the *Journal of the American Medical Association* and official death certificates, some 203 psychiatrists committed suicide between 1895 and 1967, 54 of them in the 1962–67 period, "more than had done so in any previous decade." One of every three suicides occurred before age forty. Since the incidence of accidental death is almost the same as the incidence of suicide, whereas it is at least double—that is, two to one—for the general population, "There are reasons to believe that this figure (203) is low."

is that "the amount and seriousness of psychiatric symptomatology among residents' wives . . . occurs with some regularity." A psychiatrist's wife may find it difficult to adjust to a setting "radically different from what she had experienced before or had anticipated. She perceives changes taking place in her husband which she may not always understand and which may necessitate difficult adjustments on her part. Her husband is gone long hours, is frequently upset, and tends to develop ideas and concepts which she can rarely understand. In discussions with her husband and in kaffeeklatsches with her neighbors, she hears psychiatric terms, interpretations, and concepts applied to herself and her family which may not be flattering. . . . At its worst, the stress of the psychiatric residency may lead to breakdown of what appeared superficially to be an adequate marriage." [28] The early years of practice may be no less difficult and eventful as a consequence of changing self-concepts and demand patterns.

The numerous ways of coping with the stresses of training and initial professional experience include cynicism and chronic dissatisfaction, or what has aptly been termed "therapeutic nihilism." [29] In certain cases depressed morale may express itself in failure to keep abreast of developments in the field and new literature or in a tendency to move away from psychotherapy toward greater reliance on drugs and shock treatment. In other cases, there may be a shift from clinical practice to administration or nonpatient kinds of research. In extreme cases, the psychiatrist may leave his profession altogether or become one of its foremost critics; the phenomenon of the antipsychiatry psychiatrist is not unknown. Psychiatry, like other professions, has its dropouts, its underachievers, its time-servers, its neurotics, and its malcontents.

Similar problems of stress and morale beset psychoanalysis, in addition to problems which are unique to psychoanalytic training and practice. Because the analyst treats mainly patients who are neurotic rather than psychotic, with whom he can easily communicate since they share his educational and class background, he is apt to regard himself as a more competent therapist than the psychiatrist and to enjoy more prestige both within psychiatry and with the public. He may or may not have an equal or greater number of patient failures compared with a psychiatrist; success in psychoanalysis is difficult to measure, indeed, even to define. But whatever his real merit as a psychoanalyst, he tends to acquire extensive influence over the lives of his patients, in effect, as one analyst puts it, "To Be a God." [30]

To become a psychoanalyst, moreover, is to join a very select company, at any rate in the United States, of which most psychiatrists are unable to become a part. Acceptance by a training institute, it has been pointed out by one analyst, essentially means: "You're O.K.," just as the letter of rejection means essentially, "You are a second-class psychiatrist—and person." The severe psychic blow many residents suffer on receiving the second kind of letter is mitigated only if the resident is accepted by a psychoanalytic institute in another city or if he "works through" the "rejection" in his personal analysis or through self-examination.[31] One psychiatrist who had been rejected by two training institutes described the rejection as "a disappointment," but one that brought with it "some sense of relief." While he had a desire to become an analyst "because they seem to know the most about the subject," he had realized that his acceptance would have meant "being constantly involved in a trial situation where they can sort of chop you off at any time for the next eight years or so of your professional life." He attributed his rejection to his "not being intellectual enough. This is something which is a necessary attribute of analysts. They approach things by way of literature, whereas I learn more from dealing with patients and from practical experience than I do from discussions with colleagues or from reading about problems. Also, I tend to think more concretely about things. I don't abstract a situation readily."

Rejection led another psychiatrist to conclude, after much reflection, that he would have made a very unsatisfactory analyst or even suitable person for a personal analysis. "I have a tendency," he comments,

> to want to establish a positive transference with my patients. I want them to like me and I want this to be an operative factor in helping them. I don't feel I am on secure ground until I get it. Whereas I think analysts tend to operate on what we call negative or slightly negative transference. The patient is always slightly pissed off at the doctor. He's always wondering what the hell is next and why is he never getting his questions answered. I think you need some pretty masochistic patients to put up with all this. I don't know if my own masochism would have stood up to the whole thing in the course of an analysis for myself.

Paradoxically, a psychiatrist's "rejection" may result, at least in part, from his training analysis. In the majority of institutes, the opinion of the trainee's analyst is sought in evaluating the capacity of the trainee for a psychoanalytic career. Thus, information of an extremely personal nature, which in the normal course would be held confidential, may be decisive in judging the candidate "a second-class psychiatrist." The effect of such a procedure, which has been repeatedly criticized in psychoanalytic circles, is to give training analysts great power over admissions to the profession and, hence, power to determine the future course of psychoanalysis. The trainee, on his part, may seek to flatter the analyst, or side with him on professional issues, to ensure his own success as a candidate. Even if the training analyst is someone without, in Clara Thompson's phrase, "a neurotic power drive," he may be overly protective or fond of the candidate, and thus the analysis may be distorted in another direction with consequences unfortunate for both the trainee and his future patients. Hence the recommendation that training analysts take no part in the administration and policy decisions of an institute.*

There is little evidence, however, that psychoanalysts are in personality terms characterized by extreme power drives or an abundance of personal problems; indeed, the evidence suggests an opposite conclusion. According to one study of 79 psychiatrists who were accepted for psychoanalytic training, of whom 66 successfully completed training, tests showed "an absence of intense power drives" and only moderate personal problems. The outstanding students had chosen careers in psychoanalysis soon after finishing medical school, and they had been judged superior in interviews. They also were found to have "wide cultural interests."[32] While it is occasionally argued that psychoanalytic training tends to erode one's sense of humor and to produce a certain coldness and remoteness, evidence supporting such views is impressionistic and neither confirms nor denies the possibility that, in certain cases, a sense of humor and warmth of personality were absent *before* training. Certainly Freud and his followers never

* Clara Thompson, "A Study of the Emotional Climate of Psychoanalytic Institutes," *Psychiatry*, 21, 1 (February, 1958), 45–51. According to one analyst, training analysts may choose one candidate rather than another "because he looks like I did at one time, therefore I think something can be made of him." Or, "This candidate is like a patient I have treated once with great success. In other words, there's a highly personal aspect to choosing candidates as well as patients."

claimed that psychoanalysis would work miraculous changes in the personality system of the type involved in creating a sense of humor and personal warmth where neither had existed before. Most psychoanalysts and psychiatrists, as will be seen in subsequent chapters, do not make the claims for themselves that are sometimes made in their behalf by laymen; in particular, they do not pretend to have answers for all of the problems of their patients, or even for their own.

III

Who Does What to Whom

PERHAPS more than other professionals, psychiatrists and psychoanalysts tend to be highly individualistic, and it is the nature of the subject matter, that is, the abundance of theories and conceptual frameworks, that the 184 therapists and analysts in our study should represent a variety of approaches or viewpoints. Nevertheless, certain generalizations are possible, and these suggest that the 184 are fairly representative of the profession as a whole.*

For example, 92 percent of them are men, and 83 percent were born in the United States. Forty-three percent were born between 1920 and 1929; 34 percent between 1910 and 1919; and 13 percent, none of whom is an analyst, were born in or after 1930.† Approximately 10 percent were born before 1910. In other words, the most typical respondent was a male psychiatrist in his early forties.**

---

* Henceforth distinctions are made between the 149 psychiatrists and the 35 psychoanalysts where there are important differences between the two groups, or where the topic under discussion requires differentiation. In all other cases reference is to the entire study population of 184, or to that portion of it that responded to the particular question. Where percentages do not total 100, the missing percentage represents the "don't know" or "no opinion" replies unless otherwise indicated. In some instances (for example, "mother's profession") categories were deemed to be too insignificant, or percentages too small, to be included. Total percentages above 100 indicate multiple choices. Except where noted percentages relate to the number of those responding to the question, not the total number of those in the study group (184). When other studies of the psychiatric community have been drawn upon, there is a notation to that effect.

† Since it takes longer to become an analyst, the average age of the 35 analysts in the study is higher than that of the psychiatrists. Forty percent of the analysts were born between 1920 and 1929; 31 percent between 1910 and 1919; and 17 percent between 1900 and 1909, as contrasted with 13 percent of the psychiatrists.

** A 1965 questionnaire survey of 16,454 psychiatrists, or about 88 percent of the total, found that 88 percent were men whose median age was forty-three years;

Family backgrounds are heavily weighted toward the professional and middle-class occupations. More than 12 percent of the total group have fathers who were physicians, and another 42 percent are the sons or daughters of fathers who were businessmen or white-collar employees. Only 12 percent come from blue-collar families, and approximately half that number have fathers who were teachers or professors. Of the mothers, more than 82 percent were housewives, with another 5 percent having been in business.

More than 86 percent of the group are married, and most of them have children. Fifteen are single, three are divorced, one is separated, and six are widowed. Of those married sixteen are involved in a second marriage, and four in a third marriage.*

The popular suspicion that psychiatrists and especially psychoanalysts are mainly atheists and agnostics is confirmed by the responses of the study population. As Table 4 demonstrates, more than a third of the analysts and a fifth of the psychiatrists are not affiliated with any religion.

In the case of analysts, "other" almost always refers to nonreligious Jewish identification in terms of birth, culture, or ethnic loyalty, whereas for psychiatrists "other" includes one member each of the Church of Christ and Bahai World Faith, in addition to nonreligious Jewish categories. One psychiatrist describes himself as a "not strict Catholic, on the agnostic side," and another indicates that he "attends wife's church (Presbyterian) but is not affiliated with it." †

Whatever the religious affiliation, church attendance for both the analysts and the psychiatrists tends to be minimal. Only two of the analysts (6 percent) and thirty of the psychiatrists (20 per-

---

the median age for the 12 percent who were women psychiatrists was forty-six. Ninety-six percent were United States citizens. Mental Health Manpower Studies Unit, Training and Manpower Resources Branch, National Institute of Mental Health, "Occupational and Personal Characteristics of Psychiatrists in the United States—1965." The average age of the 77 psychiatrists and analysists who returned the brief follow-up questionnaire referred to earlier was fifty-two (in 1968).

* The marital status of the sample is of special interest in view of the widely held belief that among psychiatrists the divorce rate is high. The single-marriage pattern of the group is in keeping with a study of psychiatrists in Minneapolis and St. Paul which found that 90 percent of the respondents, or a total of 54, had been married once only. National figures for marriage and divorce indicate that one of every four marriages ends in divorce.

† It is generally true of this and other studies that atheists of Protestant and Catholic origin are apt to describe themselves as atheists (period) whereas most Jews who are atheists or agnostics are inclined to identify themselves as Jews, no matter how strongly irreligious.

Table 4. Religious Affiliation

	Psychoanalysts		Psychiatrists	
	No.	*%*	*No.*	*%*
Jewish	9	26	37	25
Catholic	3	8	17	11
Episcopalian	1	3	11	7
Methodist	0	0	11	7
Presbyterian	0	0	9	6
Baptist	0	0	4	3
Unitarian	1	3	4	3
Congregational	1	3	3	2
Seventh-day Adventist	0	0	3	2
Quaker	0	0	2	1
Mormon	1	3	0	0
Other than above	7	20	15	10
None	12	34	33	22

cent) attend church frequently. Twelve analysts, or more than a third of the total, attend church seldom, and nineteen, or 54 percent, never go to church. Among psychiatrists sixty, or 40 percent, seldom attend church, and forty, or 27 percent, are never found there. In the analytic group there is widespread endorsement of Freud's view that "the whole thing [belief in God] is so patently infantile, so incongruous with reality, that to one whose attitude to humanity is friendly it is painful to think that the great majority of mortals will never be able to rise above this view of life." [1] While analysts tend to agree with this statement, and to believe, like Freud, that religious conviction is likely to be a neurotic manifestation, psychiatrists are much less inclined to treat religion as a neurosis. Thus 55 percent of the analysts support the statement quoted (which was not identified in the questionnaire as originating with Freud), as compared with 24 percent of the psychiatrists. It is also the case, as will be seen later, that some analysts are not at ease with patients who are devoutly religious, and are apt to regard a diminution of religious belief as a concomitant of successful analysis.

As may be expected, the parents of both psychiatrists and analysts had a larger number of religious affiliations and attended church more frequently. The decline in affiliation is particularly marked in the case of psychiatrists and analysts whose parents were Catholic or Jewish. Thus, for the sample of analysts, 15 mothers and 13 fathers were identified as Jewish-affiliated, and 7 mothers and 4 fathers as Catholic. Among the psychiatrists there were 49 Jewish mothers and 46 Jewish fathers, 24 Catholic mothers and 16 Catholic fathers. Twenty-six percent of the mothers and 31 percent of the fathers of analysts never attended church, compared with 9 percent of the mothers and 19 percent of the fathers of psychiatrists.[2]

The cultural level of the study group, measured by its reading habits, is much above that of the general population, and probably a good deal superior to the level of other physicians. Sixty percent of the analysts and 49 percent of the psychiatrists read "quite a few" books each year. Preferred reading for both analysts and psychiatrists is history, followed closely by fiction, biography, and books dealing with science and technology. A fifth of the analysts read detective novels, and the same proportion read poetry; among the psychiatrists the corresponding figures are 25 percent and 19 percent. But whereas only 11 percent of the analysts read medical books exclusive of those dealing with psychiatry and psychoanalysis, almost 20 percent of psychiatrists read such literature.* Psychiatrists, apparently, also watch more television than analysts, but the differences are not of major significance. Sixty-six percent of analysts watch television "hardly at all," with 26 percent averaging two hours per day of viewing time. The comparable figures for psychiatrists are 60 percent and 30 percent.

Both groups read a wide variety of magazines, and, as Table 5 suggests, there are some interesting differences between them in terms of magazine preference.

While the reading tastes of the analysts would appear to be somewhat more "highbrow" than those of the psychiatrists, it would be a mistake to exaggerate the difference in view of the high rankings among psychiatrists of such magazines as *The New Yorker*, *Harper's*, *Science*, and *Scientific American*. On the other hand, there are some conspicuous readership differences between the two groups when so-called intellectual and liberal journals are taken into account. These differences are indicated in Table 6.

---

* According to *Publisher's Weekly*, of 1,211 medical books published in 1964, 171 or 14 percent dealt with psychiatry. Only books concerned with general medicine constituted a larger category. *International Journal of Psychiatry*, 2, 6 (November, 1966), 597. In 1968 psychiatry books constituted 7 percent of the total medical books.

Table 5. Magazines Read Regularly or Occasionally

Magazine	*Psychiatrists* %	*Psychoanalysts* %
Life	86	80
Time	80	60
The New Yorker	76	86
Look	67	74
The Atlantic	58	65
Newsweek	58	69
Holiday	54	43
U.S. News	53	43
Science	52	80
Harper's	51	83
Scientific American	49	66
Saturday Evening Post	47	40
Reader's Digest	46	11

While it is something of a mystery that analysts should prefer *Harper's* to *The Atlantic,* and psychiatrists *The Atlantic* to *Harper's,* perhaps it is less of a mystery that 34 percent of the psychiatrists and 37 percent of the analysts are regular or occasional readers of *Playboy.* The markedly liberal political inclinations of the analysts are clearly reflected in the high rankings of *The Reporter, The Nation, The New Republic,* and *I. F. Stone's Weekly,* and the somewhat more conservative leanings of the psy-

Table 6. Intellectual or Liberal Magazines Read Regularly or Occasionally

Magazine	*Psychiatrists* %	*Psychoanalysts* %
The Reporter	23	57
Commentary	16	54
The Nation	16	51
The New Republic	23	48
I. F. Stone's Weekly	5	46
Saturday Review	14	20
Daedalus	4	14

chiatrists in their preference for *Time-Life* and *Reader's Digest.*

Almost a third of the entire study population were involved in a different occupation or profession before embarking upon psychiatry, the great majority in some other branch of medicine. For the most part, the time spent in these other occupational or professional areas was five years or less, which suggests that the decision to become a psychiatrist or analyst is made fairly early in one's career, whether or not that career begins in medicine. Those whose decisions came later in life frequently mention boredom with their previous profession as an important factor, or loss of interest. One analyst who formerly was in internal medicine stresses his discovery after some years of practice that the ailments of at least 50 percent of his patients were due to psychic causes, chiefly involving stress and nervous tension and that, therefore, there was little point in approaching their problems from the perspective of physical medicine and its cures. Another psychiatrist, formerly a pediatrician, mentions that with the decline of children's diseases as a consequence of great progress in immunology and the prevention of illness, pediatrics had become "boring beyond belief." After a considerable number of years "hoping that a really sick kid would come into the office, I gave up. I had also come to the conclusion that the parents I saw were a hell of a lot sicker than their children—mentally, that is—with the result that I was spending more and more time on referrals of both parents and kids to psychiatrists I knew. So I finally decided that psychiatry must be pretty interesting, at least as compared with pediatrics, and that turned out to be correct."

While 30 of the analysts, or 86 percent of the total, have been certified by the American Board of Psychiatry and Neurology, only 77 psychiatrists, or 52 percent, have been Board certified. Motivations to seek Board certification include the desire to hold appointments for which such certification is required, as is the case in certain state and Veterans Administration hospitals, and salary increases which result from certification, frequently ranging up to $100 or more per month in public and private mental institutions. Despite increasing feeling that Board certification should be required of psychiatrists, a feeling reflected in the growing number of positions for which such certification is a necessity, most psychiatrists do not regard the examination involved as a measure of proficiency, and there is, therefore, great resistance to requiring Board certification as a condition of practice.

The psychiatric training of most psychiatrists and analysts in the study was either eclectic, that is, broadly based in terms of theory and technique, or psychoanalytic; almost a third of the psychiatrists have had some psychoanalytic training. For both groups, the principal institution for residencies was a university-affiliated department of psychiatry, but almost twice as many analysts as psychiatrists spent their residencies in the armed forces, whereas twice as many psychiatrists as analysts were residents in state and Veterans Administration hospitals.

There are marked differences between psychiatrists and analysts in terms of the distribution of working week time. About 71 percent of the analysts devote 60 percent or more of their time to private patients, compared with 41 percent of the psychiatrists devoting the same proportion of time to private patients. Four analysts are almost entirely engaged in private practice, and seven, or a fifth of the total, devote at least 80 percent of their time to private patients. No analyst treats patients who receive public assistance or who are in Veterans Administration hospitals, and only one sees any patients in state or county hospitals. While the psychiatrists deal mainly with private patients, a total of eighteen, or 12 percent, are employed in state, county, or Veterans Administration hospitals,* and fourteen devote at least 10 percent of their time to patients receiving public assistance.†

---

* Of these eighteen, ten work full time for public mental hospitals, and eight devote at least half their time to such employment. For some differences between these eighteen psychiatrists and the other 131 in the study, see Chapter VII.

† A pilot study based on 148 questionnaires returned by members of the American Psychoanalytic Association in 1966 reported that almost 10 percent do no private practice at all, another 10 percent practice less than 20 hours per week, 19 percent practice 20–29 hours per week, 33 percent practice 30–39 hours per week, and 28 percent practice 40 or more hours per week. In the course of a year, the pilot study reported, "the average analyst had in treatment 28 patients and saw another 23 in consultation. In addition he supervised the treatment of another 10." While 29 percent of analysts had fewer analytic patients than in 1960, and 23 percent fewer than in 1963, the increase in psychotherapy patients was not commensurate with the decrease in analytic patients, suggesting that "where there has been a decrease in analytic patients, at least part of the time of the analyst has been diverted to teaching, research, organizational or other activities." Eight percent of the analysts were on the staffs of state mental hospitals, 3 percent on the staffs of federal mental hospitals, and 4 percent on the staffs of community mental hospitals. Thirty-six percent were staff members of general hospitals, and 12.5 percent staff members of "University Mental Hospital Units." A portion of

Approximately 20 percent of the analysts do some teaching, mainly in psychoanalytic institutes, consulting, or supervising of psychoanalytic candidates, whereas the psychiatrists are more likely to be involved in administration, teaching, and consulting. Professional activities other than psychotherapy or psychoanalysis cover a large number of areas including editing of journals, organizational and committee work, and directing training programs in a variety of institutions including theological seminaries, law schools, community mental health clinics, and social service agencies. One psychiatrist "teaches a course in aviation psychiatry to student naval flight surgeons," while another serves as an adviser to the Peace Corps.*

Eleven analysts, or almost a third of the total, and eighteen psychiatrists, or 12 percent, devote more than 10 percent of their time to research or writing that is unsponsored, *i.e.,* not supported by grants or fellowships. As may be expected, the number of analysts engaged in sponsored research or writing activities is smaller, since most research in psychoanalysis does not receive support from governmental agencies or private foundations: only seven analysts devote more than 10 percent of their time to sponsored research or writing activities. Seventeen psychiatrists, on the other hand, devote 10 percent or more of their time to sponsored research, and of these four spend more than 50 percent of their time on research and writing. While, overall, the proportion of psychiatrists who engage in research is less than the proportion of analysts, those psychiatrists who do research are better supported than their counterparts in psychoanalysis.

Despite the relative lack of financial support for research, 14 of the analysts have published at least one book, and 27 at least one article, compared with 10 psychiatrists who have published at least one book and 91 who have published articles. More than a quarter of the analysts have published at least twenty articles, whereas only 7 percent of psychiatrists have published twenty or

---

the pilot study, which was conducted by the Committee on Public Information of the American Psychoanalytic Association, was reported in the *American Psychoanalytic Association Newsletter,* September, 1967.

* Of the 27 brief-questionnaire respondents, 51, or two-thirds, are primarily occupied with private practice, 7 of them mainly with analytic practice. Sixteen also do some teaching, 16 are involved in administration, and 22 serve as part-time consultants. Eight of the group are employed in public mental hospitals, and one works for the Veterans Administration.

more articles. Forty-eight percent of the psychiatrists and 46 percent of the analysts have published between one and ten articles.*

In their dealings with patients, the preferred therapeutic technique of both psychiatrists and analysts is a dynamic approach, which may be generally defined as the "study of the active, energy-laden, and changing factors in human behavior," with special reference to their motivation, evolution, and progression or regression.† More than 90 percent of the analysts and 67 percent of the psychiatrists employ such an approach, with an even larger percentage of the former (94.3 percent) describing themselves as Freudian with reference to that portion of their practice that is psychoanalytic as distinguished from psychotherapeutic. Twenty-eight percent of the psychiatrists rely extensively on drugs and shock therapy, 20 percent utilize a psychobiological approach to patients, and 14 percent are primarily engaged in family and marital therapy. Only 6 percent of psychiatrists are involved in group therapy, while among analysts more than 11 percent do some family and marital therapy.

When the analysts reject the Freudian label, they tend to substitute for it such terms as "eclectic" or "neo-Freudian," by which they usually mean they have been influenced by Erik H. Erikson or by concepts of ego psychology associated with Heinz Hartmann and Ernst Kris.** Since the analytic sample was entirely drawn from the membership of the American Psychoanalytic Associa-

---

* Thirteen of the 77 brief-questionnaire respondents have published twenty or more books or articles, 5 between ten and twenty, 9 between five and ten, and 36 between one and five. Fourteen have no publications.

† American Psychiatric Association, *A Psychiatric Glossary,* 3d ed. (1969). See also Appendix II.

** Although there is no simple definition of ego psychology, it may be understood to refer broadly to the autonomous cognitive, adaptive, synthesizing, and problem-solving functions of ego activities. In effect, exponents of ego psychology are more inclined than Freud to emphasize "the degree of independence of ego activities from drives and from involvements in conflict . . . [and] capacities and abilities . . . to perceive, to learn, to remember, to think, to move, and to act; talent and inborn gifts of all kinds, as well as dispositions to organize, to synthesize, to achieve balance from disequilibrium." George S. Klein, "Psychoanalysis: Ego Psychology," *International Encyclopedia of the Social Sciences,* 13 (New York: Macmillan and Free Press, 1968), 11–31. The leading theoretician of ego psychology is Heinz Hartmann, who, together with the late Ernst Kris, Rudolph Loewenstein, and the late David Rapaport, has done much to explicate the concepts involved. See his *Essays on Ego Psychology* (New York: International Universities Press, 1964). For a critique of ego psychology as developed by Hartmann and others, see Robert S. Holt, "Ego Autonomy Re-Evaluated," *International Journal of Psychiatry* (reprinted from *International Journal of Psycho-Analysis*), 3, 6 (June, 1967).

tion, it is to be expected that the so-called Freudian revisionists or deviationists have only a minute following; specifically, only one analyst indicates that his approach to patients has been influenced by Adler and Horney, and none describes himself as a follower in any sense of Jung, Rank, Melanie Klein, or the existential school. Four analysts, or 11 percent, refer to themselves as influenced by the theories of interpersonal psychiatry associated with Harry Stack Sullivan.

Those psychiatrists who employ a psychoanalytic approach in dealing with at least some patients are, in the main, Freudian, but not exclusively so. While thirty-three describe themselves as Freudian, nine indicate that they have been influenced by Sullivan, five by Horney, three by Jung, two by the existentialists, and one each by Adler and Klein. Many of them substitute "eclectic" for these labels, and other self-chosen terms include "somatic," "sociotherapeutic," "sector psychotherapy," and "adaptational." One indicates that he has been influenced by Adolf Meyer, and several say that their approach is determined "according to the patient's need," which, perhaps, is another way of describing themselves as eclectic. A few psychiatrists claim that they use all or most of the various approaches; as one of them puts it, "I rely on a mishmash of all these, mostly Freudian, some Horney, little if any Adler or Rank."

These approaches are brought to bear on a large array of problems, especially with reference to the practices of psychiatrists who deal with a considerable number and variety of ill individuals, but there are distinct preferences among both psychiatrists and analysts in terms of problems and patients. Both psychiatrists and analysts prefer to treat neurosis, followed, in the case of analysts, by characterological problems. Psychiatrists rank schizophrenia as their second preference, followed by other psychoses, and characterological problems. Beyond these categories the preferred disorders cover a large area: depressives, "borderline cases," marital problems, "psychiatric factors in physical illness (this is broader than psychosomatic)," "developmental problems," "hysterical personality problems," anxiety and phobic reactions—these are only a few of the categories mentioned. Here the data support the impression that some psychiatrists and analysts are extremely specialized in their practices, dealing exclusively or mainly with certain types of disorder, whereas others, in the words of one psychiatrist, "take anyone who comes through that door." *

In terms of age groups there are, again, clear preferences. Both psychiatrists and analysts prefer to treat adolescents, college students, and young and middle-aged married adults. The least preferred categories of patients are the very young (children and preadolescents), and the very old, although there are a few psychiatrists and analysts specializing in the problems of very young children and the aged. Overall, however, the preferred patient is between fifteen and sixty years of age.

And there are other preferred characteristics as well. Many analysts and psychiatrists emphasize the importance of education and/or intelligence, feeling that there are serious communications and hence treatment problems with patients of below-average intelligence or inferior education. Some feel that age is important on the grounds that personality changes are difficult or even impossible in late middle age or beyond. A few psychiatrists and analysts say they do better with middle-class patients, or those in the professions and white-collar occupations. A number of analysts express a distinct preference for patients who are creative or who have demonstrated leadership abilities; some stress the importance of empathy and rapport, of "mutual understanding." One analyst says that he prefers "introspective" patients who have basically "a good ego, and potential for growth and contributions to family and society." A psychiatrist expresses a preference for "high-ranking persons in the so-called 'power structure,'" and others emphasize the importance of "motivation" and being "psychologically minded."

The "rejects," so to speak, are headed by alcoholics; with both psychiatrists and analysts the least desired patient is an alcoholic, at least partly because such patients tend to have records of recidivism and missed appointments, and in other ways to perform badly as patients. It also appears that the rate of cure is very low.

* According to a study of Boston psychiatrists, between 20 and 50 percent of those in private practice do not accept for treatment adolescents with behavior problems, adult sociopaths, alcoholics, drug addicts, delinquent minors, persons suffering from acute and chronic brain syndromes, mentally retarded, and those afflicted with convulsive disorders. Most of the psychiatrists accepted for treatment patients with psychoneurotic disorders, chronic borderline disturbances, marital problems, sexual deviations, psychotic disorders, and symptoms of acute disturbance. H. C. Schuberg, Private Psychiatric Services in Massachusetts, as cited by Max Rinkel *et al.* in "Private Practice of Psychiatry: A Symposium," *American Journal of Psychiatry,* 122, 12 (June, 1966), 1372–77.

Among psychiatrists the next least preferred category of patient is the homosexual, whereas among analysts it is the schizophrenic. Almost a third of the analysts enjoy working with homosexual patients, as compared with 16 percent of the psychiatrists who enjoy working with homosexuals. While therapy or analysis tends to be more successful with homosexuals than with alcoholics, schizophrenics, and drug addicts, some psychiatrists and analysts feel that the demands made by homosexual patients are frequently prohibitive. One psychiatrist, comparing them to alcoholics, observes that most of his homosexual patients

> come to me with the request that I help them become happy homosexuals. I tell them I can't do that, that if they come for therapy the end result is that they will not be homosexual any more, that they will stop being homosexuals if they want to be free of their anxiety and tension and so on. Or else they will quit because we're not going where they want to go. The same thing is true of alcoholics. In fact, I don't take them at all because I haven't the time to waste with their broken appointments, their constantly having to be bailed out of jail, and their calling me at all hours of the night when they're drunk. Some of them come to me and ask "teach me how to be a social drinker," and I won't do that. I feel very strongly that there's no such thing as an alcoholic who can become a social drinker.

A woman psychiatrist who has had some success with lesbian patients, although "they invariably make a pass at you by saying that they'll give it up if only you'll do it with them once," reports that her success with homosexuals is limited to those who are relatively young and not wholly committed to homosexuality. The problem is that

> they're having a [homosexual] relationship on the outside, or if they're in a homosexual society the others are so threatened by the fact that this one might break away that they put too much pressure on him to stop and he usually does drop out. It's too much of a threat. The few cases I have had that have been successful are not the hard, died-in-the-wool homosexuals, but younger boys in their late teens or early twenties who have had a few homosexual experiences but who still have had some heterosexual experience and they're sort of flexible.

Not all psychiatrists, however, regard homosexuality as an illness in itself, and consequently not all of them deal with the problem even when a patient is manifestly homosexual. If, says one psychiatrist, there were no motivation to change,

> I wouldn't push it. Most homosexuals come for treatment because they're depressed over the breakup of a relationship, and so the treatment for them, it always seems to me, is to alleviate the depression. Not from a moral ground, but from clinical grounds.

An analyst comments that those homosexuals he has treated successfully

> have clearly been non-accepting of their homosexuality, have not wanted it, have been uncomfortable with it, have been limited, have experienced it as a self-destructive thing. People like this, I find, are capable of shifting sexual orientation and becoming heterosexual. Of course, other homosexuals come in for treatment, but that's not what they want help for. They want help for something else, and even where I may see what I think is a connection between the homosexuality and the other symptoms, unless the patient comes to see it, I leave it alone. And there are still other patients about whom I feel that homosexuality hasn't got a damn thing to do with their psychiatric problems.

With alcoholics and drug addicts the social setting, too, can be a factor limiting treatment success; in effect, report a number of psychiatrists, there is an alcoholic and drug subculture or "world," as there is a homosexual "world," from which patients may be neither able nor willing to separate themselves. A West Coast psychiatrist who has a large number of alcoholic patients observes that

> this county is a bastion for alcoholics if ever there was one. Maybe because it's a frustrated county, but I really don't know. We have a lot of discussions about it. For one thing, it's a rich county so people can afford to indulge their feelings in alcohol. Our divorce rate here is now 50 percent and our alcohol rate seems to be approaching something like that. I think that too much money around plays a role. Anyhow, since I have some success with alcoholics—I'm not sure why, perhaps because I'm rather direct and can be a forceful type of person—I get a lot of

> referrals, including some people who are really dying of alcoholism. I usually try to motivate them into AA and everything else I can think of that might help.

In discussing alcoholics, addiction, and delinquency one analyst makes the point that the Synanon approach to addiction could be followed in connection with other problems that analysts have trouble in treating. Synanon, he comments, has made great strides because

> they recognized years before we did that these people were untouchable by psychoanalysis. We should have been able to predict that you should never try to analyze an addict, that what he needed first was to make up for a deficiency in his early mothering relationship, give him a home, take him in, make him a member of the family first. Only with that can he become neurotic, only then can he advance to being a neurotic. *Then* you can treat him with analysis. Analysis can treat neurosis, but nothing else. I realize this is a controversial point, but I firmly believe that the psychotics, the borderlines, the addicts, the delinquents, all need preliminary forms of treatment to make them analyzable people.

For psychiatrists and analysts who are atheists or who, like Freud, regard religion as a form of neurosis, there can be serious treatment problems with patients who are deeply religious and especially patients who are members of fundamentalist sects. Some analysts say bluntly that they would regard the analysis as a failure if a patient continued to be religious following his analysis, while others declare that they do not do well with patients who are reluctant to discuss the obsessive aspects of their religious convictions. A psychiatrist who confesses to past difficulties with patients who were devout Catholics has the impression that

> the Catholic community tends to find out who the Catholic psychiatrists are, and the referrals are directly to them. For example, the closest Catholic university to here is Loyola—just about five minutes from here—and the university refers its people to Catholic psychiatrists in ———. I don't know how the Jewish people handle that. Of course, there are enough Jewish analysts to go around. There is no shortage of them, so far as I can see.

One view frequently expressed is that deeply religious people tend not to go to psychiatrists and analysts, but when they do the effect is to promote less rigidity and more open-mindedness. An analyst with a rather diversified practice comments:

> There can be no question that religious beliefs are often used by patients for neurotic purposes. The interesting thing to me is what happens to these people as their neuroticism is alleviated. I recall one patient, a very religious Catholic and an intensely neurotic personality, who developed an acute fear of going downtown. She was in treatment for some time, and the thing that interested me was to see how her view of religion changed. Not that she became less a Catholic. She remained a Catholic, but the flexibility, the interest in all aspects of Catholicism, increased. Whereas before all she did was to take all the punitive, limiting parts of the religion and make them into what she thought was good Catholicism.

Another analyst, discussing a patient in treatment who belonged to a fundamentalist Protestant sect, said that while he did not directly "touch" the patient's religion,

> I do touch other things that connect with it. For example, he was very upset today because he thought of doing a certain act which was sexually aggressive. He didn't do it, but he was terribly upset, as though he had done it, so I pointed out, "You know, it's strange that you react to the thought of the deed as though you did it." And he said, "Well, it says in the Scriptures that this is a sin." But I said, "Well, let's face it, there is a big difference, isn't there? You did not do it, you did not offend your wife, you did not seduce this woman. You made yourself miserable. There is a big difference." Now I know that afterwards, when he walked out, he probably thought "What is ——— trying to do, undermine my religion?" Well, what *could* I do? There is a difference. But I don't directly raise the religious issue with this guy because he's too sick for that. He's got to get around to it when he's ready, and I've got to wait until he is ready. But I can't let this episode go by without pointing out that here *is* a difference, no matter what the Bible says.

An encounter with another patient, who was very upset, had the patient telling his analyst that "he had decided to pray." "Well," queried the analyst,

> "What else might you have done?", meaning "How come you didn't think analytically and ask yourself why you were so upset?" And he said instantly, "Oh, you think I shouldn't pray?" I said, "No, that's not the point. I didn't mean you shouldn't pray, but after you've finished praying, couldn't you ask yourself 'What's upsetting me?' Think about it. You did the easy thing. It's easy to pray. I want you to do something harder, to take a step away and look at yourself, and ask 'what am I so upset about?' " Now, you see, eventually this is going to happen to this man.[3]

Political fundamentalists also raise problems for psychiatrists and analysts, who, as will be seen in a later chapter, are themselves preponderantly liberal Democrats. While members of the John Birch Society, the Ku Klux Klan, various paramilitary organizations, and the Communist Party, like those who are devoutly religious, are not likely to become psychiatric or psychoanalytic patients (unless, of course, they become patients in mental hospitals), many psychiatrists have an occasional patient whose political affiliation is extreme right or extreme left. Usually, the experience is not a successful one, with either the patient or the psychiatrist terminating therapy after only a few consultations. The major reason for the termination is the discomfort of the patient, or his doctor, or both, occasioned by the lack of personality rapport and the absence of shared values, whether therapeutic or other. In one reported instance involving a patient who had been a Nazi Party member in Germany and a Jewish psychiatrist, both the patient and the doctor found themselves extremely uncomfortable, and the relationship came to an early end.

But the problems raised by rigidity and inflexibility on the part of patients, religious or political, are not confined to extremist and fundamentalist affiliations. Some psychiatrists and analysts are ill at ease with conservative Republicans, but this feeling may reflect the strength of the therapist's personal commitment to a different set of values; others report that they never discover, or discover only at the end of treatment, the political conviction of their patients. One psychiatrist claims that most patients as well as psychiatrists are Democrats, and that there is also some relationship between the type of treatment administered and the politics of both patients and their doctors. Specifically, he feels that psychiatrists who rely mainly on shock therapy, and their patients, are likely to be Republicans, whereas those who do psychotherapy or psychoanalysis, and their patients, are likely to be Democrats.* Having conducted a "private poll" since 1952 that reveals he has a 99 percent Democratic practice, he comments:

> There is a connection between the people who come for therapy and are willing to look inward, and being Democratic. They want true independence. There have been times when I wanted to interrupt treatment and I am told "Please don't. I want to continue because I'm not finished." The wish is to assume an independent position. These people are willing to give up the dependency advantages that are offered by institutionalization. People stop very often when they have relief from symptoms. But with the liberal Democrats who come in for therapy there is a willingness to move beyond relief from symptoms to real independence. Some of these people at the beginning present too fluid a tolerance for ambiguity—almost an excessive tolerance—and an excessive belief that they might be wrong. They are almost too flexible, which shows that passivity and acceptance or tolerance sometimes get mixed up.

The consensus of both psychiatrists and psychoanalysts is that successful psychotherapy, by promoting open-mindedness, relative freedom from intrapsychic conflicts, and a decrease in rigidity of belief, moves patients toward a moderate or middle-road political position if they were not already there at the commencement of treatment. Of course, a good many private patients, perhaps a majority, like most psychiatrists, are liberal Republicans or Dem-

---

* It is of interest in this connection that high scores on the F-scale, a measure of right-wing authoritarian personality tendencies, appear to correlate with administration of drugs and electric shock treatment by psychiatrists. It also appears that patients with high F-scale scores receive more electric shock therapy than those with low scores, the latter being more apt to receive psychotherapy. Since many psychiatrists believe that lower-class and nonwhite patients respond better to drugs than to psychotherapy, because of limited verbal facility and ability to express themselves, the use of drug therapy by psychiatrists varies inversely with class, color, and income of patients. An unproven but frequently encountered assumption among psychotherapists is that high drug usage by psychiatrists goes along with a tendency to value status differences, self-control, and sense of duty. See Gerald F. Klerman, Milton R. Sharaf, Mathilda Holzman, and Daniel J. Levinson, "Sociopsychological Characteristics of Resident Psychiatrists and Their Use of Drug Therapy," *American Journal of Psychiatry,* 117, 2 (August, 1960), 111–17; M. Greenblatt, Daniel J. Levinson, and R. W. Williams (eds.), *The Patient and the Mental Hospital* (Glencoe, Ill.: The Free Press, 1957), 356–79; and Robert L. Kahn, Max Pollock, and Max Fink, "Sociopsychologic Aspects of Psychiatric Treatment in a Voluntary Mental Hospital," *Archives of General Psychiatry,* 1, 6 (December, 1959), 565–74.

ocrats before they begin therapy, which may be an important reason why politics in general, much less party preference or voting, is seldom discussed by psychiatrists and their patients.

Members of minority groups and the poor rarely see psychiatrists as private patients, and they are even less likely to deal with analysts, for the obvious reason that they cannot afford such treatment. But there are other factors as well. Many psychiatrists feel uncomfortable working in lower-class and ghetto communities and do not relate well to patients from these areas. A Boston study of fourth-year medical students found that they developed a variety of defensive attitudes that interfered with their work. Such attitudes, to some extent based on their own depression in encountering slum life for the first time, were expressed in punitive, rejecting feelings toward the poor, overidentification with them, or withdrawn and apathetic behavior. It was only after group discussions involving experienced psychiatrists that the students were able to develop more balanced and realistic behavioral patterns.[4]

Many psychiatrists and analysts assume that the poor, and especially Negroes, are essentially unreachable by psychotherapy because of limited verbal facility, suspicion of doctors in general, and tendency to believe that pills and pills alone can work miracles no matter what it is that ails them. As one psychiatrist attached to a public clinic puts it:

> When I first came here I had high hopes of doing something about the neglected people who are sick—the Negroes, Mexicans, Puerto Ricans, the poor in general. But I've become sort of disillusioned. Most of them really can't be reached, because they live in cultures where "acting out" is habitual, where you don't talk much and practically never in intimate terms about yourself. So when I tried to discuss things with them, they just wouldn't discuss. "Look, Doc," they'd say, "forget the horseshit. I know all that. Just give me something to get through the day so I don't lose my temper so much." Well, what can you do?

But not all psychiatrists and analysts believe that the poor and the deprived minority groups are unreachable. The *American Journal of Orthopsychiatry,* the official publication of the American Orthopsychiatric Association, has repeatedly drawn attention to the possibility that middle-class biases and prejudices on the part of psychiatrists play an important role in the assumption that the poor and lower-class populations are not suitable for therapy and analysis.[5] In addition to locating their practices in areas of the cities and suburbs with which the poor are unfamiliar, and in which, in some cases, Negroes on the street would be viewed by the police and others with great suspicion, psychiatrists often are unwilling to learn the special languages or "lingo" of the poor or alter their approach to take into account the great difference between middle-class culture and the culture of poverty. One psychiatrist who has worked extensively with deprived and mainly Negro children reports that it took awhile to adjust from a white middle-class school atmosphere to this "other America" where the problems are often very different:

> In the middle class clinics where I worked the problems of adolescents usually involved lack of motivation—grades not good enough—underachievement, lack of responsibility, things like that. Whereas with the downtown [Negro] kids there are terribly acute problems that no one is aware of, not even the teachers. Many of these kids are chronically depressed, and while this would be picked up in another kind of school, downtown it's written off by the teachers as: this is an apathetic, lazy child, who just won't study. In fact, this is an acutely depressed child. . . .

In treating such children, moreover, the entire therapeutic approach must be altered to take acount of social problems that exist less or not at all in middle-class school communities. As one psychiatrist familiar with these problems expressed it:

> You learn very quickly to do some things and not do others. For example, you don't ask them who's at home. You don't ask about their parents. You don't ask what their father does. You ask "who lives at your house?" and things like that, so that you elicit the right instead of the wrong responses. You find that the kids are very concrete in their thinking, unlike middle class kids, and this raises problems for the teachers. The beginning teachers complain that everything they say is taken literally, and I have found this, too, and it can be quite a problem. Because you think you are giving an analogy and then you realize the kids have taken it literally.

There is also evidence that ethnocentricity and the existence of cultural stereotypes among psychiatrists play a role in the relative exclusion of Negroes and other minorities from the psychotherapeutic universe. While psychiatrists and analysts, as will be seen later, are much freer of race prejudice than other Americans, it appears that there is a relationship between lack of prejudice and the treatment of minority group patients. In one study of almost 600 consecutive new admissions to the outpatient clinic of the Los Angeles County General Hospital, it was found that therapists with the least ethnic prejudice treated many more non-Caucasian patients than therapists with high ethnocentricity. In ethnic terms, the most "popular" patients with therapists were, in order of popularity, Caucasian women, Caucasian men, Mexican-American women, Negro women, and lastly Mexican-American and Negro men.[6]

A further factor that creates, at the very least, some ambiguity in attitudes toward certain minorities, and especially Negroes, finds expression in some disdain for aspects of minority group culture. One analyst who has thought about the problem and the nature of his own feelings about Negroes confesses

> I've gone through some periods of very private anti-Negro feeling. I think it's because there are neurotic aspects about the Negro thing. I think, by God, I don't want this rock-and-roll, this corruption. There's nothing so wonderful about the jungle tradition. It shouldn't become our cultural norm. But sometimes I see the Negro as the height of moral and ethical position in this country right now, while at other times I see him as a retrogressive influence in the culture. I guess it's not an easy thing to explain.*

In other words, the psychiatrist, for a variety of reasons, is not entirely free of the prejudices that afflict other Americans, and this, too, influences the distribution of psychiatric services.†

* The analyst quoted added, as an afterthought, that his "ambivalent feelings" probably reflected his lack of involvement with Negroes, in addition to "ignorance, insulation and neurosis(?)." Perhaps, he suggested, such feelings represent "secondary values, as contrasted to primary values. . . ."

† Thus, it has been pointed out that the negative response of a Negro patient to a white psychiatrist may reflect the patient's awareness of some prejudice on the part of the therapist, not the "pseudofact" that the patient is untreatable. What

This distribution in the future may be significantly affected by militancy within the black community and in psychiatry itself. At the 1969 annual meeting of the APA, about 100 black psychiatrists demanded that the APA become "more relevant to black people" and, in effect, recognize that "racism is the major mental health problem in this country." Charging discrimination against black patients and psychiatrists, the group of black psychiatrists at the meeting in Miami Beach called upon the APA to revoke the membership of psychiatrists who refuse to see black or other minority group patients or who practice and work in segregated facilities. There was also insistence that more black psychiatrists be appointed to psychiatry departments in medical schools, that black psychiatrists be given more assignments in the National Institute of Mental Health, and that the APA itself immediately add five blacks to its nineteen-member council. Perhaps the most important and most difficult demand put forward was that blackness as such be accepted and even valued by white psychiatrists and analysts rather than rejected in favor of what one black psychiatrist called a " 'hallucinatory whitening' of the black resident in an attempt to assimilate him. . . ." Officers of the APA, led by its 1969–70 president, Raymond W. Waggoner, agreed to discuss the demands of the black militant psychiatrists at future meetings of the executive committee.[7]

Finally, the choice of patients is affected by highly subjective considerations that vary widely from therapist to therapist and often reflect the psychiatrist's own problems or inadequate defenses against certain anxieties and insecurities. "I do have some difficulty," an experienced psychiatrist reports,

> based on my own emotional makeup, in dealing with people who are really extremely helpless and dependent. I have trouble giving myself to these people, in fact, I get a little uncomfortable and I think, gee, I'd just like to give them a real good kick in the butt and get them out and get them going. And some people are just

---

is interpreted as the "negative transference" may simply be a reaction to the patient's therapist's "countertransference." Hence the need for psychiatrists to understand that "the black patient must come to terms with his negritude. . . . He carries into therapy a heavy predisposition to show anger, distrust, fear, and resentment . . . his self-esteem is so low that self-hatred is ubiquitous." Paul L. Adams, director of the Children's Mental Health Unit, University of Florida, as quoted in *Psychiatric News,* December, 1968.

> too sick to get out and get going and I find that frustrating. I think my easiest, my best rapport and the best work I do is with people who fight. I guess this is because I've been a fighter all my own life and perhaps have some emotional difficulty that I fought but I never gave up the fight. . . .

An analyst whose patients are mainly of the upper class admits to difficulty with

> somebody who's a member of just the Cadillac cult. I find these people terribly boring because I don't have much in common with them. I don't know anything about the stock market. I don't like to go to Las Vegas. I guess I really can't take much of the white-on-whiters, the people who are interested in making a lot of money and who don't have many or even any redeeming features.

There are analysts who try to confine their practices to creative people in the arts and theater, perhaps because, as one of them puts it who has had much experience with Hollywood personalities, "many of us [analysts] are essentially frustrated novelists, artists, or actors." A few psychiatrists whose research interests are directed toward problems of aging deal mainly with elderly patients, and some are primarily concerned with infants and very young children, but these are the exceptions.

As may be expected, the preferences of psychiatrists and analysts with respect to patients are reflected in their practices. To begin with, analysts see fewer patients than psychiatrists, and both psychiatrists and analysts see fewer patients than other physicians. A 1964 study of 250 psychiatrists in full-time private practice found that the average psychiatrist sees 7.8 patients per day, compared with 20.5 for general practitioners and 16.3 for all private physicians. Eighty percent of the patients seen were in the twenty-to-sixty age group, and almost half were between twenty and thirty-nine. About 60 percent of the total number of patients were women.[8]

Of the analysts in the study group 41 percent see between 11 and 20 patients per week, and 28 percent see between 1 and 10 patients per week. Nineteen percent see between 21 and 30 patients, and only 6 percent see between 31 and 40 patients. Almost a quarter of the psychiatrists, on the other hand, see more than 40 patients each week (no analyst sees that many patients), 21 percent see between 21 and 30 patients, and 22 percent see between 11 and 20 patients.

Most of these patients are white and from the business, professional, or white-collar occupations; more than half of them are women. About a third of the analysts do not have any Catholic patients. A fifth of the analysts, on the other hand, have Jewish patients to the extent of between 75 and 100 percent of their practice, and for another quarter of the analysts Jews constitute between 50 and 75 percent of their total practice. Among the analysts there are no Puerto Rican, Mexican, or Indian patients, and only three analysts have any Negro patients; in these instances, the Negro patient percentage is less than 5 percent of the total number of patients.

Only two psychiatrists have Catholic patients comprising between 75 and 100 percent of their practice, and only 10 percent of psychiatrists see fewer than 5 percent Catholic patients. For a quarter of psychiatrists, Catholics constitute between 30 and 50 percent of their patients, and for a fifth between 15 and 20 percent of their patients. Only four psychiatrists report that Jews total between 75 and 100 percent of their patients, whereas 28 percent have Jewish patients to the extent of 5 percent or less of their practice. For another 16 percent, Jews constitute between 5 and 10 percent of patients. Seventy-two psychiatrists, or almost half of the total group, have some Negro patients, but fifty of these psychiatrists see fewer than 10 percent of patients who are Negro. Twenty-three psychiatrists have some Mexican patients, two some Indian, nineteen some Puerto Rican, and twenty-one some Oriental patients.

Only one analyst, as compared with 83 psychiatrists, has any blue-collar patients. Almost all of the analysts have patients who are white-collar employees, businessmen, or writers, and almost two-thirds have some patients who are students. About three-quarters of the analysts see patients who are teachers or doctors, and all but six have patients who are housewives. Six analysts see some clergymen. Psychiatrists see more housewives, teachers, students, and clergymen than analysts, as well as more blue-collar workers, but fewer writers and doctors (perhaps because, with reference to doctors, the category includes psychiatrists who are undergoing a personal analysis as part of their analytic training).

Patient problems most often reported by psychiatrists are, in order of frequency, depression, character disorders, psychosis, and marital and family discord. Among the patients of analysts, on the other hand, the most common problems appear to be character disorders, followed by depression, marital and family discord, and psychosis. Psychiatrists are more likely than analysts to deal with alcoholics, and analysts more likely than psychiatrists to treat patients with sexual problems such as impotence and homosexuality.

For both psychiatrists and analysts the treatment of preference is individual psychotherapy, but 54 psychiatrists and 8 analysts do some family therapy, and 47 psychiatrists and 1 analyst engage to some extent in group psychotherapy. More than 80 percent of psychiatrists occasionally use drugs in treating patients, mainly tranquilizers and antidepressants, as compared with 46 percent of the analysts. Electric shock treatment is sometimes used by more than a third of the psychiatrists, whereas only one analyst occasionally administers electric shock. About 20 percent of psychiatrists will consider using behavior conditioning as a form of treatment, and approximately 10 percent may make use of hypnosis. No analyst indicates any preference for behavior conditioning, and only three occasionally try hypnosis.

Diagnosis of the patient's condition is mainly by interview techniques usually directed to gathering information about the patient's history and that of his family. A trial period of consultation is very much the rule with analysts, but much less so with psychiatrists, and analysts also make more use of projective tests, such as the Rorschach. Psychiatrists, on the other hand, rely more on nonprojective tests and evaluations by psychologists. Only 25 percent of psychiatrists and 11 percent of analysts require the patient to undergo a physical examination prior to treatment.

Neither psychiatrists nor analysts welcome social encounters with their patients, although in small towns and the suburbs such encounters are not always easy to avoid. Well over half of the psychiatrists and almost three-quarters of the analysts try to avoid such encounters—and there can be little doubt that the typical patient, too, makes an effort *not* to meet his psychiatrist or analyst at a cocktail party or dinner gathering. More than half the psychiatrists, however, endeavor to see the families of patients if, as is often the case, the patient's problems reflect family situations, but they are not likely to see the friends or colleagues of a patient, much less visit his place of work. Less than a third of the analysts make it a point to see the families of patients, and only two see the friends or colleagues of patients.

Unlike the situation in certain countries abroad, American psychiatrists and analysts rarely make house calls, and in general there is no systematic follow-up of patients after treatment has been terminated. But there is increasing discussion of the desirability of house calls and follow-ups, and there are several psychiatrists in the study group who endeavor to visit patients in their home settings. As one of them describes the advantages:

> The idea is very much against the psychoanalytic conception of the psychiatrist's function, but I think it is damned important anyhow. I have learned as much from one house call and seeing the patient in his home interacting with his family as I ever did in fifteen or twenty office sessions. You come to realize that it's impossible for one person to describe another person, but if you can see them together you learn more than you would from hours and hours of discussion.

Many psychiatrists and analysts who deal with marital problems make it a point to see the spouse of the patient, who, as one psychiatrist puts it, "may be the *really* sick one in the family," and it goes without saying that psychiatrists who practice family therapy will devote at least some sessions to meetings with the entire family group including children and in-laws, if any.

Those who make their way to psychiatrists' offices get there by a variety of routes. It has been estimated that about 60 percent of patients are referred by other doctors to whom they have gone with reference to a somatic complaint for which no physical basis could be found. Of course, many patients are led to a psychiatrist's office as a consequence of their own awareness of problems for which they seek a solution, problems such as chronic fatigue, marital unhappiness, depression and irritability, anxiety, and bizarre behavior patterns. College students may be referred by deans or faculty advisers, and in a growing number of corporations facilities exist for psychiatric consultations, especially at managerial levels. While psychiatrists in the armed forces see patients mainly on the basis of referrals from other doctors or requests for evaluation from commanding officers, regular screening processes have been established for individuals in sensitive positions and for some high-ranking officers in the Strategic Air

Command, NASA, and certain other agencies with heavy responsibilities for the nation's security. For the most part these screening processes are confined to personality measures and tests of the inkblot variety, such as the Rorschach, but they can and do include consultations with psychiatrists.

Because the decision to undergo psychoanalysis is a voluntary one that entails a considerable expenditure of money and time, the patients of analysts are very different from the patients of psychiatrists. According to a study reported in 1967, almost 99 percent of those treated by analysts are white persons about equally divided between Protestants and Jews; only 10 percent are Catholics or members of denominations other than Protestant or Jewish. Forty-two percent had attended college, and 36 percent had been to graduate school. More than 15 percent had incomes higher than $20,000 per year, and 25 percent had annual incomes between $10,000 and $20,000. More than half the patients seeing analysts, like those seeing psychiatrists, are women, and by age the most significant group are persons between twenty-six and thirty-five years old. Of the 3,019 patients dealt with in the study, 49 percent were in psychoanalysis and 51 percent in psychotherapy.

Since no general rules have been established by analysts for the selection of patients, each analyst has his own way of determining whether or not a given individual is analyzable and is likely to benefit from analysis. It need hardly be added that psychoanalysis overall, like other services, is affected by supply-and-demand factors, and an analyst who has several unfilled analytic hours may be less inclined to turn away patients seeking analysis, whatever their problems, than one whose time is fully occupied. As noted earlier, analysts appear to be doing more psychotherapy relative to psychoanalysis than used to be the case, and it is therefore reasonable to suppose that patients with sufficient money and time for analysis are more rather than less welcome in most analysts' waiting rooms throughout the land.*

* A 1965 study of psychoanalysts' patients in the Baltimore area showed that most of them were not in analysis but in intensive psychotherapy. The patients of the analysts, as compared with those of the psychiatrists, in the study were more highly educated and included more Jews and fewer Catholics. Only two patients diagnosed as psychotic were in analysis, whereas 16 percent of all patients in the study were psychotic. The study, undertaken by Gerald D. Klee and Jean Warthen, was reported in *Psychiatric News,* July, 1967.

Even so, there are enough likes and dislikes, and acceptances and rejections, to justify the statement that many analysts choose their patients much more carefully than many patients choose their analysts. If some analysts, in effect, welcome persons with characterological problems, identity crises, or what-not, there are others with clear preferences for patients with phobias, conversion symptoms, and obsessive-compulsive neurosis. But perhaps more important than problems—or, as many psychiatrists would put it, "labels" that may or may not have meaning—are such qualities in patients as self-knowledge, insight, introspection, and above all intelligence. In the words of one experienced analyst:

> Unfortunately, the younger analyst starting out doesn't choose, he takes everything that comes along. But when you get old enough and have enough patients, then you can choose. In my case, I soon found out that I like to work with bright adults, or post-adolescents who are in trouble but have skills and potentials that I think are worthwhile. I try to bring them to a state of actuality—get them back to school or settled in an occupation. When I do that, I feel I've accomplished something. The problem is to determine what strengths, really, does the patient have. Can he endure the self-knowledge, the confrontation with himself? Sometimes you find, as you test this out, as the patient gets a little knowledge, that he reacts so violently you think he's becoming psychotic. Because he can't stand it he begins to retreat, and you feel, well, it's dangerous to analyze this guy. I remember someone once saying, I think it was Edith Weigart but she may have been quoting someone else, that you have to be a pretty healthy person to be successfully analyzed. Well, there's something in that. . . .

The interaction between therapist or analyst and patient is such as to make it extremely difficult to specify the desirable qualities in either one. "After all these years," runs one comment,

> I'm still not sure what makes a good psychiatrist, and I'm even less sure about analysts. There is a lot of variation among the best. But I would say it's important to know what kind of patients you like to work with and what kind you do well with. It's hard to generalize, but I will say this: it's wrong for a person to commit himself too much to a theoretical position and technical aspects so that he can't play a natural role with another human being.

> After all, when two people meet, the first thing they should try to do is to understand their explicit system of communication—what kind of words the other guy is using, what are his concepts, and so forth. Once that is clear they can begin to really communicate and understand each other at the implicit level. What I'm saying is that a good analyst or therapist can communicate and also understand systems of communication that are not the same.

On the patient's side, according to several studies, successful psychotherapy is related to low authoritarianism, an active and responsible self-concept, and a conviction that the therapist or analyst is interested in him and believes in his improvement or recovery.[9]

In addition to the personal qualities, the home environment and social relationships of patients are stressed by some analysts who argue that the patient must be mature enough not to use his analytic insights as a weapon against others. "Sometimes there is a kind of paradox," runs a comment,

> in that people, individually, are helped by analysis, but their families are less helped. I think this is because analysts pay so much attention to the individual patient they aren't aware of the acting-out the patient does in working through his conflicts. So the effect on the spouse and kids is kind of left out, and the analyst may not even hear about it. Sometimes there is analysis when family therapy would be better. . . .

Sometimes, too, the title of one of Freud's papers, "Analysis: Terminable or Interminable," becomes uncomfortably relevant as the time on the couch extends to five, ten, even fifteen years, or as the first analysis is superseded by a second, and third, and so forth. At least one analyst specializes in second analyses, and it is clear that a very large number of analysts have themselves undergone second analyses and in some cases third analyses.* While not all analysts feel concern about analyses lasting a dozen years, or about multiple analyses, others share the opinion of the late Franz Alexander that in the first instance if not the second, something has gone wrong. "In such long-term cases," says one analyst,

---

* See Chapter IV, pp. 101–2.

> it may be that the person is just unanalyzable. Or it may be that the analyst is the problem. You see, when an analyst takes on a patient, he gets to feeling very comfortable with this patient. He doesn't like to give him up, and he may rationalize this with the notion that it will take more time to dig deeper, to get at the roots, the primary sources of the conflict, etc. etc. So he keeps on interminably although he knows some place he isn't accomplishing any more.

In other cases, the difficulty may not be in the analyst or the technique used, but the fact

> that there's a limit to what a person can learn, a limit to his learning capacity, and when you reach that limit, that's it. Alexander knew this, and so he tried to shorten analysis for the same reasons that psychiatrists try to shorten the hospital time of patients. They say, "When we put a patient in the hospital that patient has given up his responsibility and has become dependent upon us. He has a structured environment and he feels fine. The task then is: he doesn't want to go out, he doesn't want to go home. We've got to see to it that he doesn't become too used to this kind of environment."
>
> Alexander's idea was that we should avoid fostering dependency by making appointments irregular, by cancelling occasionally, by giving the patient vacations so that he's on his own and sees what he can do. That way he experiments with life and then we know what successes and failures he has. Alexander thought that drawing out the length of an analysis was for the benefit of the analyst, not the patient. And Alexander was right. When anybody comes to me and says he's been in analysis for ten years, I'll wager anything he hasn't learned anything in [the last] five years.*

Whether this hypothetical patient learned anything in the *first* five years is, as noted earlier, a question that does not admit to only one answer. While most patients of psychiatrists and analysts feel they are gaining in understanding of their problems—or, in

---

* One study of "reanalysis" suggests that the majority of those who have second, third, fourth, and even fifth analyses may be "addicted to analysis," and that such "addicts" may constitute a majority of analytic patients in large-city practices. In other cases, "reanalysis" may be sought because of new or reactivated traumas and strains, such as those that afflict analysts themselves in the course of practice. See Alberta B. Szalita, "Reanalysis," *Contemporary Psychotherapy*, 4 (Spring, 1968), 83–102.

some cases, "getting better"—little is known about what leads to therapeutic success and failure, or to what extent one treatment form is superior to another. Despite claims of protagonists that this or that technique is particularly successful, it remains true, as a leading analyst has observed, that *"no one has as yet devised a scientifically valid means of testing the results of any form of psychotherapy, and anyone who claims that this or that method (including psychoanalysis) is better or worse than any other method is voicing a personal impression and not pronouncing a scientific truth"* [10] (italics in original). Freud himself eventually concluded that psychoanalysis was important less as a technique of therapy than as an approach to an understanding of human behavior, past and present.

One psychiatrist, commenting on a medical journal article demonstrating that the "cure rate" for neurotic difficulties was about the same regardless of treatment or even whether the patients received any treatment, confessed that while he could not really disagree with the findings,

> it's sort of disconcerting to read this sort of thing. Many of my patients tell me they feel better. I don't know what that means. Does it mean they feel better because they saw me rather than a minister, or that in spite of seeing me they feel better?

An analyst who had confined himself to short annual vacations because of concern about his patients finally, at the insistence of his wife, went abroad for several months. He was careful to make "on-call" arrangements with colleagues so that a rapid deterioration or crisis in a patient's condition could be dealt with while he was away. When he returned, he found that only two patients had contacted his colleagues and, further, that there was no change in the proportions of his patients who improved, became worse, and stayed the same. In other words, his patients did as well or as poorly when he was absent as when he was seeing them regularly, and this unexpected result, he admits, "shook me up but good!" But another analyst finds nothing surprising in this experience. The crucial factor in analytic or therapeutic success, he feels, is the extent to which the patient's illness is reversible and treated as such. As he puts it:

> If the patient can learn, there is a good chance the analyst or therapist will be successful. But if the patient is treated in certain ways so that he develops a career as a patient, then there will be little or no reversibility. This is why, wherever you go, you'll find the figures "between 60 and 80 percent are improved," whatever the method. What is probably important, as Carl Rogers says, is that the relationship between therapist and patient be a relationship where the therapist has respect for another decent human being and hope for the potentialities of this other person. To me, that's all it may be about.

Although one study of psychoanalysis has reported that 97.3 percent of patients were judged by their analysts, and 96.6 percent judged by themselves, to have improved in "total functioning," the overall rate of "symptom cure" was 27 percent.[11] The cure rate may appear low until it is remembered that the rate is no higher in many branches of medicine concerned with chronic diseases and those diseases that, typically, are far along before they are detected. Of course, all analysts and psychiatrists have had patients who committed suicide or who became psychotic because an underlying psychosis was exposed by the analysis or therapist, but it is probable that these unfortunate results would have obtained had these patients not sought help. Somewhat more difficult to deal with is the charge that some types of analysis produce undesirable changes in the personalities of patients. According to Fredric Wertham, patients treated by orthodox (strict Freudian) analysts "often become individualistic; their philosophy becomes aggressive; some of them become over-introspective, unaltruistic, egotistical." [12] Of course, such patients may have been that way before analysis. While it is often observed that many analysts seem to lack a sense of humor, again there is no clear evidence that this is the consequence of their own analysis or a professional characteristic. Psychoanalysis, as Freud noted, cannot work and should not be expected to work a total personality change. The earlier "oversell" of psychoanalysis in America was based not on any claims put forward by Freud or his followers, but on naïve hopes that there had been found, finally, a new and certain road to human perfectibility, and in Freud himself a new deity.

What analysis and a good deal of psychiatry can and do effect has been summed up as follows:

> The more the neurotic inhibitions are dispelled and anxiety is extirpated, the more does natural self-consciousness emerge and the less stiff and cramped are the attitudes of the personality. The field of experience is enlarged, the attitude toward work and toward other people becomes more open and natural—without too much dependence, without exaggerated demands, but also without exaggerated modesty.[13]

As far as his patients are concerned, says one analyst,

> I would like them to come out of it with the capacity to love well, to work well, to play well, and to expect, well, to have some optimism about the future. If they have these abilities, that's quite enough. I'll settle for that.

Many patients, it appears, maintain some sort of continuing contact with their analysts that may go on for years after the analysis is terminated. "My patients do get in touch with me," an analyst comments,

> either to tell me about their success or to complain that they couldn't do what they expected to be able to do after analysis, and maybe therefore they should come back. I generally have an interview with them, and if there is really something more to be done, I'll do it. If not, I encourage them to accept what is. Sometimes it's all mixed up with tranference and countertransference. You know, these are never really over. You talk to almost any patient and he'll tell you, "I know if I get into trouble I can always go back to my analyst." Patients imagine the analyst is always there, sitting in that chair day and night, hardly ever goes on vacation, rarely gets sick, and is never going to die!

Unfortunately, some patients in analysis or therapy reach a point at which they are happy with life or pleased with themselves and therefore terminate treatment even though the analyst or therapist may feel they are still short of the optimal results. It may also happen that treatment is terminated by the therapist, not because the patient is restored to health or functioning with total efficiency, but because the patient has exhausted his learning capacity and there is nothing more to gain from further treatment.

In either case, some success has been achieved, and it is very likely that the great majority of the millions who have consulted psychiatrists and the thousands who have seen analysts *have* made some progress toward better mental health, or better ways of coping with problems, or the ability, in Freud's words, to love and work. Even if therapy or analysis does not, as was once claimed, lead to "a median income gain of $28 per week after a median of 57 therapy sessions,"[14] it cannot be doubted that most psychiatrists and analysts make a substantial contribution to the well-being of their patients.

IV

Career Patterns, Preferences, and Problems

"LET me freely admit," confesses psychoanalyst Theodor Reik, "that in these thirty-five years of psychoanalytic practice, I have had this wish [to change professions] more than once. I have had moods in which being a psychoanalyst appeared to me less a profession than a calamity." [1] Probably most psychiatrists and psychoanalysts have shared such moods at one time or another, but it does not appear that career dissatisfaction is a foremost characteristic of the profession. While there are complaints about a variety of working conditions, the intensity and number of job satisfactions is far greater than the intensity and number of dissatisfactions, even if some of the latter are serious hindrances to professional achievement. Moreover, few psychiatrists and analysts are known to have left psychiatry for other professions, whereas, as noted earlier, the psychiatric ranks include a number of practitioners whose former occupations range from the ministry to veterinary medicine. When psychiatrists change professional emphasis, the shifts are likely to be from clinical practice to teaching, research, or administration, or in the reverse direction, rather than toward a wholly different occupational endeavor.[2]

Both psychiatrists and analysts list helping people as the major career satisfaction, with the analysts giving equal rank and the psychiatrists second rank to the feeling of being socially useful. In third place, and ranking well ahead of such other satisfactions as status and opportunity for advancement, are income and financial security, cited by 48 psychiatrists, or almost a third of the total, and 16 analysts, or 46 percent. For both psychiatrists and analysts working conditions rank fourth, followed by status and, in last position, opportunity for professional advancement.

Some mention, in addition, "intellectual stimulation" and "intellectual excitement" or "challenge." One psychiatrist stresses the "opportunity to experiment with new and better ways of establishing interpersonal intimacy between myself and other human beings in a disciplined and professional matrix, and getting paid for same." Several mention teaching and research as important career satisfactions, and for some the "fellowship with other psychiatrists" is a rewarding factor. An analyst speaks for a majority of his colleagues in commenting that "the fascination of watching the complicated structure of the personality become apparent in analysis is, to me, the greatest pleasure. The changes in attitudes and behavior which are part of a successful conclusion are also gratifying." Others emphasize "self-knowledge," "being my own boss," and "continual learning" as significant satisfactions.

One analyst suggests that the most interesting part of analytic practice is the initial period of contact with a patient:

> It's during those early months that there is the greatest challenge. You're trying to find out what the problem is, what were the hitches in the developmental process, the disturbances in learning, what influences stopped the normal development. You're like a sleuth trying to find out what happened. Maybe you can find out in six months, and the rest of the time you spend trying to get the patient to understand what you have found out. In the trade you hear the statement: "It took me one month to analyze the patient and it took him three years to learn that." When that's the case, the rest is kind of routine. You have to pace it according to the patient's ability to take it and move along with it until you get the feeling that there can be termination. Sometimes you get the feeling that the patient is stalling, and it may be effective to set a terminating date, say, about six months away. Often, no matter when you set the date, you get a revival of everything bad, and the patient goes through the whole sickness again because he doesn't want to terminate. Everyone has his own way of winding things up.

Some psychiatrists who do not do psychoanalysis, because they have been rejected for training by an institute or are without patients desiring analysis, or have no desire to do analysis, nevertheless feel that the insights they have gained from psychoanalysis rank high among professional rewards. As one puts it:

> I think psychiatry is a terrific field because the insights that psychoanalysis has brought to the whole field are just fabulous. You're in another world once you understand what's going on in the human mind and emotions and gain some insight into the whole process. Of course, many psychiatrists don't have these insights, in my estimation. They are sort of cookbook psychiatrists. They've learned certain techniques, they've learned certain this's and that's; they are following along but they don't get a real feeling for what is actually going on, and they don't read. Sure it's involved, abstracting what is going on with the patient from his behavior and categorizing it but once you start to understand it, it's quite a thrill.

A psychiatrist who has some analytic patients feels that he is in a frontier area of medicine that can only grow more rewarding because of the "excitement of discovery." Psychiatry, he suggests,

> is now where internal medicine was maybe thirty years ago. It's new, it's developing, and it's going to offer a real opportunity to grow along with it, whereas surgery and medicine and so forth have made, I think, their great breakthroughs in the past fifty years and have sort of levelled off. Some people don't see this, and they are depressed because, up to a few years ago, about 5 percent good results was all you could expect. But then there was the advent of thorazine and some of the anti-depressants and a lot more advanced knowledge, and now the results are much higher. I can just imagine how it was twenty-five years ago when all they had was barbiturates and really no effective treatment for the manics and schizophrenics, and the results must have been very hopeless. Psychiatry then must have been a branch of the profession that only a masochist would go into, you know, and therefore it didn't interest the keen students of medicine. But it's no longer like that. Now we have the understanding and we get good results, or at least I do to the point where I enjoy my practice.

That financial reward should rank third among career satisfactions will shock only those who are naïve enough to believe that psychiatrists are or should be indifferent to their economic security and living standards. In fact psychiatrists, like other Americans, want to live well, although a great many of them are by no means as affluent as physicians in other branches of medicine. In 1965, for example, psychiatry ranked seventh in earnings among the ten largest fields of practice (although ahead of internal medicine, pediatrics, and general practice). Nevertheless, median income of psychiatrists before taxes rose 70 percent between 1955 and 1965, and it is continuing to rise. In 1966 the gross median income from practice of all physicians in solo practice was $47,900, and the net income (income minus professional expenses but before taxes) was $32,170. The gross income of solo psychiatrists, constituting 80 percent of the total of active psychiatrists, was, by contrast, $39,110, and the net $29,340.[3] * Because they deal with more patients on a daily basis, psychiatrists in private practice who dispense electroconvulsive shock therapy (ECT) or deal mainly with groups of patients have larger incomes than psychiatrists who engage in individual psychotherapy; an ECT treatment usually costs the same amount as an hour of psychotherapy, and a one-and-a-half-hour group therapy session of ten persons may produce an income for the therapist of $100 or more. Most ECT psychiatrists, however, are attached to public mental hospitals, where salary levels tend to be well below incomes from private practice.† There are also significant differences in fees charged, with the largest hourly fees characteristic of the East and West coasts and lower charges generally prevailing in the South and Midwest outside of Chicago. The income range within psychiatry is, therefore, rather extreme, with some psychiatrists charging private patients as little

* The earnings of psychiatric aides in state hospitals, unquestionably the most underprivileged group in psychiatry, are probably no more than 15 percent of the net figure and may be a good deal less. In the summer of 1968 a partial work stoppage of psychiatric aides at the Topeka (Kansas) State Hospital revealed that the starting salary for such appointments was $294 per month! According to *Psychiatric News* (August, 1968), "The situation is generally the same or worse in most states."

† Judging by the classified ads that fill the back pages of *Psychiatric News,* many psychiatrists earn less than airline pilots and certain other professionals whose jobs do not require advanced degrees, much less medical training. Starting salaries in state hospitals are frequently set at $12,000 or $13,000 per year, and it is rare for the maximum salary to exceed $25,000 even for hospital superintendents. The typical psychiatrist attached to a state hospital probably makes $15,000 to $20,000, although in high-income states, such as New York and California, salary levels for senior positions can go above $30,000. In New York the 1968 income range for licensed psychiatrists was $20,654 to $31,000.

as $20 per hour and other billing their services at $50 and more.*

The higher rates are more typical of psychoanalysts than of psychiatrists, reflecting the fact that the patients of analysts tend to be more affluent than those of psychiatrists. It is also true that analysts rarely work in state hospitals or relatively low-paid agencies; their hospital connections, if any, are more likely to be with private hospitals and clinics catering to well-to-do clienteles. Their preferred income position can be justified, of course, in terms of the fact that the training of analysts is far more expensive than that of psychiatrists, and analysts, on the whole, begin to earn money some years after psychiatrists have established practices.†

But whatever the reasons, analysts in the study have significantly higher incomes than psychiatrists, as is demonstrated by Table 7. In other words, while more than half the psychiatrists earn from practice between $20,000 and $40,000 per year, well over half the analysts are in the $40,000 to $60,000 range. No analyst makes less than $15,000 per year, whereas more than 12 percent of the psychiatrists are in that income category.

Analysts in the study group are also more fortunate in terms of outside income, that is, income from such nonpractice sources as investments, real estate, royalties, lecture fees, and so forth. Almost two-thirds of the analysts have some outside income, as compared with half the psychiatrists, although in both cases such income does not exceed a quarter of the total income. While it is true that the professional expenses of analysts are significantly greater than

* In the Minneapolis-St. Paul study previously referred to, 95 percent of the psychiatrists had a gross income higher than $15,000 per year, and 30 percent averaged more than $30,000. Psychiatrists oriented toward drugs and ECT received much higher incomes than those oriented toward psychotherapy; 79 percent of the former made more than $25,000 per year, whereas only 17 percent of the psychotherapists earned as much, and none of the pyschotherapists was in the $30,000-plus group.

† To be sure, not all analysts find their financial position advantageous vis-à-vis psychiatrists. One analyst in the study, arguing that he would be financially better off if he confined his practice to psychotherapy, points out that psychotherapy patients can generally pay higher hourly fees because they are not seen as often by their therapists. He therefore charges his psychotherapy patients five or ten dollars more per hour than he charges those in analysis. Further, "in order to see patients more frequently, it is often necessary to charge them less. Also there is the problem that if the patient gets sick or his boss says he has to go on a trip for three weeks, then the analyst is left four empty hours for each of three weeks. And he is very disinclined to fill that time, especially if the patient is doing well, because he wants to work with that patient again." Some analysts, of course, charge for missed hours that they cannot fill with other patients.

Table 7. Average Gross Income from Practice

	Psychiatrists (127)		*Psychoanalysts* (33)	
	No.	*%*	*No.*	*%*
Under $15,000	15	12	—	—
$15,000–19,999	17	13	2	6
20,000–24,999	29	23	3	9
25,000–29,999	21	17	1	3
30,000–39,999	23	18	7	21
40,000–49,999	13	10	10	33
50,000–59,999	8	6	8	24
60,000–69,999	1	1	1	3
70,000 plus	—	—	1	3

those of psychiatrists (office rents, in particular), because such expenses are tax-deductible it would still appear that analysts are rather more affluent than psychiatrists in terms of take-home pay.

Impressionistically, there can be no doubt that the living standards of analysts are in sharp contrast to those of psychiatrists, whether or not it is true, as one witty analyst remarks, that "we have been corrupted by the living standards of our patients." Even the offices tend to reflect important differences, although it would be foolish to overlook the fact that some differences are more a matter of taste than of money. But where the psychiatrist may have unpretentious office furniture—a metal bookcase and desk, for example—and a few art prints on the walls, the analyst's offices may feature a mahogany desk, floor-to-ceiling built-in bookcases, wood paneling, lithographs, and a deep-pile rug, in addition to the ubiquitous couch (covered in Naugahyde or a long-wearing fabric). There may be original paintings and some figures in wood or bronze; many analysts are discriminating art collectors, and some of them regard their offices as extensions of themselves, which is to say that the offices of analysts are more apt to reflect a personal touch than the offices of psychiatrists. In both instances the artwork, in keeping with the needs of patients, is bland, or at least restrained and undemanding in theme, since it is not desirable that too many patient fantasies be aroused, or too much excitement, much less depression and thoughts of suicide. Partly for this reason examples of pop art and action painting are rarely seen in these offices, and it would be extremely unusual to encounter any work by, for example, Larry Rivers or Richard Lindner. But whatever the taste revealed, the effect is subdued.

There are margins for taste at every income level, of course, and neither analysts nor psychiatrists are immune from those pressures that affect others, including exhibitionist tendencies and pressures toward conspicuous consumption. Thus one analyst may have a water fountain playing among tropical plants in his waiting room, while another drives to and from his office in a Morgan two-seater. In Beverly Hills analytic circles it would be considered *infra dig* not to live in a house costing at least $100,000 or to do without a swimming pool and, increasingly, a tennis court. In New York City the analysts tend to live and work in the fashionable sections of the upper East Side, especially on Fifth and Park avenues, and along Central Park South or Central Park West, and to have weekend and summer homes on Long Island or in Connecticut, Northern Westchester, and Rockland County. In Chicago the apartment and office are apt to command a fine few of Lake Michigan, while in Boston the base is a charming eighteenth-century house looking out on an old, quiet street in Cambridge or the Back Bay area. And somewhere in the house or apartment there may be a wine cellar or a collection of first editions or antique furniture of museum quality. How many patients, one wonders, have been corrupted by the living standards of their analysts?

And yet there is a hint, especially among the older generation of analysts, of embarrassment, perhaps even of guilt, about these living standards. The analyst with the water fountain complains that it is always breaking down, that it costs a fortune to maintain (with local plumbers charging a minimum of $18.00 per hour), that the fountain is there because "my wife has a thing about fountains." The analyst who has invested in a high-rise apartment house gazes out at the landscape punctuated by such buildings and says: "Well, there it is, the revolution of rising defecations." The swimming pool, it often turns out, "is for the kids," and the tennis court nearby exists because "the internist said it's exercise or else, and I didn't want to join one of these clubs where the main reason for the tennis is to work up a thirst." And so on for the art collection ("The way taxes are, that's about all the estate I'm going to have"), the weekend place ("I'd go nuts if I couldn't get out of the city most weekends, especially in good weather"), and the

1949 Romanée-Conti ("We prefer to spend the drinking money on good wine—hardly ever touch the hard stuff except for parties"). The significance of these remarks, generally apologetic in tone, is a phenomenon to which we shall return later. For the moment, let us note that such statements are more common in well-to-do analytic circles than in the corresponding circles of psychiatrists, and this, too, is a measure of the distance between the two professions.

In fixing fees for treatment, analysts also seem to reflect a more pronounced social conscience or at least sensitivity to the fact that not all of their patients find it easy to make the prescribed payments. Proportionally more than twice as many analysts as psychiatrists relate the fee to the patient's income. More psychiatrists than analysts cease treatment, or refer the matter to a collection agency, if a patient falls behind in his payments. Analysts are more inclined to negotiate deferred payments, and they are significantly more disposed to continue treating a patient who has fallen behind. While more than 71 percent of the analysts would continue seeing the patient, only 53 percent of the psychiatrists would continue treatment.*

From what has been said it is clear that lack of income and financial security do not pose problems for analysts, and, in fact, no analyst mentions this as career dissatisfaction. For almost 9 percent of the psychiatrists, however, low incomes do constitute a career dislike. More than 13 percent of the psychiatrists complain about their lack of status, by which they refer mainly to the negative attitudes toward psychiatry held by their medical colleagues, and more than 11 percent of both the analysts and the psychiatrists

* It has been estimated that about half the population has some form of health insurance covering some psychiatric expense, but there is little provision for a serious illness and/or long-term psychiatric treatment. A study reported in 1967 showed that while every fourth person seen by a psychiatrist is insured for part of the cost, 44 percent of them enjoy 50 percent coverage, but only 36 percent were insured to the extent of 80 percent of costs. About a fifth have less than 50 percent coverage. Most insurance of the "major medical" type is restricted either in total amount reimbursed or in time limit for treatment, or both. Late in 1967 the Metropolitan Life Insurance Company, a leading insurance carrier for New York City employees, reduced its psychiatric payments for office visits from $900 to $500, and the total lifetime benefits from $2,000 to $1,000, including in-hospital services. In justification for such actions, one insurance agent commented that many companies felt that mental illness was "nebulous, not like a broken arm or a ruptured appendix." Psychiatric treatment, he claimed, could be obtained merely on grounds that "I'm not feeling too well." New York *Times,* February 28, 1968. See also *Psychiatric News,* December, 1967.

mention poor working conditions as a career dissatisfaction. Only 6 percent of the analysts cite a lack of status, and the same percentage evidences doubt about helping people, as compared with 9 percent of the psychiatrists. Interestingly, the proportion of analysts who question whether they are socially useful is more than twice as great as the proportion of psychiatrists, 9 percent to 4 percent.

Exactly 40 percent of the analysts and almost 35 percent of the psychiatrists have no particular career dislikes. Among those who do express career dissatisfactions there are frequent references to long hours in the office characterized by what one calls "the tension of constant attention." Others mention "the tendency to isolation from the rest of the community," and "isolation during working hours." One psychiatrist cites the "disorganized state of psychiatric thought; variable standards of teaching and accreditation," while another refers to "the blind adherence of professionals to 'schools.' " The "dissidence between analytic and non-analytic pychiatrists" is a source of dissatisfaction for one psychiatrist. A complaint of a different type is the "damaging effects on research, development, and programming by certain vested interests—national and regional, individual and group." There are a number of references to excessive "telephoning and paper work," and "not enough time to do everything." The "immobility" and "lack of opportunity to travel" bother some of the psychiatrists, while for others the trouble is, as one puts it, "the great chaos and ignorance I encounter daily."

It is clear that feelings of inadequacy trouble at least a few psychiatrists. One of them puts it this way: "My only dislike is that I am not as effective as I would like to be in rendering assistance. I sometimes think that a practice with college students would be a more rewarding type of practice." Another who feels he does help people is nevertheless disturbed by "the lack of concrete knowledge and the limitations of our knowledge about proven therapeutic measures [that] make for frustration at times." There is "constant pressure," comments a third, as well as the question of "how to deal with patients who sincerely want and need help, yet can't seem to see it (or at least you aren't able to help)." Among psychiatrists who are attached to mental hospitals there are complaints about "administrative demands," "reports," and "too many patients, too few psychiatrists." A cause of dissatisfaction in one instance is "when background conditioning and experience of various staff psychiatrists produce rigidity of opinion, argument, and insistence on a psychotic diagnosis *Because the Patient Has Been Sent to the Hospital*" (*sic*). Another hospital psychiatrist singles out the "tremendous amount of time, effort, and delay in doing the proper thing because so many involved people must have an opportunity to discuss or participate."

Complaints similar to those voiced by psychiatrists are put forward by the analysts—"isolation from social and scientific movements," the "loneliness of practice," and "the domination of psychiatry and psychoanalysis (especially) by an establishment." One analyst mentions "its [psychoanalysis'] unctuousness, its tendency to think it has a corner on the truth; the religious tendency," while another mentions "the institutionalization of the profession and the now easy acceptance of the profession by other institutions (e.g., church, social agencies, government) and some socio-economic groups. The popularization of the profession." Perhaps this is related to the complaint of a colleague about "stupid jerks who think they know and pontificate about human behavior and especially psychoanalysis, without having studied either." And there are references to "being the object of so much conflict and aggression of patients," "the long time it takes to help people," and "the human limitations and those I can't help."

Some analysts, too, suffer from feelings of inadequacy. One mentions "the awareness of the discrepancy between therapeutic effort and therapeutic result. The awareness of the gap between one's limited efforts on a small number of individuals in the face of the vast social problems. The impossibility of becoming familiar with the progress in all related fields (for instance, communications theory, cybernetics, etc.)."

Problems frequently mentioned are passivity and the boredom that results from full-time private practice. "A really big problem," one analyst comments,

> is the fairly inelastic working day. A great deal of rigidity develops because of the scheduling, and the passivity that is involved begins to become wearing. By passivity I don't mean silence; I mean the passivity that comes with just sitting with somebody, hour after hour. If something comes up in your own life which you want to deal with immediately, you have to delay it. This seems to me to

be untypical of every other profession except psychiatry. I feel that one shouldn't postpone people, so that I don't even answer the telephone except between patients. The result is, no matter what is happening in my own life, I can't get to it until the end of the hour and I may not be able to attend to it until the end of the day. Generally speaking, if you have a fairly busy practice you spend almost all day sitting and listening to people. I work five and a half days a week and see about forty people. I usually take a three-week vacation, but this year was unusual, I took six.

The average work week for some analysts, apparently, is between fifty-five and sixty hours, but this, according to an informant,

is not talked about. Why, I'm not sure. I don't think analysts work that much for financial reasons, because there are other, easier ways to make money. For example, non-analytic psychiatry is more profitable than analytic. If you have ten people in the hospital and spend an hour visiting all ten—arranging for medication, shock treatment, and so forth—which happens—you can make a lot of money. But if you really want to see people, you end up working late in the evenings because some patients can't get away during the day. So, if you're going to be in the office from six to seven, you might as well fill in the time from five to six. One thing I find: I start with a patient who is quite sick, isn't working. I see him for a while and he gets better. Then he has a job that doesn't let him off between eight and five. So I see him in the evening. That's how it goes.

A training analyst with many years of experience feels very strongly that no analyst should engage in full-time private practice, and he accordingly tells his students,

Okay, you want to be an analyst, you want to go through training even though it's a horrible experience, means you're going to have your childhood perpetuated for another seven or eight years, going to be treated with all the indignities, going to be brainwashed, made to conform. Okay. But for Christ's sake don't do full-time analysis, because when you get to be 45 years old and you've been sitting there day in and day out listening to this *stuss* of ten, twelve patients, you're going to be so bored to death you'd like to cut your throat. Also, you won't know anything else to do, you won't have any skills, you won't have done any research, you'll be a pretty goddamned dull tool.

He therefore advises the trainees:

> Do research, teaching, psychotherapy, group therapy, family therapy, ward therapy, music therapy. Develop some hobbies. Do *anything*, but don't do only psychoanalysis or you'll die of boredom when you get to 45.

Another training analyst makes a similar point in urging candidates in his institute to

> teach, or do some hospital consultation, or work in a social agency. Whatever it is, it should have some sort of social reward. Maybe the thing is to get involved in a research project where you're not so much an analyst as an analytic consultant, and where the research has to do with something you can measure, something where you can see the beginning and the end six months later, something finite. I think it's terribly important for analysts to get out of their offices, maybe do something where they use their legs to run up and down stairs, or handle a computer.

The solution for some is a hobby, and almost all hobbies and most sports are represented, although tennis, golf, and fishing predominate. One psychiatrist turned seriously to late afternoon golf when he found that "most patients who came to see me after three in the afternoon were wasting their money. No, make that four o'clock. I really start running down about then, and I'm simply not there, no matter what the trouble is." Some of this boredom and fatigue is carried over to family life, where, one analyst admits, "I have a lot of insights but I'm often just too tired to apply them. Some days when I get home, I don't want problems, I don't want to hear about low grades, menstrual cramps, lost dogs, or whatever. I *think* I'm a better husband and father with these insights, but there are certain days. . . ."

Some analysts, however, believe that the "certain days" and problems of everyday life are made more complicated by the passivity and vulnerability of analytic practice. "It's complicated," says an experienced training analyst,

> but I lean toward the view that analysts are fairly neurotic people, in general, very sensitive people. And it's all fostered by the work. What you start out with is, in a way, increased. Maybe you get

> to be more objective as you go along, but I think there's a corresponding increase in personal vulnerability, too. I really believe that this is the wrong kind of work for men, at least, for most men. It's corrosive, it's passive, it's very hard to tolerate doing this all day, or at any rate very hard for me. I think some of life's problems are difficult to handle for me personally as a result of the work. I feel that if I had a more free-swinging kind of work activity, I would perhaps be a calmer person, and outside of my analytic work, a more mature person. I don't know. There's a kind of total suppression—muscular, emotional. . . .

One reason for the factionalism in professional circles, in this view, is related to the necessity for passivity or "suppression." Because the analyst must practice restraint and "refuse to react,"

> perhaps his professional activities give him the opportunity to "act out" what he can't "act out" in the normal course. Maybe this explains the tendency to be "prima donna-ish" and what not. I have been at quite a few meetings of the Institute where, believe me, "acting out" was only too apparent.

Whether or not the tensions, insecurities, and frustrations are responsible for high suicide and divorce rates, as has been alleged, they no doubt play a role in the incidence of so-called nervous breakdowns among psychiatrists, and in the frequency of second and even third analyses in analytic circles. But the opinion of some analysts is that a second analysis is desirable because the training analysis, no matter how long, is frequently distorted by its role in determining the suitability of the candidate for a psychoanalytic career. In the words of one training analyst who has been involved in a number of second analyses,

> the training analysis is not a good analysis because the trainee is on probation, you know, he's being looked over—are you going to be an analyst or not?—and he can't fulfill the role of the patient. But his second analysis, after he's been accepted and been working with patients who have pulled at something in him that gets him disturbed, that analysis can be a good one. Then you can really learn a lot. I think that most of the good analysts have had repeated analyses, but I don't know how many. It's not talked about.

The second (or third) analysis, however, should not be with the analyst who was involved in the first or training analysis, according to prevailing opinion. Since the training analysis was a special relationship in which the trainee functioned more as a student than as a patient, and since, further, there may be constraints on both sides, a second analysis with the same analyst might well prove, in one comment,

> so disruptive that the whole situation might become a hell of a lot worse. I just couldn't go back to ——— with my problems. He'd feel too responsible, and, let's face it, he might feel that my getting into this business was a big mistake. Once, a couple of years ago, I was having some marital troubles, nothing special, it's just that we weren't getting along. Well, I was having a drink with ——— somewhere or other, and I just mentioned casually that the marriage wasn't going particularly well. I could see that he was terribly shocked, really upset, and I quickly changed the subject. I never mentioned it again.

The decision in whom and what to confide is especially difficult for psychiatrists and analysts with career ambitions beyond private practice. Certainly a psychiatrist seeking a faculty appointment in a medical school, or an important administrative position in a public health facility, or even a high office in one of the professional associations, would not be helped by a record of several divorces or nervous breakdowns. There are instances where psychiatrists have been denied positions in state and county health services because of alcoholism or regular use of LSD. In psychiatry as in most professions, sexual promiscuity and homosexuality are not generally regarded as constituting the highest qualifications for successful private practice. No doubt a succession of malpractice suits would be a serious handicap, but such suits are rare.*

Most severe personality disorders would bar admission to a psychoanalytic institute. In the early days, when it was sufficient qualification to have been analyzed by Freud or someone in his circle, sexual deviations and nervous breakdowns were less of a

---

* In an average year there are only 200 malpractice suits involving psychiatrists, compared with 2,600 in general surgery, and most of these are occasioned by electric shock treatment or allegations of false hospital commitment, rather than by psychotherapy. Henry A. Davidson, *Opportunities in a Psychiatric Career* (New York: Universal Vocational Guidance Manual, 1964), 21.

handicap to a psychoanalytic career. There were even analysts of repute who were widely believed to be sleeping with their female patients, either for therapeutic or for other reasons; indeed, several married former patients. It is common knowledge in psychiatry that one of the most influential American figures was homosexual and that another periodically experienced a psychotic episode. Because of this history, analysts sometimes remark humorously that few, if any, of the pioneering figures in psychoanalysis would have been able to meet the admission standards of the American Psychoanalytic Association.

But if one must be beyond reproach to become an officially accredited analyst in the United States, one must be beyond suspicion of reproach to qualify as a training analyst, the most powerful position in a psychoanalytic institute. It is the training analysts who determine whether candidates will or will not make good analysts because it is they who analyze the candidates themselves. Once appointed training analysts by the institute's educational committee, of which they become members on appointment, they can determine who is qualified to become a training analyst. In effect, the training analysts in an institute are members of an exclusive self-perpetuating club that determines, directly and indirectly, what sort of psychiatrist will make a successful analyst and how many analysts there are to be.

The criteria for admission to the club include, of course, knowledge of psychoanalytic theory and practice, one's own record as a student including the supervised analyses, competence as a therapist, and professional activities such as research and publication. Of foremost importance is personal maturity and the extent to which the prospective training analyst will serve as a good model for students and trainees. "The Gestalt question," says one training analyst, "is: does this man or woman represent overall the kind of analyst needed to transmit the philosophy and practice of psychoanalysis?"

Yet, as is true in other professions, the answers often involve personal considerations. As noted earlier, the decision may be influenced by the degree to which the analyst of the prospective training analyst identifies with the applicant or has a continuing close relationship with him. "Politicking" for such appointments is not unknown—cultivating the "right people" on the educational committee, paying deference to the "right" books and articles and avoiding mention of the "wrong" ones, and, so far as possible, not making enemies of those who would also like to become training analysts. Nor are these necessities removed with the appointment, which may leave scars among those who were passed over. A successful candidate for the position of training analyst remembers vividly

> how difficult it was in a quiet way for the first few months. The other fellows were hurt, especially the fellows who were older either age-wise or in terms of having started analysis before I did. You see, It's an important ideal for an analyst to become a training analyst, no matter what they say. It may not be rational but it's goddamned important if you really involve yourself in the work of an institute. You have the sense of having arrived at the top of the analytic heap, like now you're in the elite. From a personal standpoint I had a tremendous sense of satisfaction.

On the other hand,

> Because now you *are* a model for the others, you have to be a bit careful about what you say and to whom you say it. For example, I would never open up here with ——— or ———, even where I really need to talk with someone about a case. Certainly I would never, never discuss with these guys any of my personal problems. But there's usually someone you can level with, and I generally discuss things with ———. We have a brotherly relationship because we share common professional concerns. We get together frequently to discuss matters of mutual interest.

While it is practically unknown for an appointment as training analyst to be terminated, in at least one instance a few years ago an appointment was terminated, arousing great and continuing controversy. The official reason for the action, that the training analyst in question was not fulfilling his professional obligations (*e.g.*, attending meetings of his institute, taking sufficient interest in the candidates whom he was supervising, and so forth) was widely disbelieved by some members of the same institute as well as analysts elsewhere. Instead, it was alleged that a personality clash had played a major role, and it was also argued that the training analyst had been dismissed because his own research interests had led him away from the orthodox and traditional emphases of his institute, or at least of its educational committee. Whatever the truth of the matter, the dismissal, which was practically unprecedented, was investigated by a committee of the American Psychoanalytic Association. The report has never been made public, nor was the institute decision overruled.

Clearly the position of training analyst is one of power and prestige, and as such it is greatly coveted by many analysts. But true eminence in psychoanalysis and psychiatry, as in other intellectual fields, largely depends on one's contributions to the literature of the profession, and especially on those writings that are theoretically important. While there are some doubts, as will be seen later, that theory and practice are necessarily or even customarily related, analysts and psychiatrists, asked to identify the eminent among them, are apt to single out those who have made important theoretical contributions. But because there is no consensus with regard to what theoretical contributions are of outstanding importance, the list of the eminent is a very long one and even includes names that cannot be readily identified. Perhaps, too, the lack of agreement about what is important is reflected in the very large number of journals in psychiatry, many of them catering exclusively or mainly to particular "schools" or "approaches." According to a recent count, there are some 214 journals being published in psychiatry alone, and these necessitate the further publication of journals that survey, summarize, and abstract from other psychiatric journals, including those in the behavioral sciences. The "knowledge explosion," it need hardly be emphasized, characterizes psychiatry no less than other disciplines, but what knowledge, and whose knowledge, is important?

In an effort to elicit answers to these questions, the psychiatrists and analysts in the study were asked to identify "the five most promising or significant developments in psychiatry in the past twenty years," and "the most outstanding living psychiatrists and psychoanalysts in terms of their contributions to theory and/or practice." Among the 131 psychiatrists, or 92 percent, who replied to the question about "significant developments," there is remarkable agreement about the most important development: 77 psychiatrists named psychopharmacology, or the "drug revolution," as the foremost development. Many of these replies specified certain types of drugs, such as the phenothiazines, widely used in treating schizophrenia, tranquilizers, and antidepressants.

The second most promising development for the psychiatrists was the rise of community and social psychiatry and, given equal importance, the emphasis on ego psychology. Both of these developments, however, with eleven mentions each, were rather far back in second place. They were followed in the list of most significant developments by family and group therapy, with eight mentions; the improvement of mental hospitals, six; acceptance by psychiatry and the public of psychoanalytic theory, cited by five; and, coupled together with three votes each, the increasing research devoted to the biochemistry of mental illness (including the study of brain functioning, systematic research on dreams and the investigation of rapid eye movement, or REM, sleep, and neurophysiology in general); and advances in electric shock treatment. Two psychiatrists mentioned as "most significant" the development of child psychoanalysis and psychiatry, and the Mental Health Act of 1964 together with other legislation supporting public activities in the mental health field.

Among the thirty analysts, or 86 percent of the total, who dealt with outstanding achievements, ego psychology was identified by nine of them, or almost a third, as the most significant development. Not far behind in second place was psychopharmacology, with six mentions, followed by family and group therapy and community and social psychiatry, tied at three votes each. The psychoanalysis of the child, including studies of child development, received two votes. No analyst accorded a first-place vote to either biochemistry research or advance in electric shock treatment, but the former was identified by four analysts as one of the most significant developments.

As may be guessed, the number of developments receiving one mention each was quite large, especially in the sample of psychiatrists. The list includes:

improvements in training programs
changes in the American Psychiatric Association
"reemphasis on behavior expectation"
progress in psychotherapy
"social determinants of mental illness"
"discovery that people can change"
"Sullivanian concepts"
"dropping of labels"

"reentering of psychiatry into medicine"
psychosomatic medicine
psychotherapy with schizophrenics
communications theory
"Erikson's influence"
"switch away from psychoanalysis"
"modification of psychoanalysis"

The analysts, on the other hand, accorded one vote each to:

"application of psychoanalysis to social problems (war, nationalism, etc.)"
application of psychoanalysis to psychiatry
"preventive psychiatry"
"identity concepts"
family therapy of psychotics
"transactional concepts"
"application of social science to psychiatry"
"increased openness of mental health"
"growth of individual understanding versus impersonal classification (seen most prominently in hospital setting)"

While a few psychiatrists and analysts declared that there had not been *any* significant or promising development in the past twenty years, this was far from the general view, even if there was little agreement beyond the first and second choices. But it is to be noted that only psychopharmacology, or the so-called drug revolution, ranks high among both psychiatrists and analysts, and it is the *only* development that receives more than half the first-place vote from the psychiatrists. One inference from this result is that it is in the treatment or practice area, not in theoretical elaboration, that psychiatry and perhaps also psychoanalysis have made the greatest progress in the last two decades, and we might therefore expect that those identified as "outstanding" would be chosen for their treatment innovations rather than for their theories or concepts.

This is not the case, however, judging by the names mentioned by both psychiatrists and analysts. No one connected with psychopharmacology research is mentioned, for example, either because such research is team research or because those involved, many of whom are not psychiatrists but chemists and physiologists in the employ of drug companies, are essentially anonymous.* The growing interest in social and community psychiatry is not represented by any names, and neither is the reform of mental hospitals in the direction of open wards and other measures designed to humanize the position of patients. One or two of those mentioned are identified with the increasing interest in family and group therapy, but their contributions are largely in the area of theory with special reference to the role of interpersonal relations in schizophrenia. In short, and whether or not theory as such has a major impact upon what psychiatrists do with and to patients, it is clear that the men and women of distinction in psychiatry and psychoanalysis are mainly theoreticians.

As was the case with regard to "significant developments," there is little tendency to confine choices to a few selections, although there is significant agreement on a handful of leaders. The 113 psychiatrists in the study who responded to the question produced a total of 109 "most outstanding living psychiatrists and psychoanalysts in terms of their contributions to theory and/or practice." The list of 31 analysts who dealt with the question contained 62 names. Even eliminating those respondents who named themselves, or who could not take the question seriously (there was one mention each of Lucy and James Bond), there appears to be little consensus in the sample as a whole on the criteria that identify the luminaries of psychiatry and psychoanalysis.†

Nevertheless, some names are mentioned much more frequently than others. At the top of the list for both psychiatrists and analysts is Anna Freud, with 44 mentions by psychiatrists and 21 mentions by analysts. Among psychiatrists she is followed by Karl Menninger, with 37 mentions; Erik H. Erikson, with 26 mentions; Heinz Hartmann, with 21 mentions; and Lawrence Kubie, with 19 mentions. For the analysts the order of mention following Anna Freud is: Heinz Hartmann, 20 mentions, and Erik H. Erik-

* It is of interest that while almost everyone knows the names of those who invented penicillin, the antipolio vaccine, and the tests for tuberculosis and syphilis, hardly anyone can identify the person or persons chiefly responsible for the major tranquilizers, although there are more people dependent upon such drugs than upon the Schick or Wasserman tests.

† The totals omit names that were unintelligible or so misspelled as to be unidentifiable (the handwriting of psychiatrists and analysts is at least as bad as that of other doctors). In a few cases the dead were included among the "living," and some of those mentioned have since died. Their names have not been deleted.

son, 16 mentions. Thereafter there is a sharp falling-off in both groups, as can be seen in Table 8.

Table 8. Most Outstanding Living Psychiatrists and Psychoanalysts

Psychiatrists (113) *Name*	*Mentions*	*Psychoanalysts* (31) *Name*	*Mentions*
Anna Freud	44	Anna Freud	21
Karl Menninger	37	Heinz Hartmann	20
Erik H. Erikson	26	Erik H. Erikson	16
Heinz Hartmann	21	Phyllis Greenacre	7
Lawrence Kubie	19	Rudolph Loewenstein	7
Erich Fromm	10	René Spitz	7
"The Menningers"	10	Robert Waelder*	6
Roy R. Grinker, Sr.	8	Karl Menninger	4
Jules Masserman	8	Edward Glover	3
Manfred S. Guttmacher	7	Roy R. Grinker, Sr.	3
Harold F. Searles	7	Don D. Jackson*	3
René Spitz	7	Edith Jacobson	3
Franz Alexander*	6	Bertram D. Lewin	3
Eric Berne	6	D. W. Winnicott	3
Don D. Jackson*	6		
Sandor Rado	6		
Silvano Arieti	5		
Jerome D. Frank	5		
Robert Waelder*	5		
Francis Braceland	4		
Helene Deutsch	4		
Edward Glover	4		
Judd Marmor	4		
William Menninger*	4		
S. A. Szurek	4		

* deceased

The psychiatrists accord three mentions to each of the following: Walter E. Barton, John Bowlby, Henry W. Brosin, Gerald Caplan, Martin Grotjahn, Edith Jacobson, Maxwell Jones, Lawrence Kolb, Maurice Levine, Frederick C. Redlich, Elvin V. Semrad, John C. Whitehorn, and Joseph Wolpe. A total of 20 names are mentioned twice, and 51 names are mentioned once.

The analysts accord two mentions each to: Charles Brenner, Helene Deutsch, Ernst Kris (deceased), "The Menningers," Joseph Sandler, Leo Stone, and Robert Wallerstein. A total of 41 names are mentioned once.

Despite the lack of agreement within and between the groups, it is worth noting that three of the four most often mentioned by the psychiatrists, Anna Freud, Erik H. Erikson, and Heinz Hartmann, are also among the top four names listed by the analysts. Karl Menninger and Lawrence Kubie, on the other hand, who rank high among the psychiatrists, have relatively low status among the analysts, with Menninger receiving four mentions and Kubie only one. Erich Fromm, in sixth place among psychiatrists, is mentioned only once by the analysts.

Also worthy of comment is the fact that almost all the high-ranking figures mentioned by both psychiatrists and analysts are analysts; indeed, there is little difference between them in this respect. In view of the frequency of comments regarding the decline and imminent demise of psychoanalysis, many of which carry the style but not the tone of obituary notices, it is of interest that all ten of those most often mentioned by the psychiatrists are identified with psychoanalysis. Nine of them, in fact, are members of the American Psychoanalytic Association (the sole exception being Erich Fromm). This might suggest that no body of doctrine has appeared, as yet, to take the place of psychoanalytic theory, and that notwithstanding the importance of the so-called drug revolution and other therapy innovations, the main theoretical influence in psychiatry continues to be the teachings of Freud and his followers.

It follows from this that any list of controversial figures in psychiatry and psychoanalysis should feature at the top those who had challenged at least some of the main tenets of psychoanalysis, and this turns out to be the case. Asked to identify the "most controversial living psychiatrists and psychoanalysts," the 95 psychiatrists who responded to the question displayed much more agreement than they showed in reply to the previous question about the "most outstanding." Almost two-thirds of the total, or 61 psychiatrists, named Thomas S. Szasz as the "most controversial," an opinion shared by 50 percent, or thirteen, of the 26 analysts who responded to the question. Those mentioned after Szasz are shown in Table 9.

Table 9. Most Controversial Living Psychiatrists and Psychoanalysts

Psychiatrists (95) *Name*	*Mentions*	*Psychoanalysts* (26) *Name*	*Mentions*
Thomas S. Szasz	61	Thomas S. Szasz	13
John Rosen	19	Erich Fromm	6
Erich Fromm	8	Jules Masserman	5
Joseph Wolpe	8	John Rosen	5
Eric Berne	6	Roy R. Grinker, Sr.	3
Robert G. Heath	6	J. L. Moreno	3
Rollo May	5	H. J. Eysenck	2
Melanie Klein*	4	Viktor Frankl	2
Jules Masserman	4	Heinz Hartmann	2
J. L. Moreno	4	Melanie Klein*	2
Viktor Frankl	3	Lawrence Kubie	2
Lauretta Bender	2	Joseph Wolpe	2
Ludwig Binswanger*	2		
Lawrence Kubie	2		

* deceased

Single mentions by psychiatrists produced a list of 27 names, bringing the total number of "most controversial" to forty-one. Among the analysts, 26 names were mentioned once, bringing the total number of names to thirty-eight.

As may be expected, most of those mentioned by both psychiatrists and analysts are not members of the American Psychoanalytic Association, although it is noteworthy that the most controversial figure of all, Thomas S. Szasz, is a member and has been one since 1952. Of more significance is the fact that most of those mentioned are associated with unconventional theories of and approaches to mental illness and its treatment, including behavior therapy (Wolpe), "logotherapy" (Frankl), existential therapy (May), "direct analysis" (Rosen), and psychodrama (Moreno). Szasz, as was pointed out earlier, has repeatedly suggested that mental illness itself is a myth, apart from certain organic diseases, and Eysenck, a British psychologist, has attacked psychoanalysis on the grounds that as therapy it is certainly no more effective, and may be a good deal less effective, than other approaches to neurotic behavior. Erich Fromm, the best-known of those regarded as "most controversial," presumably is listed because of his efforts to merge psychoanalysis, existential philosophy, and social criticism in a doctrinal blend that reflects Marx at least as much as Freud.

It should be obvious that those who are "most controversial" are not without a following in both psychiatry and psychoanalysis, and, equally, those who are "most outstanding" are not beyond criticism. Thus an analyst speaking of Szasz points out:

> Most analysts realize there is some value to what this man is saying. Unfortunately, he's got so many points, he is so absolutely obsessed by his point of view that it detracts from the whole understanding of him and what he is trying to say. He is terribly repetitive. He says it again and again and again. The result is, he is much more a figure with lay people than he is in psychiatry.

A comment on British psychoanalyst D. W. Winnicott makes the point that

> of course he's controversial. Anyone who is valuable is controversial. I mean, he's the man who says "Now, come on, you know that we all hate our patients. What is this business you don't hate your patients? Every time you say goodbye to him, or you interrupt him, or you answer the phone . . . ? Variety of hate. And what do you mean we don't gratify a patient? Look, you give him a soft couch, a pillow, a napkin. What is this? You might as well give him your breast." This kind of cutting away of all the stuff is very valuable, because before we just sat there in our clean, sterile chairs doing just beautiful interpretations. He doesn't go for that. And some of the things he's been writing about the early mother-child relationship and what you need to give a person who has a deficiency in this relationship, very important. But he is a controversial figure.

An analyst who "guesses" that Hartmann is important because "people who know him say that he is," admits: "I have never quite understood him, I think. His manner of expression is so involved, he is so difficult to read, I've sort of put him off. This may be why there's no really adequate critique of him at all." Fromm, on the other hand, has probably "been cast out of the Church Militant" because "he has something like genius. He's a maverick, of course, but an extremely gifted man with a literary bent. Maybe analysts are a little bit suspicious of him because he writes so well and so easily. I don't understand it all. You know, he practices in Mexico City and he is absolutely anathema to the Mexican analysts. They will have nothing to do with him. I don't quite understand the inwardness of that kind of business."

An admirer of Erikson argues that he is controversial because

> he has become increasingly anti-instinctual. I have great respect for him and I've learned a lot from him, but each one of his writings more and more tends to diminish the importance of the instinctual impulses, this kind of irreducible core with which, I say, we are stuck. And this last thing about passivity and instinct, the passivity of Gandhi. An interesting notion, but, oh, my! So fraught with danger to talk about this kind of impulse as an instinctual aim instead of as a defense against an impulse. You know, he quoted there something by Lorenz on the wolf showing the jugular vein when two wolves fight—the one who is defeated shows his jugular vein and the fight stops. I think it's unfortunate to take something from animal behavior and say it's like this with human beings. We simply don't have these good, natural instincts that animals have. We're killing each other all the time. It's that sort of thing makes Erikson controversial.

Since Erikson is far more eminent than he is controversial, it is to be expected that some of his writings are among those most frequently used in psychiatric residency programs, which is one measure, for the profession as a whole, of what is deemed to be important as "Basic Psychiatric Literature." [4] His book *Childhood and Society,* first published in 1950, is one of eighteen books most often used in psychiatric training, and two of his articles are among those that most often appear on three-year residency training program reading lists. Of the psychiatrists and analysts previously identified in the study as "most outstanding," only Anna Freud, Franz Alexander, and Silvano Arieti share honors with Erikson in the book list, and Alexander and Arieti appear there as book editors rather than authors. In the list of 118 articles each of which is used by at least seven residency programs, among the "most outstanding," Rado is the author of three, Spitz the author or coauthor of three, Anna Freud and Arieti the author of two, Hartmann and Loewenstein the coauthors of two, Alexander, Jacobson, and Waelder the author of one, and Jackson the coauthor of one.

The composition of "Basic Psychiatric Literature," like the identification of the "most outstanding living psychiatrists and analysts," also reflects a general lack of agreement on what is important in terms of contribution to theory and/or practice. Of a total of 2,799 books recommended by 140 training programs, 1,498 books, or 54 percent, were recommended by only one program, and of the 4,000 articles listed, 65 percent were recommended by only one program. Although there was a total of 205 journals recommended, 56 percent were recommended by only one program, and even the *American Journal of Psychiatry,* official publication of the American Psychiatric Association, received no more than 28 mentions.* The titles of books recommended included the *Complete Works of William Shakespeare* and the Talmud, both of which were recommended once. The Bible received four recommendations, and the *Standard Edition of the Complete Psychological Works of Sigmund Freud* received ten recommendations.

While 18 books were recommended by 50 percent or more of the training programs utilizing basic book lists, only one book, Arthur P. Noyes and Laurence C. Kolb's textbook *Modern Clinical Psychiatry,* was recommended by 90 percent, or 115, of the training programs. The remaining 17 books were, in alphabetical order of authors or editors:

August Aichhorn, *Wayward Youth: A Psychoanalytic Study of Delinquent Children Illustrated by Actual Case Histories*
Franz Alexander and Helen Ross (eds.), *Dynamic Psychiatry*
Silvano Arieti (ed.), *American Handbook of Psychiatry*
Eugen Bleuler, *Dementia Praecox: Or, the Group of Schizophrenias*
Charles Brenner, *An Elementary Textbook of Psychoanalysis*
Kenneth M. Colby, *Primer for Psychotherapists*
Erik H. Erikson, *Childhood and Society*

* Journals most often used in training programs were, in addition to the *American Journal of Psychiatry,* the *American Journal of Orthopsychiatry, Archives of General Psychiatry, Archives of Neurology, Journal of the American Medical Association, Journal of Nervous and Mental Disease, Psychiatry, Psychoanalytic Quarterly, Psychosomatic Medicine,* and the annually published *Pyschoanalytic Study of the Child.*

Otto Fenichel, *The Psychoanalytic Theory of Neurosis*
Anna Freud, *The Ego and the Mechanisms of Defense*
Frieda Fromm-Reichmann, *Principles of Intensive Psychotherapy*
Lothar B. Kalinowsky and Paul H. Hoch, *Somatic Treatments in Psychiatry: Pharmacotherapy, Convulsive, Insulin, Surgical, and Other Methods*
Leo Kanner, *Child Psychiatry*
Ruth L. Munroe, *Schools of Psychoanalytic Thought: An Exposition, Critique, and Attempt at Integration*
Alfred H. Stanton and Morris S. Schwartz, *The Mental Hospital: A Study of Institutional Participation in Psychiatric Illness and Treatment*
Harry Stack Sullivan, *The Psychiatric Interview*
Lewis R. Wolberg, *The Techniques of Psychotherapy*
Gregory Zilboorg, *A History of Medical Psychology*

The next 86 recommended books were mentioned by between 20 and 49 percent of the training programs, making a total of 104 books which can fairly be regarded as constituting a "core" of recommended reading.

No book by Sigmund Freud appears among the 18 most recommended books, but 9 of his books are found on the "core" list.[5] Of the 118 most recommended articles, 35 are by Freud, and one of them, "Mourning and Melancholia,"[6] with 57 recommendations, is the article most often used in training programs. But it may be revealing of theoretical progress in psychoanalysis that the article by Freud most often recommended was first published more than fifty years ago, in 1917, and that only 6 of the 35 articles by Freud first appeared after 1920. Three were published before 1900, 26 between 1900 and 1920, and only one of Freud's last writings, his "Analysis: Terminable and Interminable" (1937),[7] is listed among those recommended.

Yet it remains true of the most recommended books in psychiatric training, as it does of those individuals deemed to be "most outstanding," that psychoanalysis is the most influential area. Of the 104 books on the "core" list, most are concerned with psychoanalytic theories of personality, followed, in order of subject popularity, by schizophrenia, psychotherapy, and child psychiatry. And of the 118 most recommended articles, most are by psychoanalysts, even excluding the very large number written by Freud himself. Clearly, the most influential personality theory in psychiatry remains, in a word, Freudian, despite the innovations in the treatment of and approach to mental illness.

But it is far from clear to what degree theory as such, whether based on Freud or derived from some other "school," has a direct impact on the practice of psychotherapy. A number of studies suggest that the doctrinal position of a psychotherapist cannot be identified by watching him do therapy, and other studies indicate that even the most orthodox analysts tend toward eclecticism in their treatment of patients. "The point of it all," says one analyst whose writings cannot be faulted for their fidelity to Freudian principles, "is to get through to the patient. Almost no matter what. I find myself doing things that aren't exactly kosher—like seeing some analytic patients only once or twice a week. There's one I see only every couple of weeks because a lot of travel time is involved. Also, I get more involved with my patients than a lot of analysts do." A psychiatrist with much experience comments:

> People do one thing and say another, like some of those who are preaching non-directive therapy, you know, the very quiet, unobtrusive sort of thing. Actually many of them are very active when you watch them work—lots of extravagant gestures, thumping the desk, and so forth. There's a tendency to employ more techniques than you say you're using, not that this means you're more effective. About that I don't know. It varies whether you're eclectic or not. Maybe one exception where theory applies more than elsewhere is child psychiatry. I think that child psychiatry in particular has been asked to run before it can walk. In other words, we are trying to put into practice a whole lot of ideas and theories that have never absolutely been proved. There is a danger that we dash in and say "Thou shalt bring up thy children in such and such a way" before we really know what the hell we're doing.

An analyst who had previously been suspicious of certain unorthodox analytic "schools," such as those associated with the late Karen Horney and Harry Stack Sullivan, discovered in meeting the "deviants" that:

> They're just like the rest of us. They talk theory in accordance with the splintering of their groups, but they treat their patients

> exactly the same. Maybe what it comes down to is that the patient comes to us because he wants understanding, because he has failed or been deprived in a love relationship, because he is lonely, because he needs approval and acceptance. If he gets this, the analysis succeeds; if he doesn't, it fails. Of course, you won't get any analyst in the Association saying this out loud.

The major difficulty in determining whether this view or any other accurately describes the situation is the lack of knowledge about what transpires in a psychotherapeutic relationship. As noted earlier, very little is known about the determinants of success and failure in psychotherapy, and in analytic circles there is much opposition to the utilization of outside observers in efforts to study treatment techniques. "We simply do not know," runs a comment,

> what goes on, even in the case of students who are being supervised. The student reports to his supervisor. We aren't there. There are no referees, no umpires, no observers. And the real orthodox analysts are against observation through one-way screens, for example, because they claim that with such observation it is no longer an analytic situation. I don't find this to be true. Sure, it takes a while to ignore the others, but after a while you forget they're there. But this is precisely the trouble. Without observation you report what you're doing, in a paper or a talk, any way you like. You can say anything you want, make up the biggest lie. Who's to say you're wrong? With observation you don't have this freedom, and that's one big reason there's so much opposition to it.

It is extremely doubtful, however, that such opposition can maintain itself in the face of the doubts and uncertainties about psychoanalysis itself. In psychiatry, generally, the belief is widespread that the "articles, books, and lectures are important, but the essential element in the preparation of a clinician consists of his treating many patients with detailed supervision, at the same time checking assumptions which may or may not be accurate. . . ."[8] In the years ahead, the insistence on a more scientific methodology and, in particular, the empirical validation of results is almost certain to take effect.

V

The Politics of Psychiatry

IT is widely believed that psychiatrists and psychoanalysts are more liberal politically than other physicians, and every study made of their political convictions shows this view to be correct. It is further assumed that the professional associations of psychiatrists and analysts, unlike some other associations, are too well behaved and low keyed to engage in fractious in-fighting and vulgar politicking, and for the most part this assumption, too, is correct. Since patients neither know nor care whether their therapists hold office in professional associations, and since, in addition, these positions are mainly honorific, it matters little to most psychiatrists and analysts whether they are elected to any professional office.

But there are exceptions. And surely it would be expecting too much to imagine that ambitious office seekers do not exist in the ranks of psychiatry and psychoanalysis or that honorific positions in the professional associations do not carry with them a variety of personal satisfactions. In both the American Psychiatric Association and the American Psychoanalytic Association, election or selection for office is often a form of recognition for distinguished services or contributions to the profession. For those so recognized, speaking, writing, and traveling opportunities abound. The top officers of the associations are regarded by the public and the government as spokesmen for their professions, and it is to them that the mass media turn for answers to questions about the mental health of the nation. Because these questions have been proliferating, the leaders of American psychiatry and psychoanalysis rank increasingly higher in the circles of influence, and influence, whether in psychiatry or in politics, is certainly not the least of the rewards conferred by office.

Indeed, on occasion the contests for position in the associations are not totally unlike the competitions for office that periodically convulse the citizenry, even if the stakes are a great deal less. From time to time, in both associations, but especially in the American Psychoanalytic Association, a suspicion develops among some members that the organization is dominated by an establishment whose leaders and views are managing to prevail most of the time. These suspicions occasionally give birth to an antiestablishment group that attempts to impose upon the association its own leaders and outlook. The result, in a word, is "politics," with the establishment and antiestablishment functioning as political parties, the respective viewpoints as platforms, the leaders as candidates, the rank-and-file members as voters, and the final decision being rendered in the annual elections for officers. While the establishment usually wins, the contest is occasionally a close one marked by some heat and acrimony. Nor has it been unknown for the losers to withdraw and form the equivalent of a rival party movement.*

But in most cases the election of officers in the official associations passes without incident. In the American Psychiatric Association, officers are proposed by a nominating committee that usually includes one member from each of six geographical districts. Traditionally a single slate of candidates is named by the nominating committee, but any Fellow or Life Fellow can be nominated for position by a petition signed by fifty or more General Members or Fellows. Ballots identifying the candidates are mailed to American Psychiatric Association members in February, with the results announced at the annual meeting in May. Unlike the American Psychoanalytic Association, the American Psychiat-

---

* It was noted earlier that the local psychoanalytic institutes are especially prone to dissension and consequent splitting off. There is a sense in which the Academy of Psychoanalysis and the Association for the Advancement of Psychoanalysis can be regarded as the outcomes of "political" contests that were lost, bearing in mind that personality conflicts are subsumed under "politics." Thus far the American Psychiatric Association, less doctrinaire and more eclectic than the American Psychoanalytic Association, has not given birth to a major rival organization. However, several thousand psychiatrists do not belong to the American Psychiatric Association, presumably because of discontent with its politics. In recent years controversy within the APA has involved power struggles between psychoanalytically oriented psychiatrists, led by the Menningers and certain influential university-connected psychiatrists and analysts, and the hospital psychiatrists, who until 1946 dominated the APA. As a consequence, the latter no longer exercise control in the higher councils of the APA.

ric Association does not permit its president and vice-president to be eligible for reelection to the same office. Hence all American Psychiatric Association presidents since 1882, except one who served a two-year term in 1944–46, have been in office one year only.

Presidents of the American Psychiatric Association usually hold appointments in university departments of psychiatry or have made careers in public or private mental hospitals. Thus, of the ten presidents who served between 1960 and 1970, seven had as their primary affiliation a position in a department of psychiatry, not infrequently as its head. Three of these seven were members of the American Psychoanalytic Association, whereas there were no analysts among the three who had hospital backgrounds. So far as can be determined, only one person, the late William C. Menninger, has been president of both the American Psychiatric Association and the American Psychoanalytic Association. No woman has held high position in the American Psychiatric Association, and black psychiatrists so far have not been elected to high posts. If names are any guide to ethnic and religious origins, few Jews have held positions of eminence in the American Psychiatric Association; it is possible that in these offices they have been outnumbered by Catholics.

The American Psychoanalytic Association, unlike the American Psychiatric Association, does not confine its president to one term of office. In a period of fifty-nine years, from 1911 to 1970, the American Psychoanalytic Association has had thirty-four presidents, two of whom account for a total of twelve years in office. A. A. Brill, the early translator of Freud and a longtime head of the psychiatric clinic at Columbia University, was president for eight years, seven of them served consecutively. William Alanson White, superintendent of St. Elizabeth's Hospital in Washington and a leading American figure in the early days, served a total of four years as president, but this may have been partly due to the fact that there was no annual meeting of the American Psychoanalytic Association in either 1917 or 1918, leaving White in office (he had first been elected in 1916). Twelve presidents have held office for two years, but terms of two years or longer are becoming less frequent. Since 1955, only one president, Leo Rangell, has held the office for two years, and these were not consecutive years.

While American Psychoanalytic Association nominations can be made by rank-and-file members, most nominations are made by the nominating committee, consisting of all members of the executive council. The council, a large body composed of councilors representing each affiliated society, four elected councilors-at-large, and eleven *ex officio* members including the major officers of the Association, in its role as nominating committee solicits candidate suggestions from the affiliated societies and, in effect, screens those suggested in terms of willingness to serve and any conditions or restrictions of service. In the end the names of one or more candidates for each position to be filled are circulated to members, usually in November, with the results announced at the midwinter (December) meeting, which is almost always held in New York. Any twenty active members may nominate candidates for any office filled by election, but seldom does such a "revolt" take place and even less often does it succeed.

Nominees for the position of president generally have served as officers in their local societies, and they may also hold positions in university departments of psychiatry. It is rare for a candidate not to be a training analyst in his local institute or a member of its teaching faculty. A career wholly in private practice would not be an asset to an analyst who aspired to a top position in the Association. On the other hand, interest and involvement in professional psychiatry as distinct from psychoanalysis is neither help nor hindrance. One of the candidates nominated for American Psychoanalytic Association president in 1968, for example, did not join the American Psychiatric Association until 1964, although he had been a member of the American Psychoanalytic Association since 1946; in another instance, American Psychiatric Association membership followed by some months election to the presidency of the American Psychoanalytic Association.* Judging by names, most American Psychoanalytic Association presidents have been Jews, and one woman has served as president.

As noted earlier, the charge of "establishmentitis" is more often heard in the American Psychoanalytic Association than in the American Psychiatric Association, and, consequently, the nominat-

* A 1966 survey of 148 of its members by the American Psychoanalytic Association showed that 88.6 percent belonged to the American Psychiatric Association, 76.4 percent belonged to the American Medical Association, and approximately 82 percent belonged to state and county medical societies.

ing procedures in the American Psychoanalytic Association are more apt to be criticized. According to one prominent but anti-establishment analyst, these procedures practically guarantee that the president at any given time "will be a member of the Establishment—one of the boys." This is because

> the people on the nominating committee and other committees know each other very well, and they just move the presidency along. It happens that the president doesn't have much to do. He's only got a year in office and the Executive Committee does most of the work. But it's the honor, the final honor, for an analyst to be president, and therefore it's very difficult for an outsider to get in. Sure, they now have to put up two people (that wasn't always the case), and you can nominate from the floor. But it's always obvious which one is in the establishment and who'll be elected and who won't be. Never any question about that. After all, who's going to get up and question the credentials of so-and-so, who's going to ask what his great gifts are that he just *has* to be president of this organization of a thousand people?

If such questions were raised, it would probably mean "there was something personal on the questioner's side, something wrong. It could even mean that he hadn't been adequately analyzed."

Whatever it could or would mean, floor fights about elections of officers are highly unusual; indeed, it is rare to have an open and angry quarrel about any matter at the annual meeting. Divisive issues are much more likely to be discussed in the local societies or in key committees of the American Psychoanalytic Association, such as the powerful Board on Professional Standards. The Board, consisting of the top national officers and two members from each training institute, deals with membership, institutes, training, research, education, and revision of standards. Since it is only with Board approval that a new institute or society can be established, it is not least among the Board's functions to maintain a certain doctrinal purity in the definition of what constitutes psychoanalysis. Hence an important role of the Board is to keep doctrinal issues within specified bounds when a split-off is initiated by members of one of the institutes or societies. In this essential endeavor, despite the doubts and discontents within and without analytic circles, the Board has thus far succeeded.

But if it is beyond question that the American Psychoanalytic Association is a conservative organization in professional terms, it is far from the case that its members are even remotely conservative in politics. As will be seen, psychiatrists of all types and persuasions are more liberal politically than other physicians, and analysts are to the left of the psychiatrists. Psychiatrists and analysts are more active politically than other medical practitioners, and, again, analysts deviate from psychiatrists in the direction of greater involvement. Hence the paradox, if paradox it be, that the most orthodox Freudian analyst is apt to take an active interest in politics and in ideological terms to locate himself on the left wing of the Democratic Party.

The liberal commitment of psychiatrists and analysts, however, does not lead them toward political careers; in this respect they are similar to other doctors in preferring the certainties and material comforts of a medical practice to the uncertainties and less financially rewarding prospects of politics. Few physicians have held high political office since the Civil War: from 1870 to 1956, only 13 governors out of a total of 1,040 were physicians, and probably only 8 of them had ever been in regular practice. It is doubtful that the average Congress contains more than a handful of legislators with medical degrees.[1] So far as is known, no psychiatrist or analyst has served as a governor, United States Senator, Congressman, or mayor of a city, and it is not even certain that psychiatry and psychoanalysis have been represented in state legislatures. The few psychiatrists known to hold public office are found on school boards or in other types of local community activity.*

Voting, however, is another matter, and here, again, there are similarities between psychiatrists and other doctors, and, for that matter, persons with high incomes and status. According to a study of the 1952 Presidential election (Eisenhower vs. Stevenson), 97 percent of physicians voted, and 30 percent contributed financially to a political campaign.[2] In the present study, the proportion of analysts who voted in 1964 is also 97 percent, and for the

* Perhaps even this much involvement is unusual. The Hollingshead and Redlich survey of New Haven analysts found that they "belonged to the fewest organizations, participated the least in community affairs, and knew the least about the community and its activities." Quoted in Jack L. Rubins, "The Changing Role of Psychoanalysis: Beyond Action for Mental Health," *American Journal of Orthopsychiatry,* 27, 2 (1967), 156.

psychiatrists 95 percent. Sixty-two percent of the analysts and 45 percent of the psychiatrists gave money to a campaign in 1964, with political meetings being attended by 38 percent of the analysts and 26 percent of the psychiatrists. The least active political category was working for a party or candidate; only 18 percent of analysts and 15 percent of psychiatrists participated in the election to that extent.

The heavy Presidential voting turnout falls off in other elections, but it is still true that analysts and psychiatrists—along with doctors in general and other high-income and high-status groups—are fairly consistent voters whatever the contest level. For example, 88 percent of the analysts and 70 percent of the psychiatrists say that they always vote in off-year elections (that is, elections that occur between Presidential election years) for members of the United States Senate and House of Representatives. Of the analysts, 94 percent vote in elections to select governors and other state officials, and 72 percent vote in local contests to pick mayors and other city officials; for the psychiatrists the respective percentages are 75 and 62. Like the majority of citizens, neither analysts nor psychiatrists are inclined to vote a straight ticket: 64 percent of analysts and 52 percent of psychiatrists seldom or never vote only for the candidate of the party in which they are registered or to which they are generally sympathetic.*

More than half the total number of analysts and psychiatrists believe that voting is important in determining how the country is governed, but a substantial proportion of the analysts express doubts about the significance of voting and the governing competence of the major political parties. Thus 18 percent of the analysts feel that voting has little or nothing to do with how the country is run, compared with 3 percent of psychiatrists, and a surprising 47 percent of analysts do not think that either the Republican Party or the Democratic Party does a very good job of governing the country. Whereas 58 percent of psychiatrists believe

* There is also some evidence that persons in mental hospitals rank among the more politically active citizenry. A study reported in the New York *Times* indicated that inmates of the Bronx State Hospital, while they "vote virtually the same way as everybody else," vote in a higher percentage and also make fewer errors of the sort that invalidate ballots. The author of the study, psychiatrist Morris Klein of Albert Einstein College of Medicine, expressed his opinion that "no good reason existed for laws in some states that disenfranchised persons adjudged mentally ill." New York *Times,* September 4, 1968.

that both parties do a pretty good job of governing, only 26 percent of the analysts share this belief. Clearly the analysts have less confidence in the political system than the psychiatrists, but despite this lack of confidence—or because of it?—analysts are also more active politically than psychiatrists.

They also are more left-wing in outlook and voting preference. Seventy-two percent of the analysts and 52 percent of the psychiatrists regard themselves as Democrats regardless of whether or not they are registered in any party, and for the study sample as a whole the Democratic vote is substantial.* But as the following table shows, there are important political differences between the psychiatrists and analysts.

In October, 1968, according to *Medical Tribune,* 41 percent of psychiatrists intended to vote for Nixon and 35 percent indicated they would vote for Humphrey; this compares with voting intentions of 66 percent for Nixon, 14 percent for Humphrey, and 6 percent for Wallace of all physicians.†

The pronounced anti-Goldwater sentiments of most psychiatrists in 1964 was the background for a sensationalist effort to discredit the Republican candidate by suggesting that he was mentally unfit to be President. During the summer of 1964 the editors of *Fact* magazine, published by Ralph Ginzburg, sent letters to more than 12,000 psychiatrists asking: "Do you think that Barry Goldwater is psychologically fit to serve as President of the United States?" Citing a *Medical Tribune* preferential poll showing that psychiatrists preferred Lyndon B. Johnson "by ten to one," *Fact* magazine enclosed a form on which respondents could check in an appropriate box whether Goldwater "was stable enough to serve as President." They also were asked: "Does he

* Almost all studies of psychiatrists as voters show a Democratic preference, but there are important differences within psychiatry between the psychotherapists and those who practice mainly in the drug and organic areas. In the Twin Cities study, previously referred to, the psychotherapists (including analysts) were predominantly Democrats, and the drug-organicists primarily Republicans. Carl Malmquist, "Psychiatry in a Midwestern Metropolitan Community," *Mental Hygiene,* 48, 1 (January, 1967), 63–64.

† *Medical Tribune,* October 28, 1968. *Medical Tribune* surveys in past elections suggest that more than 60 percent of psychiatrists voted Democratic in both 1960 and 1964. Sixty percent or more of all other physicians regardless of field voted Republican, and even in 1964 the Democratic vote in medicine apart from psychiatry did not exceed 37.4 percent (internal medicine). It appears that the most Republican voters among physicians are radiologists (89.3 percent in 1964) and surgeons (77.4 percent in 1964).

seem prone to aggressive behavior and destructiveness? Does he seem callous to the downtrodden and the needy? Can you offer any explanation of his public temper-tantrums and his occasional outbursts of profanity? Finally, do you think that his having had two nervous breakdowns has any bearing on his fitness to govern this country?" There was space for any other comments a respondent

Table 10. Voting Preference*

	Psychiatrists		*Psychoanalysts*
1940			
	98	Number responses	28
	12	Republican %	11
	29	Democrat %	50
1944			
	104	Number responses	29
	18	Republican %	3
	32	Democrat %	83
1948			
	117	Number responses	32
	25	Republican %	12
	33	Democrat %	62
	4	Progressive %	22
1952			
	134	Number responses	33
	39	Republican %	21
	37	Democrat %	79
1956			
	136	Number responses	34
	43	Republican %	15
	43	Democrat %	85
1960			
	139	Number responses	34
	32	Republican %	6
	58	Democrat %	91
1964			
	142	Number responses	34
	24	Republican %	3
	71	Democrat %	95

* The difference between the total percentile response and 100% represents those who did not vote or were ineligible to vote.

wished to make "insofar as you are able to draw inferences. . . ." *

Despite the opposition of the American Psychiatric Association and every other psychiatric organization to the effort to poll psychiatrists on the question of Goldwater's psychological fitness for office, almost 2,500 psychiatrists participated in the survey, according to *Fact* publisher Ginzburg. Of these, 1,189 were reported as having doubts about his fitness, with 657 rendering the opinion that he was fit. Only 571 psychiatrists declared that they did not know enough about the Republican candidate to answer such questions.

It is probable that most psychiatrists and a very large number of lay citizens were appalled to find that more than 1,800 psychiatrists were willing, in the words of an *American Journal of Psychotherapy* editorial, to function as "long-range mail-order diagnosticians . . . using such dubiously reliable 'medical' reference sources as newspaper and magazine articles, television programs and newsreels. . . . These psychiatrists and the other 571 respondents unwittingly supplied grist for a mill that used them in a commercially profitable appeal to that portion of the public which is enthralled by sensationalism." While the *Journal* expressed the hope that psychiatrists "will play more active roles on the political scene," it insisted "there must be a clear recognition of the differences between one's position as a psychiatrist *per se* and one's status as a citizen with psychiatric training. If the psychiatrist confuses these responsibilities as he has in this current poll, then he fails both his country and his profession." [3]

Four years later, notwithstanding these warnings and admonitions, a number of psychiatrists again took part in a survey of Presidential fitness, this time in reference to Lyndon B. Johnson. On February 19, 1968, the indefatigable Ralph Ginzburg, in a new guise as publisher of *Avant Garde* (*Fact* magazine having

---

* The "evidence" for Goldwater's alleged nervous breakdowns came from an article in *Good Housekeeping* of May, 1964, titled "The Woman Behind Barry Goldwater" and mainly concerned with his wife, Peggy. A paragraph of the article read as follows: "One crisis occurred in 1937 when, after a period of intense work in the store, Barry suffered a nervous breakdown. After a lengthy rest, when he went to Prescott, Arizona, to help open a new branch of the store, and spent five days and nights without sleep, he cracked again. 'His nerves broke completely,' says Mrs. Goldwater. 'He couldn't sleep nights. He was very nervous. I immediately said we were going to get away to Honolulu. He was seasick all the way. But then he relaxed on the beach and just rested.' The change of pace was, apparently, all he needed."

expired), announced that more than 2,000 psychiatrists had responded to questions about the psychological fitness of President Johnson. While the responses had not been tabulated, the answers of many of these psychiatrists were "terrifying," Ginzburg reported. They had been asked, among other questions, "Does Lyndon B. Johnson seem divorced from reality? Does Mr. Johnson seem overly rigid, suspicious, unwilling to compromise, perhaps paranoid? Should Lyndon B. Johnson be examined by a board of psychiatrists before he is permitted to run for re-election?" Quoting four psychiatrists by name, Ginzburg promised to release the results of the survey well before the Democratic National Convention in Chicago.

Unfortunately for these results, which were to be published in an article titled "Lyndon B. Johnson: A Psychoanalytic Study," on March 31, 1968, President Johnson announced that he would not be a candidate for reelection. In May, 1968, a federal court awarded Barry Goldwater punitive damages of $75,000 in his suit against Ginzburg and the now defunct *Fact* magazine for its 1964 article "The Mind of Barry Goldwater." Although there was a subsequent effort by Drew Pearson to suggest in a speech, by innuendo, that President Nixon had consulted a psychiatrist in 1955 or 1956, when he was Vice President, nothing comparable to the two Ginzburg inquiries developed during the 1968 Presidential election.* It remains to be seen whether the issue of psychological or mental fitness of Presidential candidates is a recurrent one.†

---

* The Pearson allegations were reported in the New York *Times,* November 14, 1968, nine days after the election. It is possible that Ginzburg's silence during the remainder of the campaign owed something to still another loss in the federal courts. Prior to the Goldwater libel suit Ginzburg had been convicted on an obscenity charge in connection with *Eros,* a defunct magazine he launched some years ago. The *Eros* conviction, if upheld, carries with it a sentence of five years in prison in addition to a fine.

† A rapprochement of sorts between Goldwater and American psychiatry was effected in 1966 when *Psychiatric News* noted with pleasure that the former candidate for President was serving as campaign chairman for the fund-raising drive of the Maricopa County Mental Health Association in Arizona. "Those who felt," the *Psychiatric News* editorial noted, "that Mr. Goldwater's treatment at the hands of some psychiatrists during the last presidential campaign was, to put it mildly, inappropriate, will be glad to infer from this development that his reaction was one of sportsmanship and good grace and not of rancor." *Psychiatric News* expressed the hope that Goldwater's activities in behalf of mental health would have a "healthy effect" on "that mercifully small but irksomely persistent lunatic fringe that has somehow got the *idée fixe* that the mental health movement is a fiendish subversive conspiracy." *Psychiatric News,* June, 1966.

Whatever the final resolution of this issue, there will always be some psychiatrists who, because they disagree on issues with a particular candidate or because they see in his behavior potentially serious psychological problems, will be tempted to refer to the disliked candidate as a "paranoid personality," or to characterize him as manifesting "a continual distortion of reality to suit his illusions," or even to suggest that he is "suffering from insufficient cerebral blood supply and is in the arteriosclerotic range." [4] The tendency is especially pronounced when candidates are identified with programs to which the psychiatric community is strongly opposed, such as the Vietnam War and the general emphasis on a military response to the communist challenge in Asia, Latin America, and elsewhere. As will be seen, most psychiatrists view the world situation very differently from Barry Goldwater and the Johnson and Nixon administrations. It therefore was inevitable that the Goldwater of 1964, who favored "get-tough" policies abroad, and the Johnson of 1968, who was opposed to major concessions to North Vietnam and the Vietcong, would be disliked by a good many psychiatrists, some of whom were not hesitant to translate their dislike into the language of the consulting room. When Johnson was a "peace candidate" against Goldwater in 1964, he was heavily favored by the psychiatric community, few of whom raised questions about his fitness for office; in 1968, following four years of gradual but finally massive American intervention in Vietnam, many psychiatrists deserted Johnson first for McCarthy, then for McCarthy or Kennedy, and ultimately for Humphrey. Even those who supported Nixon in 1968 will need evidence, if they are to continue their support, not only that he enjoys reasonably good physical and mental health, but that he can move quickly and effectively against the problems of Vietnam, poverty, and race.

For it is clear that psychiatrists and other mental health professionals are strong supporters of peace, integration, and the welfare state. In May, 1966, members of the American Orthopsychiatric Association voted overwhelmingly for a resolution condemning the war in Vietnam and calling for a conference that would include the Vietcong and all members of the 1954 Geneva Accord; resolutions in 1967 and 1968 went further in endorsing "an orderly, phased withdrawal of American forces from Vietnam." [5] A survey of 8,000 physicians late in 1967 revealed that psychiatrists were more opposed to the Vietnam War than other physicians: 51 percent of psychiatrists as compared with 36 percent of all physicians polled favored a more active peace-seeking role for the United States, while 44 percent of psychiatrists and 18 percent of other physicians supported a cessation of bombing.[6] In August, 1968, 300 participants at the Seventh International Congress of Mental Health in London urged "an end to the war in Viet Nam and . . . a ceasefire at the earliest possible moment." The Congress, which was attended by a number of prominent American psychiatrists and analysts, heard psychiatrist Leon Eisenberg declare to a plenary session that "the central and overriding problem for mental health and human development at this point in time is the Viet Nam war." [7]

In 1968–69, petitions were presented to the American Psychi-

Table 11. Attitudes Toward Issues*

	Psychiatrists†				*Psychoanalysts*†			
	Favor		*Oppose*		*Favor*		*Oppose*	
	No.	*%*	*No.*	*%*	*No.*	*%*	*No.*	*%*
Test ban on atomic weapons	121	85	13	9	33	97	1	3
Ceasefire in Vietnam	85	62	46	33	31	94	2	6
Withdrawal from Vietnam	50	36	86	61	19	61	12	39
Medicare	74	51	58	40	30	88	2	6
More economic aid to underdeveloped countries	103	72	28	20	34	100	0	0
Greater federal effort to eliminate poverty	103	73	30	21	34	100	0	0
More federal aid to education	112	78	25	17	33	97	1	3
Recognition of Castro regime	36	25	91	63	22	65	10	29
Recognition of Chinese Communist government	91	64	42	29	27	82	4	12
Admission of Communist China to United Nations	87	61	48	34	30	91	3	9

* The exact wording of the attitude inquiry was: "There have been many issues talked about during the last two Presidential elections. As far as you can remember, how did you feel about the following issues? "

† The difference between the total percentile response and 100% represents those who were indifferent or did not remember how they felt about the issue specified.

atric Association national office urging that the Association take a strong stand against racism and poverty. At the APA annual meeting in May, 1968, more than 200 psychiatrists formed an Ad Hoc Committee for Social Action, the purpose of which was to urge an official APA stand in a variety of areas ranging from support of the Poor People's March on Washington to an endorsement of "our colleague Dr. Benjamin Spock in his consistent endeavors for peace in Vietnam." [8] A survey of more than 1,100 physicians in October, 1968, found that psychiatrists were much less responsive than other physicians to the "law and order" issue in the 1968 election and much more in favor of massive government action "with or without private help" as offering the only solution to the problems of the cities.[9]

The political behavior of the study group is consistent with these reports, but, again, it is to be noted that there are important differences between the psychiatrists and the analysts. Both psychiatrists and analysts score low on a scale measuring right-wing authoritarianism and somewhat higher on a scale measuring left-wing authoritarianism, but the analysts score lower on the right-wing scale and higher on the left-wing scale than the psychiatrists.* As Table 11 demonstrates, psychiatrists hold liberal views on most issues, with the analysts standing well to the left of the psychiatrists.

Psychiatrists and analysts are also very positive in their feelings about the United Nations. More than a quarter of the psychiatrists and a fifth of the analysts advocate transforming the United Nations into a world government of all nations, with another 38 percent of the psychiatrists and 73 percent of the analysts favoring a strengthening of the United Nations in the direction of giving it

* Scales used were a 24-item F-scale, developed at Berkeley in the late 1940's as a measure of authoritarian personality characteristics, and a 24-item C-scale, devised by Harold D. Lasswell and the author in 1955 as a measure of left-wing authoritarian tendencies. The group scores for the psychiatrists and analysts, on a range from 7 (highest agreement) to 1 (lowest agreement), were as follows:

F-scale		*C-scale*	
Psychiatrists	*Analysts*	*Psychiatrists*	*Analysts*
2.93	2.46	2.89	3.38

For the development, initial use, and defense of the F-scale as a personality test, see T. W. Adorno *et al., The Authoritarian Personality* (New York: Harper & Row, 1950). The C-scale is discussed in Arnold A. Rogow and Harold L. Lasswell, *Sex, Culture, and Politics* (New York: Thomas Y. Crowell, 1970).

Table 12. I would willingly admit . . .
(Psychiatrists, 143; Analysts, 32)

	Negroes				*Orientals*				*Jews*				*Catholics*			
	Psychiatrists		*Analysts*		*Psychiatrists*		*Analysts*		*Psychiatrists*		*Analysts*		*Psychiatrists*		*Analysts*	
	No.	*%*	*No.*	*%*	*No.*	*%*	*No.*	*%*	*No.*	*%*	*No.*	*%*	*No.*	*%*	*No.*	*%*
To close kinship by marriage	50	35	13	41	72	50	22	69	117	83	29	91	98	76	23	72
To my club as personal chums	115	80	31	97	126	87	31	97	135	94	30	94	134	94	30	94
To my street as neighbors	123	86	31	97	133	93	32	100	140	98	32	100	141	99	32	100

more power and authority. None of the analysts and only 3 percent of the psychiatrists are opposed to alliances and joint commitments with other countries.[10]

Liberal attitudes also prevail in areas of civil rights and civil liberties. In an effort to measure feelings about race and minority ethnic groups, the study group was asked for attitudes on a variety of relationships with Negroes, Orientals, Jews, and Catholics. The results of the "social distance" test are shown in Table 12.

While it is clear that most psychiatrists and analysts are reluctant to accept racial intermarriage, they are significantly less prejudiced toward Negroes and Orientals than is the population at large, and this, too, accords with their generally liberal position on social and economic questions.* For the study group as a whole, and the analysts in particular, there would appear to be somewhat less acceptance of Catholics than of Jews, either because of the prominence of Jews in psychiatry or because of the widely held view that the Catholic Church is hostile toward psychiatry and, especially, psychoanalysis. Whatever the explanation, almost a quarter of both the psychiatrists and analysts would not willingly admit a Catholic to close kinship by marriage.

In matters of civil liberties, it would be expected that many psychiatrists and analysts, who are themselves favorably disposed toward atheism and socialism, would be far more tolerant than the general population of advocacy of atheistic and socialistic doctrines in the schools, libraries, mass media, and elsewhere. But they are also much more in favor of the rights of admitted and suspected Communists to advocate Communist doctrines and to hold jobs in defense plants, colleges, and schools. As Table 13 demonstrates, psychiatrists and analysts are significantly more civil libertarian than the most liberal group in the population, the community leaders.

As opponents of the Vietnam War and supporters of civil rights and civil liberties, psychiatrists and analysts are naturally prone to admire political figures who are identified with the peace and civil liberties movements and the struggle against poverty and dis-

* A Gallup international poll of thirteen countries, released in November, 1968, showed that the United States was the most opposed to interracial marriage. Only 20 percent of Americans approved of such marriages, whereas 72 percent disapproved. Marriages between Jews and non-Jews, on the other hand, were approved by 59 percent and disapproved by only 21 percent. New York *Times*, November 10, 1968.

Table 13. Civil Liberties for Communists and Suspected Communists*

	Psychiatrists (%)				*Analysts* (%)				*Community Leaders* (%)			*National Cross Section* (%)		
	Yes	*No*	*N.O.*†	*N.R.*†	*Yes*	*No*	*N.O.*	*N.R.*	*Yes*	*No*	*N.O.*	*Yes*	*No*	*N.O.*
1 (a) Suppose an admitted Communist is working in a defense plant. Should he be fired, or not?	56	19	21	4	49	26	20	6	93	5	2	90	6	4
(b) Suppose a man whose loyalty has been questioned before a Congressional committee but who swears under oath he has never been a Communist is working in a defense plant. Should he be fired, or not?	9	62	26	3	6	83	6	6	13	82	5	18	72	10
2 (a) Suppose an admitted Communist is teaching in a college. Should he be fired, or not?	22	66	9	3	0	94	3	3	86	11	3	89	6	5
(b) Suppose a suspected Communist who swears under oath he has never been a Communist is teaching in a college. Should he be fired, or not?	3	87	7	3	0	94	0	6	15	81	4	22	69	9

3	(a)	Suppose an admitted Communist is teaching in a high school. Should he be fired, or not?	29	53	15	3	6	83	9	3	89	9	2	91	5	4
	(b)	Suppose a suspected Communist who swears under oath he has never been a Communist is teaching in a high school. Should he be fired, or not?	4	83	9	4	0	91	3	6	16	80	4	22	69	9
4	(a)	Suppose an admitted Communist wants to make a speech in your community. Should he be allowed to speak, or not?	89	6	2	3	97	0	0	3	51	47	2	27	68	5
	(b)	Suppose a suspected Communist who swears under oath he has never been a Communist wants to make a speech in your community. Should he be allowed to speak, or not?	91	4	1	3	94	0	0	6	87	11	2	70	21	9
5	(a)	Suppose an admitted Communist wrote a book which is in your public library. Somebody in your community suggests the book should be removed from the library. Would you favor removing it, or not?	2	94	1	3	0	97	0	3	54	42	4	66	27	7

Table 13. Civil Liberties for Communists and Suspected Communists (cont.)*

	Psychiatrists (%)				*Analysts (%)*				*Community Leaders (%)*			*National Cross Section (%)*		
	Yes	*No*	*N.O.*†	*N.R.*†	*Yes*	*No*	*N.O.*	*N.R.*	*Yes*	*No*	*N.O.*	*Yes*	*No*	*N.O.*
(b) Suppose a suspected Communist who swears under oath he has never been a Communist wrote a book which is in your public library. Somebody in your community suggests the book should be removed from the library. Would you favor removing it, or not?	1	93	3	3	0	94	0	6	7	88	5	17	71	12

* Percentile figures for community leaders and the national population cross-section are taken from Samuel A. Stouffer, *Communism, Conformity, and Civil Liberties: A Cross-section of the Nation Speaks Its Mind* (New York: Doubleday, 1955). The Stouffer survey, conducted in mid-1954, was based on 4,933 rank-and-file respondents and 1,500 selected local community leaders (mayors, heads of chambers of commerce, chairmen of Republican and Democratic county committees, American Legion commanders, etc.). While there are difficulties in comparisons—the Stouffer study was made at the height of the McCarthy era—it can be argued that in 1966, as in the earlier period, there was considerable apprehension about the threat of Communism both abroad (Vietnam, Cuba) and at home (alleged Communist influence in the peace movement, civil rights demonstrations, student unrest, etc.). In 1966, for example, there were at least six Congressional investigations under way of Communist and Communist-front organizations.

† N.O. = No opinion. N.R. = No response.

crimination. Presented with a list of prominent Americans and asked to name those who best represent "political maturity," the analysts confined their choices exclusively to liberals in politics, whereas the psychiatrists, while they favor political liberals, included some conservatives on the list of "politically mature" Americans.

Table 14. Identification of "Politically Mature" Leaders

	Psychiatrists No. choosing		*Analysts No. choosing*
J. W. Fulbright	48	J. W. Fulbright	27
Lyndon B. Johnson	45	Earl Warren	16
Earl Warren	41	Hubert H. Humphrey	9
Dean Rusk	34	Lyndon B. Johnson	8
Harry S Truman	29	Harry S Truman	7
Dwight D. Eisenhower	26	Dean Rusk	5
Hubert H. Humphrey	22	John F. Kennedy*	2
Richard M. Nixon	11		
Barry Goldwater	8		
John F. Kennedy*	8		
J. Edgar Hoover	7		
Adlai Stevenson*	6		

* The names of John F. Kennedy and Adlai Stevenson, both deceased by 1966, were write-ins.

Among the psychiatrists, there were scattered write-in votes for Wayne Morse, Robert Taft, Robert McNamara, Nelson Rockefeller, Everett Dirksen, and a few relatively obscure political personalities. Names mentioned once by the analysts included Eugene McCarthy, Jacob Javits, Thomas Kuchel, Nelson Rockefeller, George Romney, Arthur Goldberg, Dean Acheson, Walter Lippmann, Wayne Morse, and "Alfred E. Neuman." Of interest is the fact that Eugene McCarthy and Robert F. Kennedy, whom many psychiatrists and analysts supported for the 1968 Democratic Party nomination for President, were overlooked: Kennedy was not mentioned at all, and McCarthy received one vote.* For that

* The later standing of Eugene McCarthy among psychiatrists is to some extent indicated by his being invited in 1967 to participate in a panel discussion at the May, 1968, annual meeting of the American Psychiatric Association. Follow-

matter, neither major candidate in 1968 received high ratings for "political maturity" from the study group in 1966.

Psychiatrists and analysts accord a general welcome to the civil rights "revolution" of our time and the rise of the welfare state. Almost a third of the psychiatrists and analysts regard the civil rights "revolution" as *the* most significant development in the United States since World War II and the emphasis on social welfare as the second most important change. Some psychiatrists mention the expansion of educational opportunity as an important and welcome development, while others stress the "cultural explosion," the increase in leisure time, innovations in technology and communications, and the "relaxation of repressive standards in expression and sex." One analyst speaks of the "greater awareness of the total needs of people" as the most significant change, while a psychiatrist with a similar view hails "the evolution toward a more 'socially-concerned' society," and cites the creation of the Department of Health, Education, and Welfare as evidence of this evolution. A progressive change for several psychiatrists and analysts was the election of a Catholic President in 1960, which they interpret to mean that prejudice as such is decreasing in American life.

But for a large proportion of the total group, developments that are undesirable and unfortunate offset the gains and, in certain instances, outweigh them. One psychiatrist notes "the lack of pride in achievement; the increase of 'something for nothing' philosophy in our younger generation." There are occasional references to the "decrease in personal responsibility of the individual," and the "breakdown of law and order." Much has been accomplished, runs an extended comment, "but on the unfavorable side there has occurred in our country a dehumanization, a lack of concern for the other fellow, a disinclination to risk getting involved with others. . . ." An analyst is unhappy with the thought that "the basic American attitude is becoming one of greed and aggrandizement. It seems to whet our appetites (at all levels) to consume and accumulate more and more—while real

---

ing his announced candidacy for the Presidency, the APA program committee found it necessary to withdraw the invitation "in view of the general trend of the papers, all of which might lead to some unfavorable implications." The topic of the panel session was "Private Conflict with Public Consequences"; it featured papers devoted to the lives and careers of T. E. Lawrence, Thomas Jefferson, James Forrestal, and John G. Winant.

morality is tossed away. The stereotypes, pious platitudes, and unbelievable hypocrisy of our rationalizations are depressing." Several psychiatrists and analysts mention the breakdown of the family and increased permissiveness and indulgence of the young as a significant but unwelcome change; a psychiatrist speaks of the "premature thrusting of children and adolescents into an approximation of adult behavior, and the premature thrusting of children into an approximation of adolescent behavior."

Despite their favorable attitude toward efforts to alleviate poverty and distress, many psychiatrists and analysts have misgivings about the expansion of the federal government and what one psychiatrist terms the "weakening of our economic structure by debt and inflation." There are several negative references to "socialism" and "socialization," and it is clear that a small number of psychiatrists share the view, as one of them puts it, that "the 'cradle to the grave' care of people by a paternal federal government is creating immature, dependent citizens who look to Washington for security, planning, and organizing. We are becoming too *dependent* upon centralized power and [are] losing personal freedom." (In the preceding comment the word "dependent" is underlined three times.)

But if many psychiatrists and analysts, as well as a majority of all other Americans, believe they are living "in the best of times and the worst of times," it cannot be said that they expect this delicate balance between the best and the worst to maintain itself indefinitely. For it is a fact, judging by the responses of the study group, that psychiatrists and analysts are far from sanguine about the future. Whether because psychiatry as such attracts those who are pessimists by nature, or because a daily exposure to the griefs and ills of mankind is not conducive to a happy disposition, an optimistic outlook is definitely not characteristic of American psychiatrists and analysts. It is possible, of course, that there is a great deal, objectively speaking, *not* to be optimistic about. Whatever the explanation, an air of gloomy foreboding characterizes the expectation of many, although not all, of the participants in the study.*

* A hopeful outlook was not characteristic of any significant American opinion in 1968–69, and perhaps there was no more optimism two years earlier when the study was conducted. In August, 1968, a poll of more than 16,500 readers of *Psychology Today* showed that 52 percent of white respondents believed that

Thus, more than 61 percent of the psychiatrists (145 responded to the question) believe that there is a "pretty good chance" or a "fair possibility" of a third world war; 7 percent regard such a catastrophe as "practically certain." Of the 33 analysts who replied to the question, 67 percent feel that there is a "pretty good chance" or a "fair possibility" of another world war, while 3 percent are "practically certain" it will occur. Twenty-seven percent of the psychiatrists and 30 percent of the analysts hold that a third world war is "unlikely" or "very unlikely."

The possibility of a major depression is seen as a "pretty good chance" or a "fair possibility" by 45 percent of psychiatrists, with 6 percent maintaining that a depression is "practically certain." For the analysts, the "pretty good chance" and "fair possibility" category is 44 percent, with 3 percent indicating "practically certain." Thirty-eight percent of the psychiatrists and 35 percent of the analysts regard a depression as "unlikely" or "very unlikely."

In 1966, when black-white relations were less tense, the prospect of race riots in major cities was viewed as "practically certain" by 38 percent of the psychiatrists and 44 percent of the analysts, with 43 percent of psychiatrists and 38 percent of analysts in the "pretty good chance" category. A further 17 percent of psychiatrists and 18 percent of analysts thought there was a "fair possibility" of riots; only three psychiatrists (2 percent) and no analyst dismissed the possibility of riots as "very unlikely" or "unlikely."

Many psychiatrists and analysts are no more hopeful about a variety of social and mental health problems facing the nation. As Table 15 shows, the feeling is general that most of these problems will remain with us in the decade ahead or even worsen. "In your view," respondents were asked, "are the following problems likely to increase, decrease, or stay the same during the next ten years?"

It is significant that no problem is viewed as diminishing over the decade 1966–76, and that only the problems of mental illness and suicide receive a substantial margin of votes as likely to "stay about the same." These problems will probably not increase, some

---

the "quality of living" in cities was worse than twenty years ago, and only 37 percent thought it was better. The percentages were almost reversed among black respondents, but less than 3 percent of the respondents, or fewer than 500 persons, were Negroes. *Psychology Today,* January, 1969, pp. 22 *supra.*

Table 15. Expectations About Increase or Decrease of Social Problems

	Increase				*Stay About the Same*				*Decrease*			
	Psychiatrists		*Analysts*		*Psychiatrists*		*Analysts*		*Psychiatrists*		*Analysts*	
Problem	*No.*	*%*	*No.*	*%*	*No.*	*%*	*No.*	*%*	*No.*	*%*	*No.*	*%*
Alcoholism	68	47	16	47	69	48	17	50	7	5	1	3
Crime	86	60	25	73	49	34	7	21	8	6	2	6
Divorce rate	82	57	20	59	58	40	13	38	4	3	1	3
Drug addiction	67	47	21	64	64	45	12	36	12	8	0	0
Illegitimacy	70	49	19	58	49	34	10	30	25	17	4	12
Mental illness	37	26	8	24	88	61	21	64	19	13	4	12
Suicide	41	29	9	27	87	61	19	58	15	10	5	15

psychiatrists and analysts indicated, because they are susceptible to treatment and at least partial control through psychopharmacology, especially the tranquilizers and antidepressants. The belief that alcoholism will yield in the near future to control through drugs explains the high response in the "stay about the same" category, whereas it is not expected that the birth control pill and other advances in contraception will have much effect on illegitimacy. Pregnancy outside of marriage, according to many psychiatrists and analysts, results less from ignorance or nonavailability of contraceptive measures and devices than from a conscious or unconscious desire to become pregnant.

The view that depression, war, and race riots—in increasing order of probability—are likelihoods for the immediate future, and that none of seven major national problems will decrease in importance perhaps is not unrelated to the liberal commitment of many psychiatrists and analysts. If one by-product of training and experience almost compels one to view the world as a darkening plain on which personal relationships proceed in accordance with Hobbesian imperatives, surely another consequence is a deep compassion for those who are troubled and sick and a heightened awareness of the conditions that make for trouble and sickness. Since the evidence is overwhelming that psychiatrists and, even more to the point, analysts are to the left of their colleagues in medicine, not to mention their other equals in education and affluence—for example, businessmen, managers, lawyers, and engineers—their tendency to adopt a politically liberal position requires some explanation. Is it possible that psychiatric recruitment, training, and experience predispose one toward the political left?

To begin with, as was noted in an earlier chapter, medical students who go into psychiatry take more liberal positions on social and political issues than do students who opt for other specialties. In fact, the more certain such students are that they are making the right choice in choosing psychiatry as a career, the more liberal their position on issues.[11] Such students also score low on measures of personality rigidity and authoritarianism and high on tests of open-mindedness and tolerance.

There is little doubt that psychiatric training strengthens tendencies toward humanism and the values associated with human dignity. An important effect of training, says one distinguished analyst, is that

> it makes one open to ideas. A good psychiatrist can't be rigid, narrow-minded, or held in tight. You tend to become more open, more generous, more tolerant. After all, you develop a fundamental respect for the human animal and all his prejudices and rigidities. You try to see beyond all that.

Another analyst points out that psychiatrists, in attempting to understand themselves and their patients, necessarily develop a basic respect for the human being. "Let me illustrate this with a book I once wrote," he begins.

> It was about a guy who was a stubborn and arrogant bastard, and I hated the guy so I had to drop the book for about six months while I worked through these feelings I had. It was like treating a patient. I worked through my own relationship to the guy and I came out respecting him and liking him. With a patient you hate you either have to drop him or find out why you really hate him and work through it. But it's more than just finding out why. It's going through some sort of inner reorganization, and when you do this enough you discover that human beings have value no matter what they do or who they are. Once you understand a person you can't hate him. That may be why most psychiatrists I know are liberals. Liberalism is less given to hate than conservatism, more inclined to see worth in everyone no matter what his color, class, and so forth.

A psychiatrist mentions that he "translates thinking about patients into my world outlook," and he illustrates this translation as follows:

> I think there is an analogy between the way we treat patients and the way we ought to treat Communist China. Obviously China is a nation in this world and as such it has to be integrated into the community of nations. Inevitable. So far we have gone through a period of pseudo-isolation of Communist China, but sooner or later we'll have to deal directly with the Chinese. I look at this the way I look at a ward or something where you have a group of people, and somebody isolates himself from the group,

or maybe it's the group that isolates him. Sooner or later that member is going to have to be drawn into the group as an active participant. Otherwise nothing but trouble and the guy getting worse. That's one way I translate my experience with patients into my world view. Also, sometimes you can see the behavior of a nation as being grossly paranoid, or perhaps narcissistic, or something like that.

One psychiatrist in the study group suggests that a partial explanation for the present liberal disposition is the preponderance of Jews who are, traditionally, liberals in politics. But while this situation is changing, since more and more non-Jews are entering psychiatry, he does not expect the liberal inclination to diminish. It is in the nature of psychiatry, he comments,

to be interested in the welfare of people and to value freedom and opportunity—in other words, to be liberal. And in our time it is the Democratic party that has given liberals a place. Not that it's been perfect. Far from that. But I don't think there are many of us who feel comfortable with the Republican party.

Several psychiatrists and analysts suggest that psychiatry is anti-authoritarian in its value system, and, in their view, it is this factor more than any other that predisposes psychiatrists toward liberal politics. One of these psychiatrists argues:

Basically, the liberal point of view is more deterministic and less directive than the conservative point of view. Liberalism doesn't involve doing something to somebody nearly so much as conservatism, which tends to be more authoritative and directive. And psychiatrists are a low-authority group, that is, we value independence, free choice, minimum coercion.

A somewhat similar interpretation is advanced by an analyst:

We spend our time struggling against the tyranny of the unconscious. You see, I'm a fighter against tyranny in a peculiar way. My patients are tyrannized by unconscious repressive forces, and these forces, that have led to their symptoms, have constricted their freedom to make choices. I try to liberate them, give them a choice, give them a vote, if you will, in psychological terms. I say: come on, now, *you* should decide, not some event that happened when you were four years old. When you're against a tyranny like the tyranny of the unconscious, you must be against tyrannies of all kinds and injustices of all kinds.

Most analysts, he adds, identify the struggle against tyranny with the Democratic Party, since it is the Democratic Party that is most opposed to the "tyranny of poverty, discrimination, bad health, and lack of education." But not all analysts. Estimating the Republicans in his psychoanalytic society at between 15 and 20 percent, he surmises that "we have booming practices out here and some of these guys, once they start making money, start worrying about how to protect it." One of the worriers, perhaps, is the only psychoanalyst known to be a member of the John Birch Society. If there are others, their identity is not known to their colleagues, and perhaps they are no more eager to reveal their professional identities to their confreres on the extreme right who regard psychoanalysis as a much more evil influence in the world than fluoridation.

It remains true, however, that political conservatism even in diluted form is not a foremost characteristic of either psychiatrists or analysts whatever their income levels. Less certain is the effect upon patients of the dominant liberal persuasion of their therapists. An earlier chapter noted that most patients, whether Republicans or Democrats, probably adhere to moderate or liberal political positions prior to entering therapy or analysis, and to that extent there are not likely to be conflicts over political preferences. But it is doubtful that political discussions as such take up much time in the fifty-minute hour. Traumatic political events, such as wars, assassinations, riots, and perhaps elections of more than usual interest are sometimes talked about by patients or therapists, but it is not likely that the ordinary happenings of politics play an important role.[12]

Nevertheless, the patient's politics may be affected as he comes to understand the relationship between his life history and his political views and begins to ask himself why he believes as he does. To the extent that his political convictions are based more on the remote past than the present, or serve personality needs that change or disappear under therapy, these convictions are likely to undergo modification. The revision of political views, of course, need not be, and probably rarely is, dramatic, such as a shift from one party to another or from one ideology to its direct opposite. On the whole, it is doubtful that as a result of therapy or analysis, a patient would transfer his loyalties from, say, George Wallace to Eugene McCarthy, but it is conceivable that his allegiance might shift from Barry Goldwater or Ronald Reagan to Nelson Rockefeller. The effects, if any, are likely to find expression as a move from more extreme positions to the moderate center of American politics, whether in the Republican or Democratic party. The primary reasons for this, as one analyst observes, is that successful therapy or analysis "opens one to a broader range of experience and information. Such a person would be more concerned with human relationships. He would be more aware of his own feelings and motives. This could alter to some degree his political opinions, but not because he had ever been aware of the therapist's political views or social values, except the value which the therapist places on the worth and self-actualizing potential of the individual." The patient, in this view, is apt to be drawn to that political platform or candidate, regardless of party label, who also attaches importance to human dignity. Whether or not many psychiatrists and their patients are right to regard the recent standard-bearers of the Democratic Party as ideological allies is a question that need not concern us here—and it goes without saying that any possible answer, given the vagaries and vicissitudes of American politics, is subject to change.

A different and much more difficult question is the extent to which official psychiatry should become more involved in political issues and problems. Certainly, there are occasions when the behavioral insights of psychiatry and psychoanalysis seem relevant to an understanding of political developments. The *Fact* magazine attempt in 1964 to exploit psychiatry for political purposes may be a miscarriage of the purposes of both psychiatry and journalism, but illness in office with consequences for policy-making *is* a reality of the past and present. It has been suggested, for example, that the physical and mental illnesses or personality disorders of statesmen may be significant for understanding the rejection of the Versailles Treaty by the United States Senate, the British policy of appeasement in the 1930's, the leadership of the Russian Revolution in 1917 and the movement for Indian independence, the failure of the Democratic Socialists in Germany following World War II, and certain aspects of American policy in the Cold War.[13]

It has been noted, further, that there are substantial neurotic components in race prejudice, anti-Semitism, crime, violence, the behavior of mass movements, and a large number of political "causes" and crusades. The psychological underpinnings of totalitarian political parties have long been apparent to political scientists and psychiatrists. Freud himself was a pioneer in the psychoanalytic exploration of the conditions of war and peace, and, indeed, much of what he wrote has a direct or indirect bearing on the whole relationship between psychoanalysis and politics.[14]

In short, the effort to make psychiatry and psychoanalysis relevant to public affairs is not new. As psychiatrist Howard P. Rome has noted, Benjamin Rush, regarded as the father of American psychiatry, was as much a political activist as he was a physician, and since his time a number of leaders in psychiatry have stressed the connection between mental health and the social condition. "Mental health is not only related to individual life," said a speaker at an International Medical Congress in 1876, ". . . there is also a 'mental hygiene in communities,' which necessitates that students of mental hygiene enter 'the wide domain of sociology and social science.' [Mental hygiene] must . . . be considered from an individual, social, and national point of view."[15] In 1941, George H. Stevenson, then president of the American Psychiatric Association, urged his colleagues to view war as a public health problem with roots in "psychological and psychopathological factors."[16] More recently, psychiatrist Jerome D. Frank, pointing to a number of similarities between the behavior of nations moving toward or threatening war and the behavior of mental patients, has suggested that the insights of the clinic and hospital must be utilized if mankind is not to destroy itself.[17]

Many psychiatrists and analysts, however, while agreeing in principle that their professions must take an interest in the social and political context of mental health problems, nevertheless have difficulty specifying the exact content and form of such interest. No doubt psychiatric illness in high office should be safeguarded against, but how, and by whom? Given the difficulties in diagnosing and prescribing for psychological problems, would anything be gained by having psychiatrists screen candidates for office or, in accordance with one suggestion, by including a psychiatrist among the President's physicians?[18] Are analogies between patients and nations sound enough to warrant giving psychiatrists a major role in the determination of foreign policy? Is enough known about the political, social, and economic causes of mental illness to justify the inclusion of psychiatrists and analysts on governing boards at local, state, and national levels?

Those who supply negative answers to these questions tend to argue that psychiatrists and analysts are no more competent than anyone else to deal with political problems. It would be the gravest mistake, one analyst observes,

> to become involved in political decisions because we really know very little about political theory or foreign policy, or even domestic policy. Sure, we have to become interested in community affairs if there is going to be any meaningful social and community psychiatry. The National Institute of Mental Health would not have developed as it has if there hadn't been psychiatrists who were politically informed, who knew how to lobby and pressure for funds, that sort of thing. But if you go too far into politics, you cease being a psychiatrist and become a politician. I very much fear that some of the social and community boys are busier politicking than they are being psychiatrists, and in my opinion that is not a good thing.

The public itself is partly to blame, says a psychiatrist, for the "emergence of the psychiatrist as political expert," because the public,

> like the patient, thinks the psychiatrist is a magician, and some psychiatrists play up to this. Instead of talking about the dynamics of war and peace, which is fine because it's an extrapolation of dynamic theory, they make a statement that the war in Asia is, well, you know, absurd, idiotic, that it has no good purpose, that Americans have no place over there. They are drawing conclusions they have no right to draw. Just because we know something about internal processes in interpersonal relationships among individuals and small groups doesn't mean we can extrapolate this to nations. Nations are just not people. I'm not against anyone making statements about Vietnam or anything else, but it is very important that when we make statements we identify ourselves as private citizens, not psychiatrists.

Another psychiatrist is doubtful that psychiatrists should become involved in community activities just because they are supposed to know a good deal about human relations. "I don't think," he comments,

> there is anything particular about psychiatric training that makes one better able to deal with community problems. As a matter of fact, I'm kind of impressed by the fact that psychiatrists who, in their clinical work, may be highly sensitive and perceptive in their reactions, seem to lose all of their sensitivity when they move out of the clinical sphere into some other sphere. It's really a role component. When you take a psychiatrist and try to make him the administrator of a program, in his dealings with employees and others he'll do things that are shockingly tactless. In personnel dealings and dealings with other departments, he won't utilize his sensitivity or psychiatric skill.

It is even possible, he adds, that

> psychiatrists are worse in these roles than others, because the orientation generally of anybody in a scientific or parascientific field—clinical psychiatry is probably more parascientific than scientific—is toward introspection and evaluation of issues rather than toward decisiveness and action.

But a psychiatrist who favors expansion into political and social areas regards the refusal of his colleagues to support such efforts as itself a neurotic manifestation of the

> professional isolationism that is characteristic of the typical American psychiatrist. I would say that 85 to 90 percent are a-social in orientation. They don't want to get involved in community affairs, they don't want to get involved in politics, they don't want to get involved socially with their patients. They want to keep to a hyperprofessional isolated system. It's very easy, you know, it's extremely less anxiety-provoking to sit in your office with your identity structure on the other side of the desk. Some years ago, to see what it felt like, I tried changing positions, having the patient sit in my chair and me sit where he was. This changed the session considerably. At other times I try sitting on the floor and I find it makes a lot of difference if the patient looks down at me and I look up at him. Most psychiatrists are too rigid for

> this. They resist change of any kind, and especially change that would make them more anxious and insecure. That's one big reason they are happier in their offices than they are out there in the big bad ugly political world.

But unhappy or not, he continued, psychiatrists will be increasingly drawn into politics because of demands that they contribute whatever expert knowledge they possess to the solution of pressing social problems.

There appears to be little reason to doubt this view, which has long since been influential in the Group for the Advancement of Psychiatry (GAP), the American Orthopsychiatric Association, the American Academy of Psychoanalysis, and other organizations.[19] The movement of official psychiatry and psychoanalysis, in the form of the American Psychiatric Association and the American Psychoanalytic Association, toward socially relevant concerns is attested to by the frequency of editorials and articles in the *American Journal of Psychiatry* with such titles as "Psychiatry and Foreign Affairs";[20] the appointment by the APA of special committees and task forces in subject areas traditionally regarded as the exclusive domain of social scientists;[21] the creation by the APsaA in 1969 of a Standing Committee of Social Psychiatry, an area formerly of little interest to analysts; the establishment of training and research programs in universities administered jointly by psychiatrists and political scientists[22]; and other developments. As an October 1968 editorial in *Psychiatric News* remarked, there is "increasing consensus in our own and other science fields that something more is called for than what one scientist has dubbed 'over-professionalized particularizations and academic irrelevancies.'" Noting that the professional organizations were being urged to take stands on a variety of issues and problems, the *Psychiatric News* editorial admitted that the "something more" position pointed toward a future for the professional societies that was bound to be "more difficult, perilous, and uncertain than the comfortable nonpartisanship of the past." Nevertheless, concluded the editorial, "we would get on with it. We suspect that our very survival depends importantly on its success."[23]

The title of the editorial, appropriately, was "The Death of Inaction."

VI

America as the Patient?

THE view of Lawrence K. Frank and other social critics[1] that society itself is the patient, or culprit, and not human nature, much less man's fall from grace or original sinfulness, is apt to characterize reformers of any time and place. The "sick society" position underlies the thought of Rousseau, Marx, and Veblen, to mention a few luminaries in political thought, and in our own day it expresses the point of view, in muted or extreme rhetoric, of liberal Democrats, black militants, Students for a Democratic Society, and most varieties of pacifists and socialists. The assumption, in brief, is that people are neurotic, or cruel, or selfish, or bigoted because they have been made that way by social conditions, and especially the conditions under which they live and work in a capitalist society. It follows that if society were to be changed, there would be little or no neurosis, cruelty, selfishness, and bigotry. Wars would cease, poverty would be abolished, and blacks and whites would relate as brothers. Then, too, presumably, there would be much less need for mental hospitals, and perhaps also less need for psychiatrists and analysts.

The "sick society" position as stated above is somewhat simplified and exaggerated, to be sure, but to one degree or another it is a position taken by many psychiatrists and analysts. As they see the world, from their vantage point behind the desk or adjacent to the couch, it is indeed a sick world in which it is becoming more and more difficult to remain healthy even if one has had the best of parents and the happiest of childhoods. Moreover, since psychiatrists and analysts themselves are not without troubles, they know, even if some of their patients do not, that psychotherapy or psychoanalysis in and of themselves do not point the way toward the good life, or the good marriage, or even simple euphoria. But the diagnosis of a "sick society," unfortunately, does not produce a cure, either in the circles of psychiatry or elsewhere. Unlike the militant students and political reformers, psychiatrists and analysts (like many social scientists) view the possibilities of significant improvement with deepening skepticism. Inclined toward pessimism about the future, they are not disposed to believe in happy solutions for problems of war, race, and poverty—or even any solution. The alternative to solutions, for some psychiatrists and analysts, is to base one's life, in Freud's words, on love and work. For others, more cynical or already disappointed in love and work, the alternative is, in the French slogan, *sauve qui peut.* For still others, it is some combination of the consumption ethic, or privatism (to use David Riesman's phrase), and professional ambition, or careerism. And in psychiatry and psychoanalysis, too, there are nihilists and existentialists for whom the multitude of life styles, fads, and indulgences provide abundant "acting-out" opportunities. Of course, in the "sick society" it is not impossible to stay healthy, but it is difficult for many people, including psychiatrists and analysts, and, it need hardly be emphasized, some are more healthy than others.

The case for the "sick society," as C. Wright Mills and others have argued, is founded on the argument that while any particular suicide, homicide or other act of violence, divorce, drug addiction, or whatever is a private matter, a rising incidence of suicides, murders, divorces, and so forth is a public issue and as such calls for social analysis. In other words, if our neighbor down the street kills himself, it is a tragic event but a private one; and if our friends Bill and Mary obtain a divorce, we may be unhappy about it, but, again, it is significant only at the private level. If, however, more and more people are killing themselves, and more and more marriages are dissolving, it is possible that the causes are less to be found in private lives than in a social condition, broadly speaking, that leads people to destroy themselves, their marriages, and each other. The question, then, is whether the frequency of personal disorders and disruptions is such as to suggest that today's society itself is, or should be, the patient.

Certainly most of the available statistics lend some urgency to the question.[2] In 1966 there were 10,920 murders, according to the FBI, an increase of 10.8 percent over 1965; put another way, more people died from murder so to speak, than from tuberculosis, ulcers, or bronchitis. There were more than 22,000 suicides, of whom about 1,000 were college students, 652 boys and girls of high school age, and 92 children aged fourteen and younger; among college students, who made an estimated 9,000 attempts, suicide is now the second ranking cause of death (after accidents).* For the United States as a whole, one in every four marriages ends in divorce, with the rate approximating 50 percent in California, and the divorce rate is increasing. Although no one knows the exact figures, it is probable that between 500,000 and 1,000,000 women obtain illegal abortions each year, of whom 5,000 die as a result.[3] Of all children born about 7 percent are illegitimate; the rate increase is from 7.1 percent in 1940 to 23.4 percent in 1964.† Perhaps one-fifth of all brides, and one-third of all teen-age brides, are pregnant before the marriage ceremony.

Studies of homosexuality in America suggest that at least 5 percent of males are full-time homosexuals, and another 10 percent part-time homosexuals (*i.e.*, bisexual), and it is thought that homosexuality is increasing. According to the Kinsey reports, two of every five married couples engage in extramarital affairs; no doubt, given the so-called sexual revolution and more permissiveness in morality, the incidence of adultery has grown substantially since the Kinsey books appeared in 1948 (male) and 1953 (female). Premarital sex, on and off the campus, is commonplace.

Nor is this the only tribute to the age of the Pill. In 1966 a Gallup Poll reported that 19 percent of men and 30 percent of women, mostly under fifty years of age, had taken tranquilizers at some point in their lives. The manufacture of tranquilizers in 1964 amounted to 1,500,000 pounds, worth almost $8,000,000 at wholesale. The consumption of tranquilizers no doubt owes something to advertisements of the sort that appear in psychiatric

---

* According to Edwin S. Schneidman, chief of the Center for Studies of Suicide Prevention in NIMH, the true suicide rate is two or three times as high as the official figure. New York *Times,* December 11, 1966. Assuming the lowest estimate of 22,000 per year, suicide ranks tenth among the causes of death for adults; a suicide rate of 50,000 per year would change the rank to sixth. The suicide rate has been increasing in the under-twenty age category, but decreasing in the over-sixty-five bracket. Among children and teen-agers the suicide rate doubled between 1954 and 1964, the last year for which detailed statistics are available. It is estimated that 15 percent of accidents are related to suicidal intentions.

† "Rate per 1,000 unmarried (never married, widowed, or divorced) women aged fifteen to forty-four years enumerated as of April 1 for 1940 and 1950 and estimated as of July 1 for all other years." *The U.S. Book of Facts Statistics & Information for 1969* (officially published as *Statistical Abstract of the United States*), 51.

journals: one such advertisement for a meprobamate tranquilizer in the *American Journal of Psychiatry* showed a woman giving her daughter a bath, with the caption: "Her kind of pressures last all day . . . shouldn't her tranquilizer?" The clear implication of the advertisement was that the "pressures" of everyday life—certainly there was nothing out of the ordinary about the woman, her child, or the bath—are such as to require one to take tranquilizers.*

The known number of narcotics addicts in 1967 was 62,045, with those under twenty-one years of age constituting 17.5 percent of the total; some estimates placed the unknown number of addicts at ten times the known total. It is generally believed that 2 percent of college students are familiar with LSD and that between 30 and 50 percent have smoked marihuana; in April, 1967, it was reported that 15 percent of Princeton students had "experimented with marihuana, hashish, or LSD," [4] and in January of that year it was stated that "dozens" of high school students in Princeton were smoking pot.[5] Late in 1968 a number of mental health authorities expressed fear that drug usage was increasing among grade school children.[6] Across the nation an unknown number of adults and students were experimenting with amphetamines such as Methedrine ("speed"), banana-skin smoking, mescaline, barbiturates such as "goofballs," peyote, morning-glory seeds, and other hallucinogenic or "mind-expanding" drugs. In 1968 the offspring of certain prominent personalities including the daughter of a Presidential candidate were arrested for possession of illegal drugs, and it was disclosed that among LSD users at one time or another were the late Henry R. Luce and his wife, Claire Booth Luce, Cary Grant, Danny Kaye, Peter Fonda, and other Beautiful People. While the leading medical and psychiatric journals condemned the usage of LSD and related types of drugs, a defense of LSD by a well-known West Coast psychiatrist was published in 1967,[7] and in 1968 another psychiatrist wrote affirmatively about marihuana under the heading "The AMA Lies About Pot." [8] Alcohol, in need of no defense, continued to appeal to an estimated 7,000,000 confirmed alcoholics and more than

* A study by Hugh J. Parry of George Washington University suggests that the use of tranquilizers has risen from 7 percent of population in 1957 to 27 percent in 1967. Highest use, apparently, is among women with family incomes over $10,000 who have three or four children. By religion, Jewish use of tranquilizers and sedatives is greater than that of Protestants and Catholics.

50,000,000 occasional or part-time drinkers. It was said that a teenagers' Alcoholics Anonymous chapter had been established in Beverly Hills.

As already mentioned, there are about 1,000,000 persons in mental hospitals or the psychiatric wards of general hospitals, and another 1,000,000 people visit psychiatrists each year. Whatever the afflictions of well-to-do patients who consult psychiatrists and analysts, there is little reason to doubt that poverty as such increases the chances that one will fall victim to serious mental illness, and by now it is no secret that poverty is hardly a minor problem in the United States. Studies in Chicago, New Haven, Boston, New York, and other areas demonstrate that the proportion of schizophrenics and other psychotic persons is much higher in lower-class populations than in middle- and upper-class groups. In a 1958 New Haven study by sociologist A. B. Hollingshead and psychoanalyst F. C. Redlich, the study most often cited, the poorest section in the community accounted for 38 percent of patients suffering from severe mental illness, although the very poor constituted only 18 percent of the population. Many of these patients were in public mental hospitals. Ten years later, a follow-up study revealed that 57 percent of such patients were still hospitalized, whereas 39 percent of patients in the highest social classes remained in hospitals.[9] As noted earlier, the mentally ill poor, when and if they receive psychiatric attention, are more apt to be treated with simple custodial care and drugs than with intensive psychotherapy, and they are likely to remain in hospitals longer than more affluent patients.

In 1962 *Medical Tribune* reported that 80 percent of physicians have had to deal with "serious psychiatric emergencies" ranging from acute psychotic disturbance to attempted suicide. Excluding psychiatrists, almost all of whom experience emergency situations, the physicians most familiar with psychiatric emergencies were general practitioners, of whom more than 90 percent had experienced emergencies, and internists, almost 90 percent. Despite the frequency of psychiatric emergencies, 26 percent of the communities represented by the physicians lacked "readily available" psychiatric emergency facilities.[10] Meanwhile, the Selective Service System reported that 11 percent of all medical deferments in 1960–62 were for psychiatric disorders including homosexuality and enuresis.[11] Emotional illness in business and industry, according to one estimate, was costing business annually $3,000,000,000 in direct costs and another $9,000,000,000 in indirect costs, and was held to be more accountable for absenteeism than any other illness except the common cold.[12] Mental illness has been blamed for more than half of fatal automobile accidents, and "nervous tension" has been suggested as a cause of infertility and declining birthrates among human beings as well as animals.[13] In March, 1969, an American Bar Association committee reported "a definite upsurge" in the number of "mentally unstable lawyers." [14]

During the last decade the percentage of college students consulting the psychiatric facilities of university health services has doubled (from 4 percent to 8 percent), leading universities such as Stanford and Princeton to increase sharply the number of psychiatrists and clinical psychologists employed in student health facilities. At present, outpatient psychiatric clinics serve more persons in the ten-to-nineteen age group than in any other decade of life; in 1963 one-quarter of *all* clinic patients were adolescents. The number of patients under age fifteen in state and county mental hospitals was 325 percent higher in 1963 than in 1950 (the percentage does not include the large number of young people in private psychiatric hospitals and special schools). The National Institute of Mental Health predicts that during the next decade the rate at which young people are hospitalized will double. Between 1956 and 1960, the number of veterans seeking treatment in psychiatric clinics administered by the Veterans Administration increased by more than 100 percent.

The "sick society," however, is not entirely a matter of gloomy statistics. Questions can also be raised about the meaning of the more extreme attacks upon President Johnson during his last years in office—the play *MacBird* suggesting that he had plotted John F. Kennedy's death, the dart boards with his face as the target, the posters mocking his masculinity, the buttons carrying obscene slogans. Since the "sick society" is rooted in problems that are not confined to America, the face on the dart board in London was that of Harold Wilson; while in France caricatures of De Gaulle were no more flattering than those of Johnson.* In

* The incidence of suicide, drug addiction, and mental illness appears to be increasing in most of Western Europe and the Far East. In 1963 eleven countries had higher suicide rates than the United States, including some regarded as oases of

London it was also possible in 1968 to see a play depicting a lesbian relationship between Queen Victoria and Florence Nightingale and an attempt by Victoria to poison her husband, Prince Albert.[15] Another play of 1968 made Churchill personally responsible for the bombing of German civilians during World War II and for the murder of Polish General Wladislaw Sikorski.[16]

Whether or not Victoria and Churchill were "borderline" characters, two psychiatrists maintained in 1967 that the "theater of the absurd," especially Edward Albee's *The Zoo Story* and Samuel Beckett's *Waiting for Godot,* was mainly given over to the dilemmas and conflicts of "borderline" personalities, namely, feelings of emptiness, isolation, loneliness, and despair.[17] Defined in that fashion, the "borderline" type may be found everywhere, not least in the novel. "Today," says Binx Bolling, the leading character in Walker Percy's National Book Award-winning novel, *The Moviegoer,*

> is my thirtieth birthday. . . . Now in the thirty-first year of my dark pilgrimage on this earth and knowing less than I ever knew before, having learned only to recognize *merde* when I see it, having inherited no more from my father than a good nose for *merde,* for every species of shit that flew—my only talent—smelling *merde* from every quarter, living in fact in the very century of *merde,* the great shithouse of scientific humanism where needs are satisfied, everyone becomes an anyone, a warm and creative person, and prospers like a dung beetle, and one hundred percent of people are humanists and ninety-eight percent believe in God, and men are dead, dead, dead; and the malaise has settled like a fallout and what people really fear is not that the bomb will fall but that the bomb will not fall—on this my thirtieth birthday, I know nothing and there is nothing to do but fall prey to desire.[18]

Or perhaps alcohol, drugs, and suicide. "I'm sick," says J. D. Salinger's Franny Glass, "sick of ego, ego, ego. My own and every-

---

tranquillity, such as Switzerland and Denmark. *Psychiatric News,* January, 1966, from figures compiled by the United Nations. In 1969 it was reported that "one-third of all New Zealand goes to sleep on pills" and "a large proportion of the population is suffering from an anxiety state or mental depression." The dependence of New Zealanders on tranquilizers and sedatives was termed "a major epidemic" at the annual convention of the Medical Association of New Zealand. See the New York *Times,* March 23, 1969.

body else's." Franny and Binx, in effect, and the millions like them, are sick of life.

In 1968 clues to the health of the society could also be found in the language of everyday discourse. The endless variety of deceptions known as the "put-on" was in such vogue that the *New Yorker* found it appropriate to devote a lengthy article to the subject. "Stop putting me down," said millions of angry, humiliated wives to presumably hostile husbands, and millions of angry, humiliated husbands to presumably hostile wives, at innumerable cocktail parties. People complained to each other and to their doctors that they were feeling "turned off" or "up tight." The manic, or erotic, phase of behavior was popularly referred to as being "turned on," and somewhere between manic and depressive was the everyday phase of simply surviving or "hanging in there." For a great many Americans, "hanging in there" from morning to night, day after day, was an extraordinary feat.

For others, as for Binx Bolling, there was sex. Pornographic material catering to every taste was readily available, and in various erudite studies of sexual response it was demonstrated with reference to orgasm that, contrary to popular belief, it only takes one to tango; and not only that: one may be better than two. ("The book proves conclusively," began one unpublished tongue-in-cheek review of *Human Sexual Response,* "that sexual intercourse is no substitute for masturbation.") A fashion writer in the New York *Times* of August 3, 1968, noted that women of all ages were ceasing to wear underwear, whether bras or panties, and that the "see-through shirt or dress" was becoming fashionable even among "middle-aged matrons." In some parts of the country one could be served food by waitresses nude from the waist up, and in other sections there were "art studios" where it was possible to fingerpaint on female models nude all over. The folk-rock musical *Hair,* playing to packed Broadway houses, featured nude men and women, and the audience's view was not confined to their backsides; *Che!* and *Oh! Calcutta!*, among other theater offerings in 1969–70, featured simulated, perhaps even actual, sexual intercourse, fellatio, cunnilingus, and sodomy on stage. Nudity, sex, and psychotherapy have been combined at certain so-called sensitivity training centers where a principal intention is to free persons of their "hang-ups." At the Democratic Party convention in Chicago late in August, 1968, a number of women demonstrators made unsuccessful efforts to "bare a bosom for peace." In America, in 1968, it was sex with everything.

Some psychiatrists, and analysts, who despair of cures for the sick society, whether in terms of individual psychotherapy or social change, have attempted to reverse definitions of normality and illness. If, they argue, society is sick or, in the wording of British psychiatrists R. D. Laing, "dysfunctional," people who are perfectly adjusted to the society are themselves sick although regarded as "normal," and those deemed to be sick may be reasonably healthy or experiencing their sickness as a "growth process." Noting that "normal" men have killed perhaps 100,000,000 of their fellow "normal" men in the last fifty years, Laing suggests:

> There are forms of alienation that are relatively strange to statistically "normal" forms of alienation. The "normally" alienated person, by reason of the fact that he acts more or less like everyone else, is taken to be sane. Other forms of alienation that are out of step with the prevailing state of alienation are those that are labeled by the "normal" majority as bad or mad.
>
> The condition of alienation, of being asleep, of being unconscious, of being out of one's mind, is the condition of the "normal" man.[19]

Hence, for Laing and others who share his view,* "normal" man is the truly alienated individual and can be far more dangerous than the hospitalized psychotic, not to mention those on the outside conventionally regarded as alienated. "The perfectly adjusted bomber pilot," he argues, "may be a greater threat to species survival than the hospitalized schizophrenic deluded that the bomb is inside him." †

---

* The view of alienation as an expression of health or maturing is shared by, if I understand them, Erich Fromm, Erich Kahler, Herbert Marcuse, the late Lenny Bruce, Paul Goodman, Norman Mailer, and most of those who contribute to the *New York Review of Books* and *Ramparts* magazine.

† Coincidentally with the publication of this statement in Laing's 1967 book *The Politics of Experience,* the New York *Times* reported that "even during bombing runs on the most hazardous missions over North Vietnam American pilots remain remarkably cool, judging from a study of their heart rates in combat." In its story of April 11, 1967, the *Times* indicated that the "over-all average heart rate" of thirty experienced Navy pilots monitored during combat missions was 94.9 beats a minute, as compared with 80-beat-a-minute heart rate of normal adults. The increase was attributed to the physical exertions of flying, rather than to the dangers involved. It was noted, in conclusion, that "the pilots were described as experienced men with the highest skill, motivation and morale." A

While Laing's position is not without support in psychiatric and psychoanalytic circles, psychotherapists for the most part do not recommend to the patient that he strive to remain or become alienated or "blow his mind" with one or another of the psychedelic drugs. Even psychiatrists and analysts willing to admit that concepts of mental health and illness are relative to historical time and place[20] tend to accept the prevailing cultural norms for attitudes and behavior, and it is to these norms that their patients are helped to adjust. But in a time of rapid change and confused values it is not always easy to determine what the norms are, especially with reference to the raising of children and adolescents. Psychiatrists as parents are no less aware than other adults of the rebellion of the young against the generation in authority and most of the institutions it supports. And psychiatrists as psychiatrists are familiar with the evidence suggesting that mental illness among children and adolescents is increasing at a faster rate than that of any other age group. But whether as parents or doctors, psychiatrists and analysts express a variety of views about hippies, drop-outs, and that section of the youth constituting, in the apt terminology of psychiatrist Louis Jolyon West, the "Green" (for "grass" or marijuana), "Red" (for revolutionaries and radicals, such as the Students for a Democratic Society), and "Black" (referring to black militants) rebellions. But whatever their views, they are in unanimous agreement on one point: unlike many commentators on the American scene, psychiatrists and analysts do not blame themselves, Dr. Spock, John Dewey, or Sigmund Freud for the youthful unrest.*

---

possibly related phenomenon is the low incidence of neuropyschiatric illness among Army troops in Vietnam. In 1965 and 1966 the rate for soldiers hospitalized or excused from duty on psychiatric grounds was 12 per 1,000 soldiers per year compared with the Korean War rate of 73. About 6 percent of Vietnam soldiers have been evacuated for psychiatric reasons, compared with 23 percent during World War II. The low Vietnam rate has been attributed to relatively short-term combat service, rotation policy, high morale, excellent training, and application of the "cardinal principles of combat psychiatry." William J. Tiffany, Jr., colonel, Medical Corps, Department of the Army, "The Mental Health of Army Troops in Viet Nam," *American Journal of Psychiatry,* 123, 12 (June, 1967), 1585–86.

* The unrest has also been attributed to "an immigration in time with the people over forty the migrants into the present age, and the children born int. it as natives" (Margaret Mead, quoted in the New York *Times,* August 16, 1968); "disrespect for authority" (Bruno Bettelheim, quoted in the New York *Times,* August 22, 1968); "symbolic parricide" (Lewis Feuer, quoted in the New York *Times,* February 14, 1969); "utopianism" and the "Welfare State" (Malcolm Muggeridge, quoted in the New York *Times,* January 21, 1968); and the New York

Insofar as blame can be attached to any source other than politics, Vietnam, and the state of society in general—conditions which many psychiatrists and analysts regard as the root cause of unrest—the tendency is to be critical of the family and social culture in which adolescents grow up. Asked to name those problems of child raising that their patients most frequently want to discuss, more than half the psychiatrists and almost 47 percent of the analysts name as the foremost problem "inadequate communications between parents and children." In second place is "trouble in school" (poor grades, bad relations with teachers, etc.). Thereafter there are certain differences between psychiatrists and analysts. For the psychiatrists the next most important problems are disobedience, too much permissiveness in making and enforcing rules, and too much rigidity in rule making and enforcing. For the analysts, however, too much rigidity is in third place, followed by permissiveness and disobedience. Only 16 percent of the psychiatrists and 20 percent of the analysts report that the sexual problems of adolescent children are frequently mentioned by patients, and only a handful indicate that confusion about parental roles plays a major role.

On the other hand, 46 percent of the psychiatrists and more than 51 percent of the analysts believe that the "typical American family" is "too permissive" with children, as compared with only one psychiatrist and two analysts who say that the family is "not permissive enough." Since psychiatrists and analysts are widely regarded—and attacked—as exponents of extreme permissiveness

---

Times itself as the alleged publisher in the late forties and early fifties of opinions emanating from "the new school of permissive education" (Mrs. Grete Hillinger in an irate letter to the *Times* of January 7, 1968). Sociologist Christopher Jencks concluded that it was not Dr. Spock's fault in an article titled "Is It All Dr. Spock's Fault?" (*New York Times Magazine,* March 3, 1968), and parents in general were absolved by psychologist Fred Brown, speaking at a symposium reported in the *Times* of May 12, 1968. Jencks, Brown, and other commentators are inclined to attribute the unrest to the weaknesses and failures of society itself, including, in Brown's words, the habit of "talking peace, peace, peace and conducting a murderous, ruthless war." For still others the main reason for the unrest of the young and their disrespect for authority is, in the words of one angry mother of a rebellious teen-ager, that "the adult world has capitulated on every point—hair styles, the dress code. Everybody is busily jumping on the band wagon making money, writing songs about the drug habit, movies about LSD. Sensationalism is rampant. Filthy, pornographic literature and perverted obscenities are readily made available to our children under the guise of freedom of expression. Little children are talking about pot like lollipops. The stuff is handed to our children free of charge by their good friends" (Mrs. Susan Harris in the *New York Times Magazine,* December 10, 1967).

in child raising, this attitude of the study group may appear paradoxical, but only at first glance. Those who deal with children and adolescents have long known that they need help, as Ilse Hellman has put it, "in the difficult task of mastering their urges and [controlling] the anxiety aroused by them." [21] Instead of offering such help, many psychiatrists and analysts complain, parents are inclined to indulge a child's wishes or desires, the expression of which can give rise in the child to almost intolerable anxiety. Most psychiatrists and analysts, therefore, would agree with Paul Roazen that: "By saying 'No,' one can help a child overcome the anxiety of his drives." [22]

The analysts are also more critical of the relations between parents and children in the "typical American family." While eight of the analysts describe these relations as "generally good," seven refer to them as "generally bad." The division among the psychiatrists, however, is 40 percent "generally good" and only 13 percent "generally bad." The analysts also appear to be more critical of parents, particularly with reference to the parents' failure to establish desirable standards for their children's behavior, or, in analytic terminology, their failure to establish themselves as "ego ideals." Agreeing with Freud that the superego, or, broadly, conscience, represents the internalization of parental and social ethics of behavior, many analysts feel that the parental role in superego formation has tended to diminish in recent years. "Let me give you a gross illustration," says one analyst:

> The third or fourth time I saw this patient he mentions that his teen-age son is drinking heavily, already picked up once for drunken driving, and so forth, would I talk to him? So I had the boy come in, and he sits there, very sullen, withdrawn, obviously resentful. I don't want to say right off what this is about, but he guesses right away, and does he take off on his *old man's drinking!* "Why are you talking to me?" he says. "Talk to him, he drinks more than I do." You know, I didn't know what to say. All I could think of was something from my Sunday school days long ago, I think from Ezekiel, about how the fathers have eaten sour grapes and the children's teeth are set on edge.

Of course, not all psychiatrists and analysts are reminded of Ezekiel. A psychiatrist observes that "the central and basic issue is the failure to establish an intimate relationship of candidness, openness, straightforwardness, and matter-of-factness between the two generations." Several analysts suggest that troubled relations between parents and children may reflect only the desire for independence and self-identity on the part of the young as against, in the words of one analyst, "the anxiety of the parents that their child's behavior will be used to judge *them* as to their adequacy as parents, both in the eyes of others as well as in their own eyes. This can lead to a severe disturbance in the interaction between parents and children." Many parents would do better, say a number of psychiatrists, if they worried less about making the same mistakes with their children that their own parents made with them.

Whatever their views of adults as parents, almost all the psychiatrists and analysts believe that most adults are capable of making happy marriages, although not without considerable effort. Almost 58 percent of the psychiatrists and 60 percent of the analysts feel that for most people "a happy monogamous marriage is difficult but not impossible," and 24 percent and 17 percent, respectively, believe that a happy monogamous marriage is "neither difficult nor impossible." In the entire group only two psychiatrists and one analyst take the position that a happy monogamous marriage is so difficult as to be rare, and a similar number agree that "monogamy, like celibacy, should be neither expected nor required of most people."

Yet these responses are not unqualified. "I don't know about 'most people,' " say a number of psychiatrists and analysts, calling attention to the fact that each case is different. " 'Happiness' may or may not suitably apply as a criterion," runs a comment, "and it is always relative to the expectations of the individual." Another observation is that "a great deal depends on the intelligence, culture, and social upbringing of the married partners." An analyst insists that "there can be no happy marriages unless the partners work at it," and one emphasizes that the husband "not be an 'absentee' husband and father whose career puts *all* the burden on the wife. Monogamy is quite secondary to that issue."

There is much awareness of marital unhappiness since, according to some estimates, at least half the patients seen by psychiatrists and analysts have significant marital problems.[23] Indeed, many psychiatrists specialize in marital problems, and there are now institutes specialized for training in family therapy.[24] Some of the so-called sensitivity training centers, of which the best known is Esalen at Big Sur, California, feature "workshops" for couples under such titles as "For the Good Marriage: More Authenticity," "Close Yet Free," and "Man and Woman," many of which are conducted by psychiatrists and psychiatric social workers. Variations of psychodrama and simulation, including Esalen's "Fight Training for Lovers," and Beth Israel Hospital's "Interpersonal Behavior Game Test," in which husbands and wives express their problems by operating electric trains, have also been enlisted in efforts to save marriages.*

Nevertheless, the divorce rate continues to rise, and there are very few psychiatrists who expect it to fall anytime in the future. "I don't blame a lot of the kids," says one psychiatrist who is also the father of teen-agers,

> for deciding that they'll never get married. What do they mostly see around them? Quarreling, fighting, or dead silence, love-hate relationships which finally settle down to a tolerant dislike on both sides. It's what I see all the time. Not that either partner is sick or expressing some sort of psychopathology—it's just that they don't get along together, can't make it in interpersonal terms. They would like to, but can't.

An analyst, making a similar comment, suggests that it may be wrong for psychiatry and psychoanalysis to continue to take marriage for granted. "Maybe [Karen] Horney was right," he suggests,

> to think that some of the qualities needed in a good marriage are simply not achievable, such as dependency and the need for each other. Maybe these things should be renounced, at least by most people, I don't know. Almost all of my patients tell me they are putting out everything and the other side is putting out nothing, and what should they do? I often say, okay, if that's the way it is, accept it. Don't expect more and you'll be happier. I think maybe that's true for life in general.[25]

---

* According to Dr. Robert Ravich, one of the game's developers and director of Beth Israel's Family Therapy Service, the couple makes "about 20 trips during a test. The way they play, what they say, the decisions they make, who backs down the most (to avoid collisions)—all of these are recorded. Several days later I go over it with them. Inevitably they soon start making analogies between things that went on in the game and what goes on in their lives." *Psychiatric Reporter* (Smith, Kline & French), November–December, 1967. The Esalen approach is dealt with in Chapter VII.

Thought and discussion of marriage, however, do not lead to any agreed-upon solution for marital unhappiness and the rising divorce rate. While some psychiatrists and analysts feel that increased sexual permissiveness plays a role, others blame the "cult of youth," and there are some who accuse both. Many psychiatrists, like many social scientists, are aware of the extent to which middle-aged adults, envious of the youth and fearful of their own old age, desperately imitate the life styles of the younger generation. Hence the mothers and grandmothers of adolescents wearing miniskirts or frugging to Beatle records while their husbands shop for the latest hairpiece and Cardin jacket.* Indeed, this may be the first time that the roles of the generations have been reversed—in other words, the first time that an older generation has modeled much of its behavior on that of a younger age group. Small wonder, say many psychiatrists, that youngsters feel lost and confused; looking to their elders for example and guidance on values, they are apt to see, to their consternation, merely older and infinitely more pathetic versions of themselves.

Nor is sex, in the opinion of psychiatrists and analysts, unimportant as a cause of family dissolution, although by sex they are not thinking so much of difficulties within a marriage in traditional terms (impotence, frigidity, etc.) as of culturally sanctioned trends toward unlimited experimentation and promiscuity. "Even if he doesn't read *Playboy*," says a psychiatrist of the American middle-aged male,

> he suspects what's going on, and he *knows* he's not getting any of it. And his wife, unless she's sick or menopausal, may have some hankerings that way, too. Maybe one or the other or both will try to swing, but sooner or later they finally have to take a long look at themselves and at the paunch, bald head, and sagging breasts on the other side of the marriage bed, and it's the moment of truth. Of course, the fantasy life may go on, but

* "How did this 38-year-old housewife pass as a teenager?" says an advertisement for Ivory Liquid in the November, 1967, *McCall's*. It turns out that Mrs. Hilary Byk, shown in a miniskirt and playing a guitar, "fooled a whole roomful of teenagers" because "Creamy Ivory Liquid leaves hands with that creamy young look." The New York *Times* of April 13, 1969, reported: "More and More 'Average' Americans" are demanding plastic surgery for "thigh lifts, arm lifts and abdominal lifts as well as facelifts, hair transplantation, removal of wrinkles, frown lines and baggy eyelids, reduction of oversized breasts and augmentation of undersized ones, and reconstruction of the nose, ears and chin."

> somewhere he knows that he's not going to make it with some miniskirted girl, and she knows that the kid with the long sideburns is out. Even so, they may quit on each other.

For still other psychiatrists and analysts, the incidence of marital breakdown reflects larger issues of American society, although they find it difficult to define these issues with precision. "In my view," says a West Coast psychiatrist,

> the underlying reality is that the whole population of the United States is getting more emotionally and mentally disturbed by the day. You know, here's an interesting thing. I took my residency in a state hospital in the Middle West where I expected to see the sickest people in the state. And I did see a lot of poor people who were very sick. But what surprised me then and even more out here is the number of rich people who are sick, really sick, although they have important jobs with corporations. Many of them are alcoholics, and the degree of psychopathology was really quite a surprise to me.

The divorce rate, he continued, is only part of the story:

> If you ask me, the family itself is breaking down, maybe society itself, as a result of all the change, urbanization, and what not. I think the whole structure is crumbling, and this much I'm sure of: when I see the number of frankly and fantastically disturbed marriages in this area, and the products coming out of these marriages—let's say four, maybe six children, and four of them are just as neurotic as they can be by the time they're fifteen years old, or even ten—and the kids from these marriages are going to grow up and find more disturbed people to marry because a normal person won't marry them, and so on through the generations—when I think about this, even though it's oversimplified, I know we're in deep trouble.[26]

Despite the view of some psychiatrists and analysts that the so-called sexual revolution is an important factor in marital unhappiness, there is no disposition to reject it in favor of a more puritanical code of behavior. On the contrary, the psychiatrists and analysts in the study are more permissive about sex than the American population as a whole, although they are far from being as permissive as some of their critics maintain. While there have been a few studies suggesting that psychotherapists in general are "less orthodox" in their value orientations than certain other social groups, and while it is still believed in some circles that Freud was a dirty old man promoting free love and all types of sexual excess, there is no evidence that psychiatry as such should be equated with bohemia. In fact, in terms of his private life, the average psychiatrist and analyst, committed to marriage, children, and affluence, might even be regarded as "square." The Playboyvilles, marina cultures, "islands in the sun," and Bunny Clubs supply psychiatry with many more patients than practitioners.[27]

Nevertheless, the sexual values and attitudes of psychiatrists, as measured by a variety of tests, are characterized by permissiveness and lack of rigidity, and it would appear that the analysts are even less restrictive. Most psychiatrists and analysts believe that the laws regulating sexual behavior are far too strict, and there is strong support for the view that sexual relations between consenting adults, including homosexual relations, should be freely allowed. A majority is in favor of permitting men in prison to have sexual relations with their wives. Of a national sample of 5,000 psychiatrists, most favor reform of the abortion laws, with one in every four believing that a pregnancy should be terminated "whenever the woman requests it." * Judging by the study group, psychiatrists and analysts are most tolerant of premarital sexual intercourse among college students, and least tolerant of extramarital sexual intercourse and premarital sexual intercourse in the high school population. With regard to unmarried college students, 38 percent of the psychiatrists and 17 percent of the analysts who responded to the relevant questions thought that sexual affairs should be "avoided at all costs" or warned against them because they "are likely to lead to trouble." More than 20 percent of the psychiatrists and 29 percent of the analysts, however, felt that such affairs were "all right so long as no one was hurt" or "serve a useful purpose and may be engaged in without guilt."

By contrast, 55 percent of the psychiatrists and 29 percent of

* *Psychiatric News,* May, 1966. In a survey of almost 1,300 physicians, reported by *Medical Tribune,* October 31–November 1, 1964, psychiatrists were most in favor of permitting abortions and obstetricians-gynecologists and pediatricians least in favor!

the analysts held that extramarital affairs should be "avoided at all costs" or "are likely to lead to trouble"; only 7 percent of psychiatrists and 6 percent of analysts regarded such affairs as "all right" or "useful." Perhaps the general view of extramarital sexual relations was expressed by one psychiatrist who observed:

> The issue for me is not whether it's right or wrong, good or bad, and so forth, but whether the affair is a destructive thing, like most such affairs. Few people can handle them so that no one is hurt. In fact, my view is that the individual is probably using a drive toward pleasure which he doesn't really accept as a valid drive, and he's using it as a destructive weapon. Most people I see are having affairs in a way that practically guarantees someone will be hurt—their wives or husbands, or the other person, or the kids. Their purpose is partly to get pleasure and partly to hurt, to punish. In other words, it's the motivation that's important. I usually ask: Why are you doing this? You don't really enjoy it, you feel guilty, you can't accept it, so why? And most of them quit, finally.

But the most negative view of sexual relations outside of marriage was reserved for premarital intercourse among high school students. Fifty-nine percent of psychiatrists and 40 percent of analysts maintained that sexual affairs in high school "should be avoided at all costs" or "are likely to lead to trouble," and only 5 percent and 9 percent, respectively, approved them as "all right" or "useful." * In other words, combining the responses of the psychiatrists and analysts, 55 percent disapproved of premarital sexual intercourse among high school students while only 6 percent approved; 50 percent disapproved of extramarital sexual intercourse and 7 percent approved; and 34 percent disapproved of premarital sex among college students while 23 percent approved.

* A large number of psychiatrists and analysts, it should be mentioned, were reluctant to deal with sexual questions and other value issues in the abstract. One general response, especially with reference to sexual behavior, was "it would depend on the particular situation" and "my personal feelings might or might not fit the circumstances of a particular patient." Some analysts, denying that they advise patients in such matters, declared that they confined themselves "to the meaning of the act for the patient" or "determining what the motivation was—punitive or destructive or something else." These reservations and many others may be accepted by way of qualification, yet it remains true that psychiatrists and analysts do hold certain sexual and moral values, which may or may not be communicated to patients. The main intention here is to make these values explicit rather than to assess their importance in psychotherapy.

The psychiatric response to sex on the campus, like the response to other phenomena of our time, embraces almost every kind of attitude. For that matter, there is little agreement on the facts of campus sex life, with some university psychiatrists denying there has been any major change in sexual behavior, much less a sexual revolution, and others suggesting that, at the very least, there has been a significant change of attitude and possibly behavior as well.[28] Thus, according to Harvard psychiatrist Graham B. Blaine, Jr., the principal change in campus sexual mores has not been a "sexual revolution" but "a move away from the double standard" in the direction of female sexual equality.[29] Certainly many psychiatrists believe that the proportion of nonvirgins in the coed population, estimated by Kinsey in 1948 at 20 percent, has not changed appreciably during the last two decades, although it need hardly be emphasized that reliable information on the subject is notoriously difficult to obtain. Hence some colleges have put the nonvirgin female population at 7 percent or less, while others, such as Oberlin, have found that 40 percent or more of unmarried women undergraduates engage in sexual intercourse.[30] Whatever the facts, there is reason to believe that attitudes toward sex have changed substantially, comparing one generation with another. A study of more than 200 coeds found that while 88 percent of their mothers considered virginity "very important" until marriage, only 55 percent of the coed daughters agreed that virginity was "very important." Asked about sexual intercourse for engaged couples, 83 percent of the mothers thought it "very wrong," compared with 35 percent of the daughters.[31]

Psychiatrists in student health services frequently deal with a variety of problems brought to them by premarital couples, and it is clear that sexual relations and questions about birth control are often on the agenda. Those who deal with such problems are inclined to favor the distribution of birth control information and contraceptives to unmarried students, policies increasingly favored by college and university administrators,[32] and it has not been unknown for student health psychiatrists to bypass restrictive regulations by putting students in touch with physicians who will prescribe the Pill or any other contraceptive that may be indicated. Most of these psychiatrists also know where safe, although not necessarily cheap, abortions can be obtained, and this information, too, is usually made available to the student "in trouble," especially if the student is unmarried and without any prospect of marriage. Unfortunately, the trials and torments of such students do not end with the Pill or the abortion. According to Seymour L. Halleck, psychiatrist at the University of Wisconsin, the rate of premarital intercourse among psychiatric patients in the student body is much higher than it is among nonpatients, accounting for 86 percent of the total female patients. Of these patients, 72 percent had had intercourse with more than one person, leading Dr. Halleck to conclude that "a significant number of students are casualties of the sexual revolution." [33] The increasing permissiveness in sexual areas apparently has not penetrated to some superego areas of the mind where the older, more traditional mores remain entrenched.*

Many psychiatrists on and off the campus view student demands for sexual freedom as part of the larger youth rebellion that in recent years has been a troublesome issue in a number of countries. Because the discontents of some of the young have been expressed in locales as far apart as Columbia University, Mexico City, the Sorbonne, and Tokyo, psychiatrists, like social scientists, have not produced general explanations for the unrest which is fast approaching global proportions. It is manifestly difficult to frame hypotheses that would deal adequately with the various styles or expressions of youthful alienation such as hippies, Yippies, acid heads, drop-outs, Students for a Democratic Society, pacifists, war resisters, Maoists, socialists, Marxists, Black (and white) Panthers, and other New Left groups, much less the *enragés* of France and the followers abroad of Daniel Cohn-Bendit and "Rudi the Red." And, again, psychiatrists and analysts are by no means of one mind about the meanings and implications of youthful unrest whatever its form, whether here or abroad. At one extreme are those who endorse and sympathize with most varieties of

---

* For other students, there are the college presidents, deans, and the other representatives of the societal superego to contend with when certain taboos are violated, but in some instances the contest is not without its humorous aspect. For a week or so in April, 1968, readers of the New York *Times* were entertained almost daily by the saga of Miss Linda LeClair, a twenty-year-old Barnard College sophomore who was living openly with her Columbia College boyfriend, in defiance of Barnard regulations. After a lengthy discussion in the pages of the *Times* that ultimately involved, in addition to the president and other Barnard officials, Linda's parents, certain faculty members, a minister, a rabbi, and some Barnard alumnae, a student-faculty committee "disciplined" Miss LeClair by denying her access to the cafeteria and snack bar and participation in social events on the campus. Not surprisingly, Miss LeClair termed these restrictions "sensible."

alienation; indeed, the psychiatrists and analysts who take this position are very often themselves individuals who are alienated in some degree from the main trends in their profession and American society itself. At the other extreme are those who regard alienation only as a form of individual disturbed behavior and partial breakdown—in a word, as an illness. Most psychiatrists, no doubt, would locate themselves somewhere between these extremes, and few would dissent from the proposition, no matter what their persuasion, that certain modes of alienation are more reasonable, more understandable, and therefore more personally rewarding and socially useful than others.

But what constitutes alienation in the first place, and how can the various styles of alienation be distinguished? Unfortunately for discussions of alienation, whether in psychiatric or other circles, there is much confusion and carelessness in the definition of terms, to such an extent that the runaway youngster in New York's East Village who is a heavy user of drugs is often talked about as if he were identical with the student at Berkeley or Columbia who is active in Students for a Democratic Society. Thus there have been frequent articles in psychiatric journals, many of them otherwise informative and important, that discuss *the* alienated college student as if there were no distinctions to be made between the varieties or types of alienation on campuses. Some of these discussions, no doubt influenced by the exaggerations and sensationalism of the mass media, proceed as if an entire generation of youth had turned against the established institutions, beliefs, and traditions of society.

In fact, only a few thousand young people have become hippies or student activists. For example, while there were an estimated 221 student protests at 101 colleges and universities in the first six months of 1968, the students involved totaled only 38,911 or 2.6 percent of the students enrolled in the institutions involved.[34] Membership in Students for a Democratic Society, early in 1968, amounted to 7,000, compared with a combined total of 250,000 student members of Young Republicans and Young Democrats, the latter two organizations representing less than 5 percent of the 6,000,000 students currently attending America's colleges and universities.[35] Since it would appear that apathy, not involvement, is the dominant mood on campuses, the popular impression that most students are radicals may owe something to the tendency of mass media to inflate the size of student demonstrations and in other ways overly dramatize the extent to which another "lost generation" is manifesting itself. It is just possible that a majority of students, including even those affiliated with SDS, have never read anything by Herbert Marcuse, never taken LSD, and never thought or said to each other: "Don't trust anyone over thirty." [36] It is more certain that their anguished elders, never having read Boswell's *Life of Samuel Johnson,* are unware that the diminution of respect for authority, the alleged evils of affluence, the so-called generation gap, have been complained about in other times and places. "Subordination," Johnson complained to James Boswell and others in April, 1778, almost two hundred years before another Johnson withdrew from politics for reasons among which subordination was not unimportant,

> is sadly broken down in this age. No man, now, has the same authority which his father had,—except a gaoler. No master has it over his servants: it is diminished in our colleges; nay, in our grammar-schools. . . . There are many causes, the chief of which is, I think, the great increase of money . . . gold and silver destroy the feudal subordination. But, besides, there is a general relaxation of reverence. No son now depends upon his father as in former times. Paternity used to be considered as of itself a great thing, which has a right to many claims. That is, in general, reduced to very small bounds. My hope is, that as anarchy produces tyranny, this extreme relaxation will produce *freni strictio* [a tight rein].[37]

Johnson's hope no less than his complaint has a modern ring; indeed, insofar as the student unrest has contributed to strengthening right-wing political forces in the United States, France, West Germany, and elsewhere, both hopes for and fears of a *freni strictio* may be said to have been partially realized.[38]

But whatever the number of alienated young people on and off the campus, two principal types of youthful alienation can be identified, defining alienation as a state of separation and estrangement from many although not necessarily all of the conventional values and institutions of society. From this point of view, the alienated student or nonstudent may reject his family, the religious faith in which he grew up, monogamy and marriage, the free enterprise system and a business career, suburbia, the necessity for government and authority in general. He may or may not have smoked pot or taken a "trip." Almost certainly he has nothing good to say for former President Johnson and the Vietnam War—but these are attitudes shared by a good many nonalienated older Americans. The point is, alienation entails some rejection of society and its beliefs, but such rejection need not involve a condemnation of all institutions and values.

Until recently, most attention focused on those alienated young people known as hippies, mistakenly referred to in the press as the "flower children" or the "love generation." (Yippies, who are hippie members of the so-called Youth International, and Diggers, hippies who help other hippies— in effect, hippie social workers—do not warrant separate treatment.) Commonly regarded as physically dirty and addicted to drugs, free love, and freeloading, hippies in typical dress—usually faded and patched blue jeans, sandals, beads, bracelets, bells and peace symbols—have been known to arouse hostile emotions in respectable people, notwithstanding the fact that many of these same people, when they are touring in New York and San Francisco, visit hippie areas by the busload, staring and taking pictures. The spread of hippie styles of dress, especially the jewelry and ornaments, among the middle class and middle aged is also an aspect of life in contemporary America.

The hippie, to most psychiatrists, is a disturbed individual who experiences himself, one psychiatrist has written with reference to alienated college students, "as being detached from his own feelings as well as from those around him." In addition to using drugs such as marihuana and LSD, and being sexually promiscuous, the hippie tends to live in the present, avoiding commitment to people, causes, and ideas. He is unable or unwilling to communicate with his parents or other adults. Because his self-concept is ill-defined and confused, anxiety is "pervasive and relentless," leading toward severe depressions that may be accompanied by suicide attempts. When seen by a psychiatrist he is apt to complain of "apathy, boredom, meaninglessness, and chronic unhappiness." Although he may be far above average in intelligence, he is unable to concentrate on his studies or achieve more than low grades.[39]

A second type of youthful alienation is expressed in political activism, and here again it is important to distinguish between the various styles and extremes of activism. One end of the activist spectrum is the revolutionary element in the New Left and Students for a Democratic Society; black student revolutionaries are apt to be affiliated with the Black Muslim movements or the Black Panthers. The heroes of the revolutionary students include those who have led popular revolutions to victory, such as Lenin and Mao, and the guerrilla intellectuals among whom the most outstanding are Franz Fanon, Che Guevara, and Régis Debray.* It is these students, at Berkeley, San Francisco State College, Cornell, and Columbia, with a scattering of faculty support, who have been the most militant and uncompromising in their demands for a radical reconstruction not merely of American higher education but of the whole society.

The moderate activists who may also be members of Students for a Democratic Society eschew revolutionary activity in favor of discussion and negotiation. Unlike the extremists, they do not desire to take over the university but to reform it in the direction of student representation on administrative and faculty committees and greater university responsiveness to the local community, especially in those parts of the country, as in New York City, where the university is contiguous to the black ghetto. Unlike some revolutionaries, the moderates are opposed to violence or "going undergrcund" in their efforts to change the university.

Middle-road moderates on the campuses overlap with nonalienated student liberals who, while they support the demands of the moderates, may be more involved in off-campus political and civil rights movements and less involved in the affairs of the university. Student supporters of Robert Kennedy and Eugene McCarthy in 1968 were liberal and moderate activists, and it is probable that they form the core of youthful protest directed at Vietnam and the draft. Willing to work within the existing institutional framework, the liberal activists participate in the volunteer teaching of underprivileged children, assisting in prisons and state hospitals, helping with the rehabilitation of tenements and slum housing, and caring for the children of migratory workers. Until a few years ago a number of liberal activists spent summers in the Deep South, where they worked in voter registration drives and other areas of the civil rights movement as then

* It is not without interest in this context that Fanon was a psychiatrist and Guevara a physician who for a time considered specializing in psychiatry.

constituted. During or after their college years many liberal activists spend a year or more in VISTA, the Peace Corps, or one of the Quaker work camps here or abroad.[40]

The moderate activists and student liberals elicit the most approval from psychiatrists and psychoanalysts who themselves are critical of major social trends in the United States and elsewhere. The student activists at Columbia University, as one sympathetic psychoanalyst put it in 1968, are merely following "the longest tradition in American history," and also "the example of the President of the United States" in deciding that "violence in the name of righteousness is permissible, indeed, when the cause is just, a duty." Another analyst, commenting on the Columbia disturbances, suggested that the turmoil on the campus helped students "cope with this madness in high places which asks them to sacrifice their lives for irrational, immoral purposes." [41]

A related view of the moderate student activists is that the majority, in the words of a psychiatrist in charge of psychiatric services at a distinguished private university,

> are sensitive, creative kids. I think what they want is change, change in themselves and change in society. They are increasingly dissatisfied with the structure of society itself, with its over-specialization, its over-emphasis on conformity, its emphasis on oneness and togetherness, the "great society" and all that. It frightens young people, because in this society there is little opportunity for individuality, for original development. . . . If you ask me, this questioning, this probing, is a good development, not a sick one. Sure, there are drugs mixed up in this, especially marijuana, even more than you might think. But I don't take the dim view of pot that most of the administrators here do. You know something? In my years on this campus I have yet to come across an alcoholic student, and I'm just a little amused when some alcoholic dean or parent raises hell about drugs on the campus!

This view of moderate activists as "sensitive, creative," is supported by almost all studies that have been made of student unrest by behavioral scientists. Compared with the politically less involved students, activists are more intelligent, more aware of social issues, and more stable from a psychological point of view. Far from having rejected their parents' outlook, the activists are likely to have taken to heart their parents' idealistic, liberal values and to be critical of departures from these values by the parents and society at large. As Kenneth Keniston and others have noted, the activism of the young is often a response to their perception of the parental and social failure to live up to professed values rather than a reflection of alienation as such or the influence of any radical ideology.[42] Indeed, many activists maintain close ties to their largely middle-class, college-educated, affluent, and permissive families, a disproportionate share of whom are Reform Jewish.* While the activists may regard their parents and their parents' generation as hypocritical because of the gap between beliefs and acts—which was one important reason for their intense dislike of President Johnson, Johnson having been regarded as the archetypal practitioner of deception and guile—their concern is less with the general failure to live up to ideals than with the creation of a social order in which the gap between beliefs and acts can be closed.†

Student revolutionaries and hippies, viewing this gap as inevitable and unalterable in present-day society, have fewer supporters in the ranks of American psychiatry, but they are by no means universally regarded as disturbed types. Although younger psychiatrists and analysts are more apt than older ones to respond favorably to the hippie phenomenon, there is much support in psychiatry for the view that the hippie, in words of a prominent lay analyst, is "rebelling against the nothingness breeding in the suburbs . . . [against] parents [who] are leading hollow, empty, shallow lives and not giving their children anything to hold onto." From this standpoint "the evil is in Greenwich and Great Neck, not Greenwich Village," and hippies are to be wel-

* It is also of interest that an estimated 20 to 25 percent of the 5,000 hippies in San Francisco's Haight-Ashbury are Jewish, and it is probable that an equal or greater percentage of New York's hippies are Jewish. The hippie appeal to Jewish youth, a cause of concern to the American Jewish community, is so far unexplained. It is possible that alienation of all types is more prevalent among young Jews than it is in other ethnic and religious groups, but if this is the case, the reasons are far from clear.

† In a study of 986 student campaigners for Senator Eugene McCarthy during the Wisconsin primary in March, 1968, it was found that 82 percent "seldom" or "rarely" believed what was said by the Johnson administration. The sons and daughters of affluent parents—28 percent of their fathers had incomes of $18,000 or more—the McCarthy volunteers were found not to be alienated, rebellious, or members of the New Left, but youngsters for whom the Vietnam War was the overriding issue. Melvin Kahn, "Students for McCarthy—What Unites Them," *Trans-action,* July–August, 1968, 30.

comed because "they are not dead yet." [43] It is perhaps for this reason that occasional encounters between psychiatrists and hippies tend almost to produce a reversal of therapeutic roles. Following one such meeting between "a handful of hippies" as panelists and "some 500 psychiatrists and their wives and friends," the president of the Society for Adolescent Psychiatry, pointing out that some of the hippies present had once been patients in mental hospitals where "all kinds of diagnoses and tags [were] placed on them that were very serious," concluded:

> Many of us admire them now and even envy them. I hope enough of that has come through tonight so that psychiatrists don't hurriedly apply labels—like schizophrenia—to people. To be different is not to be sick. To understand them is to see it in different terms than pathology.

The "applause was explosive," the New York *Times* reported, in a story subtitled "Doctors at Forum Appear Charmed by Panelists." *

Whatever the approach to hippies, a widely held view in psychiatry and elsewhere is that today's hippie is tomorrow's sober and responsible adult; as psychoanalyst Jules Masserman has put it, most hippies "will achieve more maturity and wisdom, and may even become 'staunch Republicans.'" [44] Meanwhile, of course, hippies and other varieties of alienated youth make their way in increasing numbers to the wards of mental hospitals and offices of psychiatrists. As noted earlier, the number of college students seeking psychiatric aid has risen sharply in recent years, and it is continuing to rise. In 1967 it was estimated that about one in every ten students, or approximately 640,000 each year, consulted a university psychiatrist or psychologist, but the proportion varies from campus to campus. At the Ivy League uni-

* Robert E. Gould, quoted in the New York *Times,* October 20, 1967. And not only the doctors. Between 1965 and 1968 hippies were generally treated favorably, even romantically, by many newspapers and magazines. One consequence was a tendency of some middle-aged, middle-class Americans to regard hippies as modern vagabonds and gypsies, living lives of love, freedom, and spontaneity. To that extent, hippies were made to carry the burden of almost everyone's fantasies (as in the folk-rock musical *Hair*) and, inevitably, the brunt of public shock and disillusionment when the seamy side of hippie life became known. For a time it was even believed that the hippies were the only poor who were able to live happily in the American city. By 1969 many of the "flower children" showed evidence of hard-core narcotics usage and severe mental disturbance.

versities, for example, the number of students seeking assistance has more than doubled during the past decade.* Nor does this take into account the 40 percent of students who drop out of college, many of them for psychiatric reasons.[45] Yet in 1967 only 76 of the nation's 2,252 colleges and universities had psychiatric facilities, and only another 100 had a psychiatrist available part-time.[46] The total number of physicians certified in child psychiatry—which does not include all those who treat children and adolescents—is 500, or roughly one child psychiatrist for every 140,000 children and adolescents.[47]

Clearly, this acute shortage of personnel must be remedied if there is to be any significant decrease in mental illness and drop-outism on campuses. At present most colleges and universities solicit information about the psychological state of an applicant for admission, and while it is desirable, and apparently the case, that high school students not be disqualified because they have consulted a psychiatrist or analyst, it is not certain that such information is always put to the best use during the student's college career.[48] To be sure, a university is a mental institution rather than a mental hospital, but steps could be taken to ensure that troubled students do not go back and forth from one to the other. Course requirements, grading systems, relations with faculty, housing arrangements, opportunities for leisure and recreation, the physical location of the campus, financial needs—these and many other aspects of college and university life have a bearing on the health of students, but not only their health. Rationality and creativity are also important values in higher education, and a great deal could be done on the campus to promote them.

The problem of alienation, however, goes far beyond the campus to the problem of society itself. The typical university cannot escape the sicknesses of the larger society, as the typical individual cannot remain healthy in the center of the epidemic or plague that is raging around him. A particular hippie, a drop-out we know, a certain Maoist student, a friend's young son who is in a mental hospital, a niece who has been "busted" for possession of drugs, these are individuals in whose lives—perhaps

* It is tempting to suggest that the number of students consulting university psychiatrists may have declined on campuses where student grievances have been channeled into demonstrations and protests. Unfortunately, no evidence is available proving or disproving such a hypothesis.

in whose genes, cells, or hormones—something has gone wrong. But when the number of these individuals is such that one is tempted to refer to a generation, then, clearly, something has gone wrong in the society, and increasingly there is evidence that these forms of alienation are not phenomena of the young only. "I am the wife of a promising young businessman," a letter to the New York *Times* begins,

> the mother of two small boys and I work at home as a freelance copy editor. I have been out of college almost five years. The college was Smith. At 25, I am faced with the crisis of finding some meaning in life or, if that proves impossible, finding a satisfactory way of living and functioning despite it. . . .
>
> The question is, how do you find something to look forward to? And how do you achieve that sense of purpose in what you are doing that will end this questioning? . . . Basically, what good are goals of any kind in the face of death? Yet how is it possible to be happy in the present, forgetting goals, if there is no sense of accomplishing anything?
>
> . . . What is the answer? Keep busier? See lots of people and communicate like mad? See a psychiatrist? Drugs? [49]

Psychiatry in its present state, unfortunately, does not have a satisfactory answer, and there are many psychiatrists and analysts who would object to the way the question is phrased. Politicians and ministers also lack answers, and they, too, would object to the phrasing of the question. But whether the question is sick or healthy, clinical or existential, it would appear that an answer must be found if an ethic of alienation is not to take the place in America of the earlier ethic of work, faith, and commitment.

VII

Toward the Year 2000

"INTROSPECTIVE autobiography," André Malraux comments in his *Anti-Memoirs,* "has changed its character, because the confessions of the most provocative memorialist seem puerile by comparison with the monsters conjured up by psychoanalytic exploration, even to those who contest its conclusions. The analyst's couch reveals far more about the secrets of the human heart, and more startlingly too. We are less astonished by Stavrogin's confession than by Freud's Man with the Rat [*sic*]; genius is its only justification." [1] Coming from a distinguished man of letters, this is high praise indeed, especially at a time when it is more fashionable to believe that Dostoievski will be read long after Freud's writings have been consigned, once and for all, to the literature of quackery.*

But in psychiatry, too, extremes of opinion are hardly unknown, particularly in regard to questions about its future.[2] "I feel safe in predicting," writes British psychiatrist William Sargant, "that in the course of the next twenty-five years nearly all psychiatric patients will be readily cured with simple drugs mostly prescribed by general physicians." [3] On the other hand, there is the forecast that during the twenty-first century "periodic psychiatric examinations will become compulsory in advanced countries. The average *normal* adult will consult his psychiatrist more often than his dentist" (italics added).[4] Still others believe that the future psychiatrist for a good many people will be a computer extremely sophisticated in gathering and evaluating data supplied by patients; some even envisage an extensive therapeutic role

* Malraux's point is to some extent illustrated by Philip Roth's 1969 best-selling novel *Portnoy's Complaint* (New York: Random House) in which the hero confides the secrets of his life to his analyst, "Dr. O. Spielvogel."

for such computers.[5] Finally, there are a few utopians who believe that psychiatry and psychoanalysis will eventually disappear, not because they are unscientific in method and doubtful in result but because the world of the future will be perfect enough, or at last free enough of mental illness, not to require psychiatrists. There are no psychiatrists or analysts in either Edward Bellamy's utopian novel of the past, *Looking Backward,* or in B. F. Skinner's more recent *Walden Two.*[6]

Most psychiatrists, however, do not predict their own demise, although they are willing to admit that the future will see important changes in techniques of dealing with mental illness. As one of them puts it, advances in drug therapy and our understanding of complex brain functions will not change the fact that harmony in human relations is difficult to achieve. "One hundred years from now," he suggests,

> psychiatrists will still be talking with patients about their marriages, kids, jobs, hang-ups in general. The human transactional process, after all, goes way back before psychiatry, and I doubt that the need for some type of psychotherapy will ever disappear. I do think that the governing theory of it will probably be considerably changed from what we now know. There will be less of a pure culture of psychoanalysis or any other subsegment and more a blending of new and old approaches. Psychiatrists will still be prescribing medication, but there will be different medications. As I see it, approaches will still be interpersonal and chemical, and perhaps mechanical because other kinds of somatic treatments will have been developed by then.

"We will do away with psychiatrists," comments another clinician, "when we do away with people." And he quickly adds: "Not that I think that's impossible. Given the drift of things, *no* one may be around a century from now."

Assuming a continuation of civilized life and a need for psychiatrists equal to or greater than the need at present, obviously a number of manpower and economic problems will become increasingly pressing in the years ahead. In 1967 only ten states and the District of Columbia exceeded the overall national ratio of 9.6 psychiatrists and psychiatric residents per 100,000 population.[7] To bring the other forty states up to this average would require an additional 4,200 psychiatrists, and even then there would be acute shortage of trained personnel. The Job Corps, for example, employs approximately 100 psychiatrists in training 40,000 children; the Head Start program, with an enrollment of 457,000 children, or more than ten times as many as the Job Corps, has the same number of psychiatrists.[8] And perhaps more than an increase in numbers is required if there are to be adequate psychiatric services in the slums and ghettos of major cities, rural areas in general, school systems, and public mental hospitals. A study of New York City school children reported in 1969 found that 12 percent were suffering from marked to severe "psychiatric impairment," with another 34 percent classified as moderately impaired, and another 42 percent categorized as mildly impaired; only 12 percent of the children, who ranged in age from six to eighteen, were deemed to be in good mental health.[9]

In many school systems even the severely disturbed and prepsychotic children go without adequate treatment. Thus in Pittsburgh and surrounding Allegheny County there are an estimated 39,000 emotionally disturbed children of whom 3,000 are in the formative stages of psychosis. But not only are there no adequate treatment sources for these children in western Pennsylvania; it is said there are not enough facilities "in the whole state," and Pennsylvania is far from the worst state in the union in terms of medical care services.[10] Perhaps between 10 and 12 percent of all children in the country suffer from serious emotional problems, and yet at least fifteen states lack separate facilities for young people in public mental hospitals.[11] Moreover, only 500 psychiatrists are Board-certified in child psychiatry, or roughly one psychiatrist for every 140,000 children and adolescents as compared with one Board-certified general psychiatrist per 16,000 adults.[12]

The sharpest contrast between sectors of private affluence and public squalor which, as John K. Galbraith has observed, is so typical of American society, is found in comparisons between private and public mental hospitals.[13] Whether or not there are fewer "snake pits" than once was the case, the public mental hospitals lag far behind their private counterparts in the treatment accorded patients. In 1966 the ratio of *all physicians* (not only psychiatrists) to patients in public mental hospitals was 1:103, and the average daily expenditure per patient was $7.73;

by 1968 the physician-patient ratio had shown a minute improvement to 1:102. In private mental hospitals, by contrast, the ratio of *psychiatrists alone* to patients was 1:12, and the average daily expenditure per patient was $33.23. The physician-patient ratio in at least one state system of public hospitals was, in 1964, 1:345, and the lowest recorded expenditures per patient in 1968 were $3.34 in Mississippi and $3.98 in Alabama.* At the other extreme are private mental hospitals with a psychiatrist-patient ratio of 1:5 and daily charges ranging up to $119 per patient. Nor are the missing psychiatrists in public hospitals replaced by other trained personnel: private mental hospitals employ five times as many professional patient-care staff members per patient as do public hospitals.[14] Of the 300 public mental hospitals, principally state hospitals, it was reported in 1966–67 that 21 did not have a single psychiatrist on their staff, and 91 others had between one and four psychiatrists. The conclusion is inescapable that "in well over one-third of all public tax-supported state mental hospitals psychiatric time is practically unavailable." [15]

While much has been done in recent years to improve the lot of hospital inmates and former patients, the mental hospital as "total institution" (in Erving Goffman's phrase) is in some respects more like a prison than an institution responsive to the needs of the sick. In 1969 an investigation of New Jersey's largest mental hospital revealed a variety of sexual abuses including rape of female patients by staff members and the forced prostitution of patients for the benefit of male employees.[16] Alabama, previously noted as ranking forty-ninth in the amount spent daily for mental patient care, had still not integrated its three

---

* The United States is not alone in according the mentally ill the status of inferior citizens in terms of their claims upon the public treasury. In the United Kingdom, for example, less is spent on a patient in a psychiatric hospital per week than in any other type of hospital, averaging per week in 1965 £11 in mental hospitals and £10 in hospitals for the mentally retarded. There, too, a consulting psychiatrist may deal with as many as 250 patients in addition to outpatients and administrative responsibilities; a study of three mental hospitals estimated that the average amount of time devoted to individual long-term patients by all members of the medical staff (not just psychiatrists) was *five and a half minutes per week!* See Peter Mittler, *The Mental Health Services* (London: Fabian Research Series 252, 1966); Kathleen Jones and B. Sidebotham, *Mental Hospitals at Work* (London: Routledge and Kegan Paul, 1962); G. W. Brown and J. K. Wing, "A Comparative Clinical and Social Survey of Three Mental Hospitals," *Sociological Review Monograph*, 5 (1962).

mental hospitals by 1969; considering the state's ranking, it is painful to contemplate what a federal court must have meant when it stated, following an order that the hospitals be integrated, that "the medical services and facilities for care and rehabilitation of Negro patients . . . are typically inferior to those available to white patients."[17] In many states, former mental hospital patients find it difficult or impossible to acquire driving, hunting, and professional licenses, and they frequently are discriminated against in employment and business.*

There may be other problems as well. Approximately one of every four psychiatrists is a staff member of a hospital, with the greater number employed by the 300-odd state, county, and Veterans Administration hospitals. Judging by the eighteen public mental hospital employees in the study group, there are important differences between psychiatrists who work in these hospitals and those in private practice. As mentioned earlier, ten of the eighteen are employed full-time in public mental hospitals, and the remaining eight devote at least half their time to such employment (there are no analysts among them). Almost all of them do much more drug and shock therapy than psychotherapy or confine their research to these areas. The eighteen public hospital psychiatrists are more religious than other psychiatrists, and proportionally there are more Catholics and fewer Jews at-

* Recent court decisions evidence an increasing concern for the rights of patients and former patients of mental hospitals. A 1968 California appellate court decision set aside a commitment of a "mentally disordered sex offender not amenable to treatment" on the grounds that he was denied his right to confront and cross-examine the psychiatrist who ruled on his condition, a right protected by constitutional due process. *Psychiatric News,* March, 1969. A U.S. Court of Appeals in New York held, in 1969, that a prisoner being transferred to a state mental hospital has the right to a jury trial before his transfer. New York *Times,* April 27, 1969. In another case heard by the U.S. Court of Appeals for the District of Columbia, the court raised doubts about the constitutionality of a Washington, D.C., ordinance providing for the commitment of persons "unable to control their sexual emotions . . . so as to be dangerous to other persons. . . ." In a case on appeal involving an exhibitionist, the three-man court (one judge dissenting) held that the words "not insane" and "not mentally ill" were not synonymous despite the language of the ordinance, and that, while the appellant had been deemed "ill" by psychiatrists, "there was no evidence of any actual harm to adult women from appellant's past exhibitionism." It added that "very seclusive, withdrawn, shy, sensitive women are in a minority," thus implying that most women were too worldly or sophisticated to be disturbed by an exhibitionist. *Psychiatric News,* February, 1969. The majority opinion was written by Chief Judge David L. Bazelon, an honorary fellow of the APA and a member of the board of trustees of the William Alanson White Psychiatric Foundation. In 1969 Judge Bazelon was elected president of the American Orthopsychiatric Association.

tached to public mental hospitals. They watch television more often and read fewer books; whereas nonpsychiatric medical books are far down on the reading list of the private psychiatrists and analysts, the public hospital psychiatrists put them in third place, not far behind the popularity of the history books and biographies. They are more apt to read *Reader's Digest, U.S. News,* and *Harper's* than the other psychiatrists—*Reader's Digest* is sixth among favored magazines—and less apt to have published books and articles.

Not surprisingly, the public hospital psychiatrists have different career likes and dislikes. Like the private psychiatrists and analysts, those who work in public mental hospitals list helping people and being socially useful as the chief career satisfactions, but these are the only major satisfactions mentioned. Income and financial security are cited by three of the eighteen public hospital psychiatrists, and only one of the three is employed full-time in such a hospital. One of the half-time public hospital psychiatrists checks status as a career satisfaction, and another one says that he likes "nothing at all" about his career. The most important career dislikes are low income and a variety of hospital conditions including admission, diagnostic, and treatment procedures. But four, three of whom are full-time in public mental hospitals, have no particular career dislikes.

For the public hospital psychiatrists the only promising or significant development of the last twenty years in psychiatry is the "drug revolution": eleven give it first-place mention, and no other development receives more than one first-place vote. Four of the eighteen do not list any development. Only nine of the group identify one or more outstanding psychiatrists or analysts, while eight name one or more who are controversial. Lawrence Kubie receives four mentions as outstanding, and Anna Freud and Karl Menninger receive three each. Erik Erikson is mentioned twice, and thirty-four psychiatrists or analysts are named once (but thirteen of these are nominated by the same respondent). Thomas Szasz and John Rosen are cited twice as controversial, and eight others are mentioned once.

In their moral and political attitudes the public hospital psychiatrists are less permissive and more conservative than their colleagues. Almost two-thirds believe that the typical American family is too lenient with children, compared with 46 percent of other psychiatrists. Whereas a quarter of the entire study group of psychiatrists believes that a happy monogamous marriage is "neither difficult nor impossible," 71 percent of the hospital psychiatrists hold that view, and the rest are of the opinion that such a marriage is "difficult but not impossible." Almost two-thirds of the hospital psychiatrists oppose abolishing restrictions on sexual relations, including homosexual relations, between consenting adults, and they are less tolerant of extramarital and premarital sexual relations.

Among the full-time hospital psychiatrists Republican voters exceed Democratic voters in each election 1940 to 1960, and even in 1964, when most of their colleagues supported Johnson against Goldwater, the political division was four Republicans and four Democrats. For the part-time psychiatrists, however, the Democratic votes equal or exceed Republican votes in every election including 1952, when Eisenhower and Stevenson received equal support. The public hospital psychiatrists are less in favor of moving toward world government and strengthening the United Nations, and well over half the group is opposed to withdrawing from Vietnam, recognizing Communist China, and admitting Communist China to the United Nations. Opinion is evenly divided with reference to a ceasefire in Vietnam. The "politically mature" selections are, in order of preference, Johnson and Rusk, with third place held by Humphrey and Warren. Eisenhower, Goldwater, Fulbright, and Truman receive three votes each, while Nixon is chosen by two respondents.

Attitudes toward civil rights and civil liberties are also different from those of the private psychiatrists and analysts. In terms of the social distance scale, Negroes and Orientals are still the most excluded, but Catholics are somewhat more favored than Jews as relatives, fellow club members, and neighbors. There is less tolerance of both admitted and suspected Communists, and the hospital psychiatrists tend to score higher on the F-scale measure of right-wing authoritarianism, and lower on the C-scale measure of left-wing authoritarianism, than the other psychiatrists and analysts. They are slightly more optimistic about the chances of avoiding World War III but much more pessimistic about the future of such problems as alcoholism, crime and divorce rates, drug addiction, illegitimacy, mental illness, and suicide. *All* of these problems, the public hospital psychiatrists believe, will increase, by percentiles ranging from 53 percent (suicide) to 83 percent (crime rate).

If the admittedly small sample of public mental hospital psychiatrists is any guide, it would appear that the psychiatrists in such institutions not only practice a different psychiatry from their colleagues in private practice but that they are different people as well. Indeed it is difficult to resist the suggestion that in terms of theoretical influence and cultural level, psychoanalysts can be regarded as the highbrow, private practice psychiatrists as the middlebrow, and public mental hospital psychiatrists as the lowbrow element in American psychiatry. Unfortunately for these distinctions, the public hospital psychiatrists are more a part of the medical world than the private practice psychiatrists, and many of them are more interested in research and experimentation. To the extent that these orientations are at least as important as the provision of psychotherapy and psychoanalysis for those who can afford it, the public hospital practitioners, while different, are not necessarily inferior to many of those in private practice. The evidence, however, pertaining to similarities and differences is far from conclusive. Perhaps the only firm conclusion is that Americans, in general, receive the psychiatrist and the psychiatric treatment *not* that they deserve, but that they can pay for, and since the poor can pay for less, they usually receive less.

But the high cost of psychotherapy not only penalizes the poor and low-income groups, it also works hardship on middle-income persons if they are in need of long-term treatment. With costs averaging $35 for fifty-minute therapy sessions in many cities, and in some cases far exceeding that figure, a year of once-a-week meetings with a psychiatrist can easily cost between $1,500 and $2,500. As was demonstrated in an earlier chapter, psychoanalysis requiring a minimum expenditure of $5,000 per annum is within reach only of the well-to-do.

Given the affluent values of American society, it is extremely unlikely that psychiatrists and psychoanalysts will charge their private patients less in the future. The solution, rather, is an increase in the coverage provided by prepaid medical insurance well beyond the limits presently typical: most such plans are limited as to total amounts provided for psychiatric care so that only short-term psychotherapy is adequately covered. The seventeen low-cost psychoanalytic treatment centers, where fees are determined by the patient's ability to pay and average about $5.00 per session, need to be expanded beyond their present number. In 1968 some 400 candidates and 170 practicing analysts treated about 1,000 patients at the low-cost centers, of whom 900 were in analysis and the remainder in psychotherapy. The total of 570 practicing analysts and trainees is less than a third of the total number of trainees and post-training analysts, and apparently each averages less than two patients in treatment. Since trainees typically have two patients in supervised analysis, it is clear that much more low-cost time could be contributed by analysts past their training and especially by those who have established flourishing and lucrative practices.*

Obviously daily expenditures per patient must be doubled and even tripled in our public mental hospitals if such hospitals are to perform more than merely custodial functions; the emphasis must shift from simple maintenance of the patient (three meals per day, plus medication) to treatment of the patient. Since many states clearly cannot afford adequate public psychiatric services, a case can be made for the federal government's assuming the major financial burden of mental patient care, thus closing the gap between states such as Alaska, where daily per patient expenditure is $26.48, and those of the Deep South. Ways must be found to make service in the public institutions attractive to psychiatrists, psychoanalysts, and other trained mental health personnel. Salaries and working conditions, for example, could be made more competitive with private practice, and perhaps in some instances

---

* Fees charged by psychiatrists, like those of other physicians, have increased sharply since the enactment of Medicare, and the costs of psychoanalysis have tended to keep pace. According to Wilbur J. Cohen, Secretary of Health, Education, and Welfare in the Johnson administration, between 1960 and 1965 the annual percentage increase in physicians' fees averaged 2.6 percent. In the period 1965–67 the average increase was 7 percent, with median physicians' incomes increasing 11 percent in 1966 and 8 percent in 1967. Cost-of-living increases during those years have been estimated at about 3 percent. Fees are expected to rise a further 5 percent in 1969 and 4.5 percent in 1970. Despite Cohen's plea to physicians for "unusual restraint" in setting fees for 1969–70, it is unlikely that the average annual increase will fall much below 5 percent. *Psychiatric News,* February, 1969. At the 1969 annual meeting of the APA in Miami Beach, the executive director of the National Committee Against Mental Illness assailed the Association's endorsement of the position taken by the American Medical Association that fees charged for medical services should be "usual and customary" no matter what the medical plan coverage. Mike Gorman, the Committee's executive secretary, referred to the endorsement as "astounding." New York *Times,* May 7, 1969.

superior; many psychiatrists and analysts would consider full- or part-time public employment if inducements included lengthy annual vacations, sabbatical leaves, and generous provision for retirement.*

One certainty in the future is the continued growth of the community mental health movement, regarded by some psychiatrists as a "revolution" comparable in importance to the earlier revolutions caused by psychoanalysis and the introduction of psychotropic drugs. Established by Act of Congress in 1963, following a message from President John F. Kennedy calling for a "bold new approach" to problems of mental illness, community mental health centers are designed to provide a variety of services to mentally ill patients without removing them, except for short periods where necessary, from their homes, schools, and jobs. The centers, each of which serves a so-called catchment area with a population between 75,000 and 200,000 persons, offer inpatient treatment, outpatient treatment, partial hospitalization (day or night care), emergency services on a twenty-four-hour basis, and consultation and education aimed primarily at leaders and groups in the community. The major intent of the centers is to provide psychiatric treatment for those who, if there were no centers, would either go without treatment or ultimately find themselves in mental hospitals. Hence almost every center has some patients who work or attend school during the day and spend their nights at the center, and others who are hospitalized for short periods of time, in addition to those patients who receive outpatient treatment or who turn to the center only in emergencies.*

Whether or not the community mental health centers, like other hoped-for cure-alls in psychiatry, have been oversold, as many

---

* It may be noted, in passing, that state universities and private universities are competitive for precisely the reason that the former are the equal, and in some states the superior, of the latter in salaries, fringe benefits, and working conditions. Unfortunately, some advertisements enticing psychiatrists to certain parts of the country have dubious and even ugly overtones. Thus a *Psychiatric News* advertisement in April, 1969, designed to attract psychiatrists to Mt. Pleasant, Iowa, listed among the job advantages: "Our area is free at present of major social, ethnic, and economic problems—in short, a good place to raise your family."

* Financing of the centers is on a matching fund basis under which, by 1974, federal government grants will have totaled approximately $600,000,000, with another $600,000,000 having come from states and local governments. Efforts are under way to increase these amounts, the total of which in the years 1963 to 1974 will be much less than public mental hospitals spend in one year, not to mention the more than $20,000,000,000 annual cost of mental illness in the United States.

psychiatrists believe, some initial expectations have been disappointed. A study of eight "most nearly fully operational" centers reported in 1969 that only two of the centers had significantly reduced state hospital admissions from their catchment areas, although it had been argued before Congress in 1963, with good effect, that such reductions would be dramatic. It was further found that, while all eight centers were offering day treatment programs, four of them never had more than four patients at one time on day programs. Very few children and geriatric patients were receiving help, and the educational and consulting functions were little understood. In one center no one received inpatient treatment without paying for it, and there was little spreading of outpatient services away from the centers and into the communities themselves, for example, through the neighborhood health centers.[18]

In some parts of the country, however, the results have been more impressive. According to Lawrence C. Kolb, APA president 1968–69, two New York City centers serviced by the Department of Psychiatry at Columbia University succeeded over a five-year period in reducing the transfer rate to state hospitals from 40 percent to 20 percent in one instance, and from 40 percent to 10 percent in the other. Many of those who favor an increase in the financing and services of the community centers feel that it is in such centers, not the large public mental hospitals, that the bulk of the mentally ill should be treated, with the hospitals providing supportive and custodial care for the chronically ill, the aged, and those with brain damage. In effect, the hospitals would become nursing homes for incurables, and while psychiatrists would be attached to general medical staffs, the larger part of their time and effort could be devoted to treating community mental health center patients and private patients.[19]

Whatever the final shape and function of the community mental health centers—or, as the controversy was developing in 1968–69, the extent to which it is staffed and controlled by representatives of the local community*—there is no reason to doubt

* In cities with large Negro and Puerto Rican populations, nonprofessional workers in community health centers tend to come from such populations, as do the patients, whereas the professional and administrative staffs are usually white and nonresident in the community. As a consequence, the issue of community control in a number of cities is not confined to the schools, although "confrontation" in the mental health field, thus far, has been more restrained.

that by 1975 there will be more than 500 such centers dealing with most of the low-income mentally ill outpatient population and many of those suffering from alcoholism and drug addiction.[20] What may still be needed, however, especially if the large public mental hospitals are gradually phased out, are community facilities for the senile aged and chronic psychotic patients who now occupy the "back wards" of such hospitals. There, out of sight of visitors and other patients, and infrequently attended by staff, the "chronics" live out their lives as a hopeless and incurable subspecies of patient. Many of them could be cared for in halfway houses on the British model, that is, institutions that represent a crossing between the mental hospital and the hostel. In many halfway houses abroad, patients are cared for by nonmedical trained personnel, and there are usually work-for-pay programs for all but the totally disabled. In the United States such programs are rare, and in general there are few community facilities for the rehabilitation and special needs of former hospital patients.[21]

Since it is beyond question that the demand for psychiatrists, psychoanalysts, and allied professionals will exceed the supply as far as one can see ahead, additional mental health personnel must be found in fields other than medicine, clinical psychology, and social work. The evidence is encouraging that a great many people can be trained to offer at least some forms of psychotherapy to those in need of it. One Pennsylvania Mental Health Center gives a two-year course in principles of psychotherapy to housewives, most of whom have children, are in their forties, and have been married fifteen years or more. Upon graduation from the course the housewives are state-certified as "Associates in Psychotherapy" and are therefore eligible for staff jobs in the community mental health centers. A Maryland State Hospital project has shown that after three weeks of intensive training a hospital aide "whose . . . job has been mainly running errands" is capable of "serving as a 'team leader' of a group of patients, can help pinpoint their 'target symptoms,' and help the professional staff develop a program of treatment." At a state hospital in Texas some of the psychotherapy, casework, and administration is in the hands of twelve nonmedical individuals, only one of whom is a social worker in the orthodox sense. One of the twelve had majored in college in political science, another had specialized in English, one had had an executive position in the Girl Scouts, several had been attendants, and a few had never gone to college. In Cleveland clergymen are being trained to deal with mental health problems; the program was inspired, in part, by a survey showing that 40 percent of "first contacts" made by emotionally ill people are with clergymen.[22]

But here, again, much more could be done than has so far been attempted. Despite the shortage of psychiatrists in university student health clinics and the increase in mental illness among adolescent and college-age youth, there is no known instance of professors receiving psychotherapy training. Yet it is to a friendly and respected professor that the student is first apt to turn when he is in trouble, whether over his grades, family problems, sexual difficulties, financial worries, or the state of the world. Few professors in their careers have not encountered depressed students contemplating suicide, and for most professors it is a rare lifetime in a university or college that has not been scarred by at least one suicide of a student or colleague. Were faculty members to receive training that elsewhere is being given to housewives and hospital attendants, it is probable that on the campuses there would be fewer drop-outs, underachievers, and students who are "acting out" in a variety of destructive ways their private fantasies and nightmares.

Training housewives, clergymen, professors, and others in some of the principles and techniques of psychotherapy would have one further advantage: no one has ever heard of a clergyman or housewife who was reluctant to make house calls, and on residential campuses it is not unusual for students to see professors in their homes and for professors to visit student residences. Among all physicians, however, only obstetricians-gynecologists make fewer house calls than psychiatrists. A 1963 survey showed that almost 60 percent of psychiatrists never make a house call, and those who do make fewer than five house calls per week.[23] House calls by psychiatrists are more common in Europe, where it is believed, with good reason, that visiting the home and meeting the family of a patient is far more revealing of his problems than a consultation in the artificial surroundings of an office or hospital ward. Indeed, many if not most American psychiatrists probably would agree with this view, and yet there has been no move in the direction of treating the patient even occasionally in his home environment. Although it is likely that psychiatrists have done more to hold marriages together than any other professionals—in this sense the *ménage à trois* as practiced in the United States includes a psychiatrist rather than another sex partner—in most cases they never observe the marriage in its only natural setting, the home. Analysts, although they, too, deal with marital problems, are usually unwilling to meet the patient's spouse, much less visit his home, even if the spouse and the home life are what led the patient to the analyst's couch in the first place.

Innovations of any sort, it would appear, are hardly the distinguishing feature of either American psychiatry or psychoanalysis. In 1957 psychiatrist Jurgen Reusch observed that "no original idea in psychiatry has ever come from an American-trained psychiatrist"; in 1968 another psychiatrist, quoting Reusch's remark, added that "this still holds today for both adult and child psychiatry."[24] The alleged lack of originality, perhaps, owes something to the nature of the profession. As one psychiatrist suggests, innovation is more apt to be found in a profession that is sure of its principles and confident of its techniques. Both of these qualities, he feels, are lacking in American psychiatry, and he also notes that many psychiatrists and analysts are themselves tense, anxious persons all too aware that their patients are quick to detect any weakness or insecurity on their part. For this reason, he suggests, psychiatrists and analysts are inevitably less innovative than other physicians, especially the surgeons and cardiologists, who, if the innovation or experiment fails, can always fall back on the comforting belief that the patient would have died anyway.

But is it certain that originality in psychiatry has been entirely a European product? The major figures in psychoanalysis, to be sure, were born and educated in Europe, and even those born in the United States, such as the Menningers, have been trained and analyzed by teachers of European origin. It equally is true that important departures from traditional mental hospital policy, such as the concepts of the "open" hospital and therapeutic community, were first developed and tested in Great Britain. On the other hand, the variety of psychotherapies and analytic techniques in use at the present time seems almost endless, and most of them have originated in the United States.

Perhaps this variety suggests that any type of human expression and communication can be put to therapeutic use. Thus, in addition to individual and group psychotherapy and analysis, there is poetry therapy, music therapy, dance therapy, and cinema therapy.[25] Psychodrama, a form of therapy associated with psychiatrist J. L. Moreno and the Moreno Institute at Beacon, New York, has been in existence for some time. A growing number of psychiatrists are practicing conjoint marital therapy (the husband and wife seen together) and family therapy (the husband and wife with the children—the entire family, in short—meet with the psychiatrist).* Psychoanalysis has been successfully conducted by correspondence.[26] Since 1964 chapters of Neurotics Anonymous, patterned after Alcoholics Anonymous but with some of the features of the group in therapy, have enrolled as many as 100 members in a number of cities.[27]

While psychoanalytic group therapy is not unknown, psychoanalysis for the most part continues to take place in a two-person environment comprising the analyst and his patient, the essential theory of which differs little from that established by Freud himself. Freudian theory does not lend itself easily to broad social applications or even the study of interpersonal relations. As R. D. Laing observes,

> The metapsychology of Freud, Federn, Rapaport, Hartmann, Kris, has no constructs for any social system generated by more than one person at a time. Within its own framework it has no concepts of social collectivities of experience shared or unshared between persons. This theory has no category of "you", as there is in the work of Feuerbach, Buber, Parsons. It has no way of expressing the meeting of an "I" with "an other", and of the impact of one person on another. . . .[28]

Whether or not Laing is correct in arguing that "the wholeness

---

* According to psychiatrist Clifford J. Sager, at least seven different methods may be used in treating married couples. The most common forms of treatment, however, are simultaneous treatment of the husband and wife by different therapists, successive treatment of the husband and wife by the same therapist or analyst, simultaneous treatment of the husband and wife by the same therapist but at different times, and simultaneous (conjoint) treatment of the husband and wife in joint sessions. Clifford J. Sager, "The Treatment of Married Couples," in Silvano Arieti (ed.), *American Handbook of Psychiatry*, III (1966), 213–24. See also Don D. Jackson (ed.), *Communication, Family, and Marriage* (Human Communication Vol. 1; Palo Alto, Calif.: Science and Behavior Books, 1968); and George R. Bach and Peter Wyden, *The Intimate Enemy* (New York: William Morrow, 1968).

of being human" can only be defined in an interpersonal context, psychoanalysis has been much criticized in recent years for its view of man as an isolate or atom—as an "*un*rugged individual." From this point of view, Freudian man is simply Lockean man rendered neurotic and, like other creations of John Locke, somewhat obsolete.

Certainly it is possible that the central weakness in Freudian psychoanalysis is not its lack of scientific method, its rigidity about the length and number of sessions, or any other of the criticisms mentioned in earlier chapters, but its neglect of socialization processes that have affected the nature of repression and altered both the conscious and unconscious components of behavior. For a case can be made that the "Americanization of the Unconscious,"[29] whatever else it has achieved, has reduced the importance of the superego in its internal and external manifestations, and immensely strengthened the forces of the id, to the extent that the ego no longer functions as the executive or "governor" of the personality system, in accordance with Freudian theory. If one interpretation of our increasingly permissive society is that the superego and authoritative institutions have largely broken down, another is that there are ever fewer impediments to those id-type indulgences commonly referred to as "doing your thing." Self-expression, of course, can take creative forms; as Freud suggested, the libido may be capable of sublimation into a variety of culture-building activities. But in a society characterized by increasing frustrations and resentments, "doing your thing" is more apt to find expression in exhibitionism, violence whether of language or deed, and other kinds of disturbed "acting out" behavior.

Whatever the expression, the decline of religion and the family, and the widespread distrust, especially among the young, of the political, business, educational, and military leaders, not to mention the forces of law and order, reflects conscious and unconscious socialization processes which the Freudian model does not take into account and to which, given its assumptions, it must be hostile. As Anna Freud has pointed out, "Young people now are not interested in man's struggle against himself, but in man's struggle against society. They see that what psychoanalysis may lead to is adaptation to society. That's the last thing they have in mind."[30]

If by "society" is meant that instinctual renunciation that Freud explicitly made a condition of culture, then psychoanalysis may also be the "last thing" the parents of the young people have in mind. As Philip Rieff and others have suggested, the historical necessity of renunciation, a necessity proclaimed by religion, law, and established institutions, has been replaced by a demand for instant, pure, and complete gratification of instincts. In the United States and to an increasing extent the rest of the world, the insistence upon gratification is sweeping before it the laws, customs, traditions, and ethical systems that have been maintained for generations, and not least among the casualties of the instinctual release that is approaching flood-tide proportions is the Freudian ethic itself as promulgated by its founder. In effect, Freud's declaration: "Where id was, there ego shall be" (he was speaking of the principal objective, in terms of personality change, of psychoanalysis), has almost been replaced by: "Where ego and superego were, there id shall be." For this reason alone much of Freudian theory about culture and personality seems dated, although it may be premature, at least, to conclude that "Freud has already receded into history. His problems are not ours." [31]

But given the history of psychoanalysis, it is not beyond question that the Freudian model will be modified to take account of changed social conditions and especially the permanent as distinct from the temporary or transient impact of increasing permissiveness, notably as manifested in the "sexual revolution." For the "Americanization of the Unconscious," that is to say, is a continuing phenomenon as, indeed, it must be. If it is impossible to imagine how psychoanalysis might have developed had it remained rooted in central Europe, it is no less impossible to imagine that psychoanalysis, transferred as it were to the United States, could have flourished without taking on a more optimistic view of basic human nature and the prospects of change and growth. It is no accident that autonomous ego functions, for instance, and the emphasis on man's ability to adapt to circumstances and successfully cope with internal and external stress have received more attention in American psychoanalytic circles than in circles abroad.

The eclecticism of many analysts, whatever their theoretical positions, in treating patients is still another "Americanism." Such eclecticism is not confined to experiments with fewer sessions per week than the number officially recommended, or shorter sessions, but extends to treatment techniques that are improvised in accordance with the analyst's perceptions of the therapeutic situation at a given time. In accordance with this perception, he may remain relatively silent, in keeping with the strictures of orthodox Freudian theory, or he may actively intervene; he may attempt to penetrate the patient's defenses and subterfuges, or he may be accepting, at least temporarily, of the patient's efforts to avoid certain topics; he may choose to appear cold and indifferent, or warm and concerned. Whatever he does, theory as such is likely to have little influence on his decision, partly because, as one analyst in the study group puts it,

> We have not really learned yet how to use theoretical advances in our technique. For example, we know much more about ego psychology than we did in Freud's day, but it hasn't influenced our technique very much at all. We know more about identity problems since Erikson, but that hasn't influenced our technique much. Maybe the problem is that some of these theories call for really new and different techniques. I feel that for certain problems of identity the ideal method isn't necessarily individual therapy but a combination of group therapy and individual therapy. Or maybe there should be residential treatment whereby the therapist lives in the home of a certain kind of family.

The tendency for theory and technique to be divorced recalls Freud's own conclusion toward the end of his career that the future of psychoanalysis was not in terms of technique or therapy but as a theory of behavior. Theory in psychoanalysis, it is tempting to suggest, enjoys a life of its own.

Whether this life is long or short remains to be decided, but it is already clear that significant changes are under way in both the theory and the practice of psychoanalysis. Analysis not only appeals less to the most talented medical students; it also appeals less to patients, more and more of whom are seeing analysts for psychotherapy rather than for psychoanalysis. Many analysts, meanwhile, have begun to doubt whether most of those in analysis can properly benefit from it. "I think our criteria for selecting patients," runs a typical comment,

> are much too crude. We know very little about what makes a good analytic patient, and much more about what makes someone impossible. I find myself, after more than thirty years in

> practice, that I recommend analysis to one in ten patients I see, whereas formerly I would recommend it for eight or nine out of ten. For the future, this probably means that the big value of psychoanalysis will be for training psychotherapists, because they won't be able to help patients much unless they have had some psychoanalytic training—you really need analytic insight for supportive therapy. As for standard psychoanalysis, it will be limited to a very few patients, I believe.

Psychoanalysis in some form, another analyst observes, will always be around,

> but it will never again have its central position in American psychiatry. Now it has to share ground with the behavior theories and the research that deals with the external manifestations of ego functions. Field theory, systems theory, controlled experimentation, communications theory—all these and more will have to find a place in psychiatry, and psychoanalysis will be part of the general theoretical structure. You can see this beginning to happen now as a number of scientists, good scientists, who became analysts, are beginning to effect some change. All this new stuff was called "dilution" in the old days, by which they meant that the sacred principles were being weakened. You don't hear that any more.

No wonder, then, that an article in the *American Journal of Psychiatry* can be titled "Is the Unconscious Necessary?" * And even less wonder that a leading figure in psychoanalysis can suggest that unless psychoanalysis makes more effective use of the behavioral and social sciences, broadens its training base, and becomes relevant to the urban community, "its very survival may be at stake." [32] This may well be true, but one ponders the form and substance of a psychoanalysis that is minus the unconscious, infiltrated by the behavioral sciences, and cross-fertilized by community problems. If, in fact, this *is* the direction that psychoanalysis must take, old-style analysts, as they contemplate their futures, may well be reminded of some words of the Beatles:

* Richard Rabkin, "Is the Unconscious Necessary?" *American Journal of Psychiatry*, 125, 3 (September, 1968), 313–20. In answering no to his own question, the author, a psychiatrist, argues the appropriateness of treating "the unconscious as nonscientific, as a basic assumption which cannot be proved or disproved but must be accepted as a given." His major point is that the concept of the unconscious is unnecessary in psychotherapy and that it may even obscure what is involved.

Will you still need me, will you still feed me,
When I'm sixty-four?

The fate of new-style psychiatrists and analysts, on the other hand, will be to combine traditional modes of psychotherapy with the advanced technologies and electronics devices that have already begun to make an impact in medicine. It may not be long before patients in analysis will be expected to tape-record their dreams immediately upon awakening, and by means of pocket-sized recorders to transcribe their daydreams, fantasies, and other material of interest to their analysts, much of which is lost to later recall; from a technological viewpoint, free association need not be confined to the fifty minutes on the couch. The verbalizations of those in therapy may be subjected to content analysis, thus facilitating the identification of recurrent themes, wishes, and word patterns. Closed-circuit television, currently used in psychiatry as a teaching aid and monitoring device for patient supervision in mental hospitals, may in the future link patients' homes with their therapists' offices, thus ensuring that treatment is little interrupted by the vicissitudes of physical illness, traffic congestion, and weather conditions.

It is certain that the role of computers will become more significant, and not merely in connection with data retrieval and storage functions. By 1969 computer programs had been developed that were sophisticated enough to yield diagnoses in "substantial agreement with diagnoses made by psychiatrists functioning in a setting in which they knew the patient well. . . ."[33] In one experiment, involving comparisons between a computer program known as Diagno II and a group of psychiatrists and psychiatric residents, diagnostic agreement among the clinicians differed little from the agreement between the clinicians and Diagno II. Greatest agreement between the psychiatrists and the computer was with reference to diagnoses of "nonspecific illness" and "not ill," with lowest agreement for "personality trait" or "pattern disturbance." Given the fact that computer usage in psychiatry is in its infancy, there can be little doubt that succeeding generations of computers will practically eliminate those margins of error and disagreements in diagnosis that are fairly common in psychiatry at the present time.

Nor is it beyond possibility that the computers of the future will be able to undertake a number of treatment functions. As early as 1965 an IBM 7090, programmed under the direction of psychoanalyst Kenneth M. Colby of Stanford University, could draw upon a stored vocabulary of some 6,000 words to carry on conversations such as the following:

> PERSON: When my father died my mother was sick for a long time.
> PROGRAM: Tell me more about him.
> PERSON: My father was a writer. He was kind but rather cynical.
> PROGRAM: What else was he like?
> PERSON: He was intelligent and knew a lot about people.
> PROGRAM: Is he now?
> PERSON: He is dead.

Subsequent improvements in programming enhanced the computer's ability to respond more intelligently to information (such as, in the above example, the reported death of the father), and direct its questions accordingly. Advanced computer models, it is clear, will be programmed for more exact simulations of therapist-patient transactions, and since these computers will also know and remember much more about patients than any human psychiatrist is capable of retaining in his mind, there is good reason to believe that computers will replace pyschiatrists in the treatment of certain categories of illness and personality disorders. If Colby and his colleagues are right to think that computers can be programmed to change a person's belief system as well as record it, the psychotherapy of the future may bear little resemblance to that of the present day. Little wonder, then, that Colby's students refer to the earlier 7090 computer as the "Mad Doctor." [34]

Like the advent of computerized psychiatry, the so-called drug revolution, regarded by many psychiatrists as the most significant recent development in treating mental illness, may have only just begun. Thus far the major achievements in psychopharmacology have been to reduce the number of patients hospitalized with severe illnesses such as schizophrenia and to relieve anxiety, depression, and other neurotic states. But the drug therapies are effective only in controlling certain types of behavior and in relieving symptoms. Hence the use of the phenothiazines in treating schizophrenia, of lithium carbonate in the treatment of mania, and of the antidepressants and minor tranquilizers in the treatment of other disorders has left untouched and unsolved the question whether there is a cure for most forms of severe mental illness. Moreover, while the number of long-term hospitalized patients has decreased, the readmission rate of former hospitalized patients is rising, possibly because of their increasing tolerance of the drugs being administered, or resistance to taking the medications prescribed once they are free of the hospital routine. It is also true that many mental patients in and out of hospitals are not significantly helped by the established drug therapies: while estimates vary considerably from psychiatrist to psychiatrist and from hospital to hospital, it is perhaps the general case that between a fifth and a third of acute or chronic patients do not respond to drug treatment. In one study of schizophrenic patients who had "uncertain prognoses" but were not likely to require more than two years of hospitalization, it was found that the phenothiazines (mainly chlorpromazine, known commercially as Thorazine, and trifluoperazine, known commercially as Stelazine) with or without psychotherapy constituted the most effective and efficient treatment for the largest number of schizophrenic patients; individual psychotherapy and milieu therapy were found to be the least effective, most expensive, and most time-consuming, with electroconvulsive therapy (ECT) somewhere in the middle. But 50 of the 228 patients, or approximately 22 percent, all of whom were in treatment for periods ranging from six months to a year, failed to improve regardless of the method used.[35]

Of course, not all psychiatrists rely on psychotherapy or drugs in treating mental illness. There are those who feel that the treatment of choice for depressed patients is electroconvulsive shock (ECT) rather than antidepressants, and despite the decline in the frequency of prefrontal and transorbital labotomies, psychosurgery continues to have its adherents who claim impressive rates of success for such surgery in treating certain kinds of schizophrenia. In 1968 a British neurosurgeon reported that a new type of brain surgery, involving the implanting of radioactive "seeds" in a section of the brain, was effective in treating several varieties of severe psychoneurosis, especially depression, that have not responded to psychotherapy, drugs, or shock. By contrast with lobotomy surgery, which has a mortality rate of 2.3 percent and an epilepsy rate of 12.3 percent, "seed" neurosurgery, it was stated, had not been followed either by death or by epilepsy, but, on the contrary, the "postoperative personality is bright with restoration of normal emotion in contrast to the blunting of emotion produced by the standard leucotomy." [36] For still other psychiatrists a combination of psychotherapy with hypnosis, or one of several forms of behavior therapy, has proven effective in treating disorders.

Many psychiatrists are convinced that the most serious and intractable mental illnesses, such as schizophrenia, have their roots in biochemical disturbances and malfunctions which, once isolated and identified, will give rise to an entirely new generation of drugs that will be curative rather than merely symptom-relieving. Certainly the evidence is impressive that some types of mental illness are coexistent with biochemical and neurological peculiarities, although it is not known whether these peculiarities are cause or effect of the mental state, and it is possible that both the illness and its biochemical or neurological accompaniment are themselves the resultants of complex processes which are still very little understood.*

Thus a higher incidence of sex-chromosome abnormalities has been found in schizophrenics, criminals, and mental defectives, but it is not known why this should be the case. Genetic links have been postulated in connection with schizophrenia and depression; for example, if one identical twin is schizophrenic, there is a high probability that the other twin will also become schizophrenic even if reared separately; there is also evidence that where manic-depressive illness exists in a family, there is a 25 percent chance that other members of the family will develop the illness. A chemical substance known as dopamine (DMPEA), not excreted by normal persons, has been found in the urine of about 70 percent of schizophrenic patients, and a blood protein, taraxein, has been detected in the brains of schizophrenic patients but, again, not in those of normal people. In 1968 it was reported that the amount of glycoprotein neuraminic acid in cerebrospinal fluid is 90 percent effective in determining the extent and severity of

* The increasing psychiatric interest in biochemical and neurophysiological approaches to mental illness is reflected in the increasing number of applications for certification in neurology. In 1963, for example, about 12 percent of all applications for certification were in neurology; by 1968 the percentage had increased to 18. *Psychiatric News,* August, 1968.

mental illness. A Washington University study suggests that the lactate ion may be implicated in the development of anxiety symptoms.[37]

One of the most controversial biochemical interpretations of mental illness was advanced in 1968 by Linus Pauling, winner of two Nobel Prizes (one of them in chemistry). An advocate of "orthomolecular psychiatry," defined as the "treatment of mental disease by the provision of the optimum molecular environment for the mind," Pauling suggested in a *Science* article that much mental illness is the result of deficiencies in vitamins and other chemical substances. Noting that low concentrations of certain B-complex vitamins, niacin, vitamin C or ascorbic acid, and other substances have been associated with physical and mental diseases, Pauling declared his belief that "mental disease is for the most part caused by abnormal reaction rates (of the brain and nervous tissue), as determined by genetic constitution and diet, and by abnormal molecular concentrations of essential substances." In effect, Pauling argued that most forms of mental illness could be cured by massive doses of vitamins, minerals, and other essential nutrilites.

As might be expected, the psychiatric world did not react favorably to the suggestion that the root of the problem was vitamin deficiency. Donald Oken, chief of the clinical research branch of NIMH, charged Pauling, in a letter to *Science,* with illustrating "elegantly the pitfalls which occur when an expert in one field enters another area . . . there is no adequate evidence to back up his view." In rejecting the sources cited by Pauling, Oken leveled criticisms very similar to those that have been made of psychiatry in general by scientists and physicians in other branches of medicine. The "serious methodological flaws" of the published reports on vitamin deficiency in mental illness, Oken wrote, "include inappropriate sampling, inadequacy of controls for extraneous intake and for activity, or the effects of hospitalization per se, loose diagnostic criteria, the opportunity for observer bias, and like defects which render them less than useful." In his reply Pauling showed no signs of distress, temper, or even a desire to continue the argument; he had little more to say than to reiterate his belief "that a psychiatrist who refuses to try the methods of orthomolecular psychiatry, in addition to the usual therapy, in the treatment of his patients is failing in his duty as a physician." *

Whatever the final verdict on Pauling's "orthomolecular psychiatry," his article provides still further evidence of the tendency of psychiatry, in the phrase of Roy R. Grinker, Sr., "to ride madly in all directions."[38] If there are those who are convinced that the cause and cure of schizophrenia will emerge from biochemical research, there are others equally persuaded that schizophrenia is mainly a disease of disturbed family and social relationships, the cure for which may be a radical revision of familial and social interaction patterns.[39] While many psychiatrists continue to favor supportive and directive psychotherapy for many varieties of mental illness, others are of the view that most forms of neurosis will yield readily to behavior conditioning and learning theory.[40] The psychoanalysts, unable to accept the view that in psychiatry, as elsewhere in medicine, the disease is successfully treated when the symptoms are effectively dealt with, remain agreed that the unconscious is of supreme importance in understanding neurotic behavior, although such agreement is fragmented by a plethora of "schools," concepts, and approaches. But no matter what the theory of cause and cure in mental illness, it is certain to have its advocates within the psychiatric world, and outside of that world each theory, no matter how questionable or bizarre, tends to become the center of a network of supportive practitioner, patient, journalist, and publisher. It needs only to be stated, with or without evidence, that such-and-such a technique has "cured" such-and-such an illness for there to be a veritable flood of books, magazine and newspaper articles, and television interviews attesting to the healing powers of Bongo-Bongo Therapy or Pengo-Pengo Analysis. Even more to the point, it is almost certain that some people *have* been helped by Bongo-Bongo therapists and Pengo-Pengo analysts, as they have been helped by

---

* *Science,* 160, April 19, 1968, and June 14, 1968. Neither Pauling's article nor Oken's letter discusses the possibility that early malnutrition as such may play a role in the origin of mental illness, possibly by depriving the brain of needed elements for its growth and development, or by making it vulnerable to certain types of physical and/or mental illness. In 1968–69 a number of studies reported that malnutrition during gestation and the first years of life may produce irrevocable physical and mental effects including brain damage, retardation, low intelligence quotients (IQ's), stunting, and impaired behavior and learning ability. Given these consequences of malnutrition early in life, it is not beyond question that some varieties of mental illness have their origins in undernourished brains, especially those deficient in protein and other vital substances, before and after birth.

psychiatrists and analysts influenced by Freud, Jung, Adler, Rank, Klein, Sullivan, Reich, Erikson, Wolpe, Skinner, Moreno, Rosen, May, Rogers, and a good many others. Classical psychoanalysis, behavioral conditioning, environmental manipulation, drug therapy, client-centered therapy, electroconvulsive shock, group therapy, hypnosis, psychodrama, lobotomy—all have their adherents who can testify to impressive results in their particular area of interest and expertise.

For a large and growing number of persons the therapeutic future lies in the direction of so-called sensitivity training programs and encounter groups which, collectively, embrace a variety of theories about behavior and techniques for dealing with neurotic problems. Most of these programs have originated in California, partly because climate is not unimportant in their functioning and perhaps partly because the California atmosphere of permissiveness and freedom from tradition is hardly less essential than moderate year-round weather conditions. But what began in California has begun to be copied in states where both climate and social atmosphere are much less hospitable, suggesting that the sensitivity training and encounter group approach fills a need that traditional forms of psychotherapy are unable to satisfy. While it is unlikely that the sensitivity programs will ever replace the couch, much less render obsolete the mental hospital, it is a fact that almost all who can enthusiastically testify to having been "turned on" at Big Sur or in Palm Springs are veterans of years in analysis or therapy. And among the enthusiasts are a small number of psychiatrists and analysts, not all of them attached to the various sensitivity-training institutes and centers, whose own experiences with sensitivity training have had positive results.

If one end of the sensitivity training spectrum is oriented toward "mind" and principles associated with Zen Buddhism and Alan Watts, the other is oriented toward "body," and especially sensual and sexual expression—not that these are clear-cut or mutually exclusive divisions. Thus one important component of the sensitivity programs is an emphasis on mysticism, meditation, Eastern philosophy, yoga, and, above all, the teachings of Zen; in recent years several Zen centers under the direction of a Zen Master (or Roshi) have been established in the United States, mainly in California. In several sensitivity programs the focus is wholly or mainly on group sex-related activities, sometimes referred to as "group grope," with nude participants urged to touch, feel, and embrace one another. One brochure promoting "Sensuality Courses" begins: "Are you making out more and enjoying it less? Are you making out less and enjoying it at all?" The list of questions concludes with the warning: "Observers and dilettantes, do not waste your time and ours," but the warning is followed by, in large print, "Let us put a bunny in your tank!" Between the extremes of Zen and "nudity therapy" there is an almost unlimited variety of sensitivity approaches, ranging from the T-group (short for training group) workshop extensively used in business circles to relieve tensions and generate ideas, to explorations and expositions of art, music, theater, and the dance.

Esalen Institute, the best-known and most copied sensitivity training center—between 1966 and 1968 twenty-five articles about Esalen were published in leading magazines and newspapers—includes in its program all of the sensitivity training approaches except the blatantly sexual. Founded in 1962 at Big Sur on the California coast, about 175 miles south of San Francisco, Esalen by 1969 had discovered that in sensitivity training, as in other fields, nothing succeeds like success. Its fall, 1968, brochure offered 120 programs, with attendance for the 1968–69 year expected to exceed 6,000 persons. It was anticipated that twice that number would attend Esalen programs in San Francisco, and there were also Esalen-sponsored activities under way at three California universities, several public schools, and a state mental hospital. At least 30 Esalen-type programs were operating in various parts of the country, and Esalen itself had developed a resident program under which 20 resident fellows spend nine months studying Esalen approaches and methods.[41] The book *Joy: Expanding Human Awareness,* by Esalen staff member William C. Schutz (Grove Press, 1967), was selling, as an Esalen newsletter proudly noted, "faster than *Games People Play,*" and another book, *Education and Ecstasy,* by George B. Leonard, an Esalen vice-president and West Coast editor for *Look* magazine, was also doing well at the bookstores. The Esalen site itself, busy with new construction of motel-type cabins and other facilities, provided further evidence that sensitivity training and encounter groups are likely to be a part of the therapeutic scene for a very long time.

While there is no one Esalen approach, it is possible to detect a "philosophy" underlying weekend seminars and workshops. In the Esalen view—although, of course, not only the Esalen view—the human condition as experienced by many Americans is an inability to enjoy life, especially in its physical and sensual aspects, and to communicate meaningfully with others. But the potential exists in almost everyone for creativity, awareness, empathy, love, and autonomy—in a word, for sensitivity. The techniques for developing this potential—and, again, there is no one technique—are designed to break down barriers to expression, feeling, and reaching out toward others, and to maximize the capacity for enjoyable sexual and nonsexual relationships. Insofar as Esalen can be identified with "philosophers" as well as with a "philosophy," the "philosophers" clearly include psychologists Carl Rogers, Abraham Maslow, and Rollo May, all identified with humanistic and existential psychology, especially its emphasis on growth and maturation. Frederick S. Perls, founder of Gestalt therapy, is psychiatrist-in-residence at Esalen, and he or one of the other "associates in residence" frequently conducts the twenty-four-hour marathon continuous group sessions which are designed to penetrate defenses and clear away obstacles to intimate communication. Joining Perls and his colleagues at Big Sur or San Francisco for varying periods of time are individuals as diverse as Professor S. I. Hayakawa, philosopher Abraham Kaplan and novelist Herbert Gold. Ravi Shankar has appeared at Big Sur on several occasions, and other Esalen participants have included psychiatrist J. L. Moreno, poet Allen Ginsberg, and Olympic track coach Payton Jordan.

Not least among the reasons for Esalen's success is that in its scenery and setting at Big Sur it combines some of the features of the therapeutic community with those of milieu therapy and the weekend resort. On the one hand, the sunsets over the Pacific Ocean, the cliffs, rocks, and coastal mountains, the sea lions and migrating schools of whales, the hot Japanese-style sulphur baths from which all this can be observed, the deep massages administered to nude recipients by trained masseurs and masseuses of the opposite sex. On the other hand, the candlelight dinners, the total absence of violence in the atmosphere whether in speech or action, the free-floating sensuality and demonstrativeness which all staff members seem to share, the tolerance of individual diversities mixed with genuine respect for certain communal rules of the game. It is easy to make friends at Esalen and to find sexual partners for a night, or weekend, or longer, but while some come there for that purpose, the majority of visitors are seekers and searchers rather than feelers and fornicators.

Yet there are questions about Esalen's place in the world and about Esalen itself. Many an Esalen weekender has experienced growth awareness and sensitivity Friday through Sunday only to find that his Monday-to-Friday world has little place in it for awareness and sensitivity. While many couples at Esalen discover new depths of feeling in themselves and their relationship, back home they may find themselves, once again, substituting depth of problems for depth of feeling. In other words, there is the possibility that Esalen offers merely temporary escape from professional and personal worlds where the Esalen values, if adopted, succeed only in making one even more vulnerable to ruthlessness and less able to cope than would otherwise be the case. As a sympathetic critic of Esalen once put it, "The world is not ready for sensitivity training. Unfortunately."

It is somewhat ironic, as well, that Esalen, hardly a member of the psychiatric establishment, charges establishment prices, which is to say that all but the well-to-do are excluded from participating in its programs. A weekend beginning with dinner Friday evening and ending with Sunday lunch will usually cost between $65.00 and $75.00 per person "shared occupancy"; when light attendance makes single accommodation possible, an additional $7.00 per night is charged. The five-day workshops, beginning with Sunday dinner and ending with Friday lunch, usually cost $165.00 to $175.00 per person, but professional and training workshops may charge as much as $225.00 per person. Travel to and from Big Sur, of course, is extra, as is massage, wine, and liquor. For a couple—and many of the encounter groups are designed for married and unmarried couples—the cost of a weekend can easily reach $200.00.

But establishment prices do not guarantee establishment recognition. In its seven-year history Esalen has been consistently shunned by ranking figures in the professional psychiatric and psychoanalytic associations, many of whom regard its programs with great skepticism. Some of them are inclined to use the term "quack" in referring to Esalen leading lights, while others, incorrectly, think of Esalen as part of the Big Sur drug scene characterized by generous use of marijuana and LSD, or as "the Playboy Club of the therapeutic world." For still others, Esalen is based on psychological theories that are untested, doubtful, and even dangerous. The twenty-four-hour marathon continuous group session, in particular, has been much criticized. According to S. R. Slavson, a founder of the American Group Psychotherapy Association, the marathon session is especially threatening to manifest, latent, and borderline "psychotics with tenuous ego controls and defenses [who] may, under the stress of such groups and the complete giving up of defense, jump the barrier between sanity and insanity." [42] Not all psychiatrists and analysts, however, view Esalen with alarm or distaste. In the words of one analyst who has spent many weekends observing people searching for happiness in the bars, boutiques, and love nests of nearby Carmel, "Esalen is better than Carmel."

In the sense intended, perhaps any type of psychiatry that promotes awareness, understanding, growth, and the capacity to love, is "better than Carmel," not to mention better than Las Vegas and Miami Beach. Perhaps, after all, most forms of psychotherapy and psychoanalysis succeed or fail to the extent that they compensate the patient for those affective deprivations and deficiencies of which, earlier in life, he was the unwilling victim. Even some "back ward" psychotics, it would appear, are not beyond reach of therapy or analysis, albeit in more extreme and dramatic forms than that given to neurotic patients, and there is also evidence that the recovery of mental hospital patients is to some extent aided or inhibited by the attitudes and expectations of ward attendants and other hospital personnel. If the hospital staff has abandoned hope for a patient's recovery or has a pessimistic view about the possibility of significant improvement, the patient's condition is apt to deteriorate. Optimism on the part of the staff, on the other hand, and good relations among staff members are likely to be reflected by a reduction of symptoms and better prospects for recovery.[43]

But whether the patient is in the hospital or is being treated privately by a psychiatrist or analyst, recovery for what? By now it is clear that however much psychiatrists and analysts try to avoid influencing their patients' values, in accordance with Freud's warning against their acting "as teacher, model and ideal to other people," few if any can avoid having some influence.* "Much as I try to avoid it," one analyst comments,

> often a patient will force me into certain judgmental positions. The degree with which this happens differs from patient to patient, but with some it happens all the time. I try to stay with the question of motivation, because I believe that when you point out the consequences of an action, you are in the situation of being judgmental. As long as you confine yourself to the motivation of the action, you are still on the side of doing analytic work. But, as I say, some patients force us to have a blueprint for their lives.

A psychiatrist who makes an effort not to take positions suggests that

> patients get to know you pretty well, and in surprising ways. I think of a woman patient I have been seeing pretty intensively who is really quite depressed. She's a very intelligent woman and it's remarkable what she has discovered not only about me but my wife as well, and she talks quite frankly about her jealousy, envy, and so forth. Just to give you an example: I change that painting over there about every three months, mainly to create a little interest, and it is kind of fun to see how patients react to the changes. I rent the painting, you know, and the last time I changed it, I didn't have time to go to the rental service, so I sent my wife. Well, her taste is different from mine, and she brought back a painting that I would not have chosen. Damn if this patient didn't spot it right away as my wife's choice. "You wouldn't have chosen it," she says, and she got quite angry about it. Of course, not all patients have this sense or intuition or whatever it is, but this one really amazes me with how much she knows about me.

For still another analyst there is no question about the role in analysis of his own values. In fact,

> one of the things that irks me no end is when analysts say that

* No matter what the temptation, Freud wrote in one of his last publications, the analyst should keep in mind that it is not his task "to make men in his own image . . . indeed that he will be disloyal to his task if he allows himself to be led on by his inclinations. He will only be repeating one of the mistakes of the parents, when they crushed their child's independence, and he will only be replacing one kind of dependence by another." Sigmund Freud, *An Outline of Psychoanalysis* (New York: Norton, 1963) (first published in German in 1940), 67.

> they have no value systems as related to their patients. Of course they do, and they also have a great deal of feeling for their patients—you can't possibly be in communication with another human being for all that time and not have any feelings. If you think of yourself as a screen, you're not going to get anywhere. But you certainly are always communicating values. When you say "yes," when you say "uh-huh," when you stay silent, you are expressing a value regarding what the patient said. He gets reinforcement immediately. Even the way you move your chair may tell him whether you like or don't like what he said. He'll bring you dreams he knows you're interested in analyzing because you pounced on a particular dream, and because you did, he'll bring you more like that.

Many patients, too, are aware of changes in values following extensive psychotherapy or analysis. For the most part, since the patients already share many values of their therapists as a consequence of similarities in class background, education, and political outlook, the major effect of therapy or analysis may be a change in attitudes toward oneself and others. As one analytic patient expresses it, after five years of analysis and psychoanalytically oriented therapy:

> I am now more open to experience of all kinds and less fearful. I have a much clearer idea of who I am and what my needs are. My goals are clearer, and I have less anxiety about pursuing them. I just feel more personal freedom.

A young woman who has had two years of psychotherapy reports that the experience is changing her relations with others, including sexual relations:

> My therapist affirmed my instinctive view about sex which I had not acted upon because it was so different from the mores of the "hip" group I wanted to be part of. The view was that sex, the physical act, being the ultimate union, should be reserved for those with whom I had an intimate love or loving relationship. Many young people, myself (before therapy) included, sleep with people as the only acceptable way to get close to them. When I looked at my behavior, I discovered that what I had been calling a "need" for sex was really a need for affection, for being close to someone, for a big hug. I was also able to admit to him some-

> thing I hadn't admitted even to myself before being in therapy, which was that with all the sleeping around I'd done, I'd never had an orgasm. Since I've been in therapy, I've had (and am still having) one really solid relationship, sexually and otherwise, in which I and my partner have been growing and digging each other really solidly, with very few resentments, and being able to tell each other what we're uptight about instead of holding it in and letting the hostilities grow. This technique I've learned through therapy, too.

But while most change through therapy or analysis is in the personality area, political attitudes may also be affected. The young woman just quoted found that her political radicalism had much to do with resentment of her parents ("sorry to sound so Freudian," she adds); however, the effect was not to change her views but to "unconfuse my motives for working toward political goals." For a male patient with four years of analysis there was no change in political attitudes, but the "analyst's influencing of my ethics helped to break down the 'double-standard' by which I was a harsh judge of other people (politicians and friends) while not applying equal standards in judgment of my own actions."

The experience of some patients, of course, falls short of what was expected and hoped for in terms of change, whether of values or behavior. An analysis of six years' duration is described by the person who experienced it as

> an opportunity to grow—to reevaluate thinking and feeling. It was a chance to be free of the neurotic baggage. However, I felt it was unsuccessful in terms of being able to bring about behavior change. Chewing over the reasons why, endlessly, expensively, doesn't help one to *be* different. I also got angry at the introverted, masturbatory nature of analysis, and the power of the analyst. One must have enormous respect for a person who is influencing your life so strongly. Few analysts are worthy of that power! Nevertheless, I do credit the analysis with a great deal of release of energy and some new fulfillment.

It is probable that the influence of therapy and analysis on values and "behavior change," even if disappointing in some cases, is not unimportant in a great many instances; the "release of energy and some new fulfillment," intended as a minimal statement of what was achieved through psychoanalysis, are hardly of no consequence. But if we can now say that therapy and analysis affect values and what some of these values are, it is far from evident what these values should be, particularly outside the disease area, given the challenges facing America and the world. Broadly speaking, Western culture has shifted its philosophical base from Descartes' "I think, therefore I am," to a question more in the spirit of Camus: I think, therefore am I? In keeping with that profound shift in consciousness has come the emphasis in psychology on man's quest for himself, a quest that so far has proved much more difficult than the probes into space and the ocean depths. Little wonder, then, as many psychiatrists and analysts report, that an increasing number of their patients are coming to them with existential questions rather than clinical problems. The Mrs. Robinsons and Alfies of the psychiatric patient world are less sick in the clinical sense than bored, confused, anxious, and, above all, tired.

To be sure, it is paradoxical in the extreme that at precisely the time more and more people turn to psychiatrists and analysts for wisdom in all sorts of areas, psychiatrists and analysts are less certain of their goals, methods, and achievements than at any time since the early days of Freud. Hardly less paradoxical is the sad truth that many a psychiatrist and analyst shares in the spiritual malaise, the growing uncertainty, the doubts and the despairs, that characterize our society. Of course, not all psychiatrists and analysts join in the "meditations" of an Allen Wheelis worried about "practice, reputation, Russians, cholesterol," or agree with R. D. Laing that " 'normal' man is profoundly alienated." On the whole, it is difficult to imagine the late William C. Menninger, happily busy with his stamp collection, his bird watching, and the Boy Scouts of Topeka, asking, as does Wheelis, "Is this the way to live? Is there a choice?"[44] A very large number of psychiatrists and some analysts are contented churchgoers, Rotarians, and active PTA members, and not all of them are employed in state hospitals. In psychiatry and psychoanalysis, as elsewhere, there are many moods, styles, and ways of relating to external as well as internal worlds, and many varieties of feeling about the problems of our time. These professions, too, also have their cynics and nihilists, their reformers and radicals, and those who are not uncomfortable in the world of the Jet Set and Beautiful People. There are even a few psychiatrists and analysts who are self-styled hippies, complete with beads, bells, sandals, long hair, and the single earring.

Perhaps in psychiatry and psychoanalysis, too, there is a developing "generation gap" marked by differing interests and orientations. Younger practitioners seem to be more interested than older colleagues in scientific research and methodological problems, and they may differ in other ways as well. As already mentioned, some analysts in the study group appear to feel somewhat ill at ease about their incomes and affluent living standards. Those who are most troubled by a social conscience perhaps were adolescents or young adults during the Depression, and became involved, through their relatives or friends, in radical politics. It is possible that the rise of Nazi Germany disposed Jewish analysts, in particular, to the political left and a lasting sensitivity to social problems. Analytic training as such, in the earlier period, may have added to awareness of suffering, want, and discrimination. Whatever the explanation, younger analysts give an impression of being bothered less by their material advantages, although there is no reason to think that their political views are less liberal than those of the older group.

But in truth there is no such person as *the* psychiatrist or *the* analyst, whether young or old. For every therapist or analyst who himself needs a therapist or analyst, there are a hundred of the "solid citizen" variety attempting to meet their responsibilities to their patients, their own families, and the larger society. If many of them do not know how they personally should relate to the problems of war, race, and poverty, who does have this knowledge, whatever his profession? If, like other thoughtful Americans, many of them are caught between the desire to do good and the desire to do well, who in the rest of the population is not also caught in this dilemma? If, like the members of other professions, they are not certain how much they do is art and how much science, how much will continue to be the result of hunch and intuition, and how much the product of new technologies, who *is* certain? Indeed, is there any guarantee that the psyche of twenty-first-century man will resemble that of nineteenth-twentieth-century man, upon which, in the form of one interpretation or another, the whole of psychoanalysis and most of psychiatry is based?

To ask these questions is to risk laboring the obvious. And yet, just as analysts find it difficult to agree with Whitehead that "a science which hesitates to forget its founders is lost," so the larger number of patients in therapy and analysis and the wider circles of the public find it difficult to agree with Freud that psychoanalysis is no more capable than psychiatry, religion, education, and science of serving as a cure-all or panacea for the ills of mankind. At least twice in his life Freud observed that there were three "impossible" professions: educating, healing, and governing. In the end he was not even able to believe that man would succeed in controlling "the human instinct of aggression and self-destruction." [45] It remains to be seen whether, by the year 2000, either Whitehead or Freud has been proven wrong.

Appendix I

Index of Names in Psychiatry and Psychoanalysis

Who's who in psychiatry and psychoanalysis with special reference to persons mentioned in this book. Identifications do not include those who once were colleagues of Freud or who are the subjects of biographical treatment, such as Abraham, Adler, Binswanger, Breuer, Brill, Federn, Ferenczi, Horney, Jones, Jung, Adolf Meyer, Rank, Reich, Sachs, Stekel, and Sullivan. For brief studies of these figures, see Franz Alexander, Samuel Eisenstein, and Martin Grotjahn, *Psychoanalytic Pioneers* (New York: Basic Books, 1966).

The late **Franz Alexander,** author of many books and articles, served as president of the American Psychoanalytic Association 1938–39 and was a founder of the American Academy of Psychoanalysis. Interested in psychosomatic medicine, new treatment approaches, and psychiatric aspects of crime and politics, he also was coauthor (with the late Sheldon Selesnick) of *The History of Psychiatry* (1966).

Silvano Arieti. Born Pisa, Italy, 1914. Professor of clinical psychiatry at New York Medical College and faculty member of the William Alanson White Institute of Psychiatry, Arieti has published papers on schizophrenia, among other topics. He is best known for his editorship of the *American Handbook of Psychiatry* (3 vols., 1959–66).

Walter E. Barton. Born Oak Park, Illinois, 1906. Past president and currently medical director of the American Psychiatric Association, Barton received his psychiatric training in Oak Park, Worcester, and London hospitals. His principal interest has been in professional and administrative areas of psychiatry, to which topics he has devoted a number of publications.

Lauretta Bender. Born Butte, Montana, 1897. Bender, a clinical professor of psychiatry at Columbia College of Physicians and Surgeons, has specialized in child psychiatry. She has long been a senior staff member at Creedmoor State Hospital, Queens Village, New York.

Eric Berne. Born Montreal, 1910. One of the few psychiatrists to have published a best-selling book (*Games People Play,* 1964), Berne has written on transactional psychotherapy and other topics. He makes his home in Carmel, California.

John Bowlby. Born London, 1907. A Cambridge graduate, Bowlby is a major figure in British psychoanalytic circles. Associated with the Tavistock Clinic since 1946, Bowlby is best known for his writings on infancy and early childhood, especially the impact on the child of the separation from parents and death of parents.

Francis J. Braceland. Born Philadelphia, 1900. In addition to writing numerous articles, Braceland has taught psychiatry at several universities. He was chief of psychiatry at the Institute of Living in Hartford, Connecticut, 1951–65, and president of the American Psychiatric Association in 1957. In recent years he has been editor of the *American Journal of Psychiatry.*

Charles Brenner. Born Boston, 1913. A Harvard graduate, Brenner received his analytic training at the Boston and New York Psychoanalytic Institutes. A past president of the American Psychoanalytic Association, he has written on a large number of subjects including repression, masochism, and the psychoanalysis of children. His *An Elementary Textbook of Psychoanalysis* (1955) is widely used for instructional purposes.

Henry W. Brosin. Born Blackwood, Virginia, 1904. A University of Wisconsin graduate, Brosin received his analytic training at the Chicago Institute for Psychoanalysis. Past president of the American Psychiatric Association, Brosin has been a fellow of the Center for Advanced Study in the Behavioral Sciences and active in the Group for the Advancement of Psychiatry. He practices in Pittsburgh.

Gerald Caplan. Born Liverpool, 1917. Educated and trained in England, Caplan practiced in Israel before coming to the United States in 1952. He has written widely on aspects of child psychiatry and psychoanalysis and has been active in the community mental health movement.

Helene Deutsch. Born Przemysl, Poland, 1884. Deutsch is a supervisory and training analyst in the Boston Psychoanalytic Society and Institute, of which she was president from 1939 to 1941. She is the author of *The Psychology of Women* (two volumes, 1944), regarded as the definitive work on the subject by a Freudian analyst.

Erik H. Erikson. Born Frankfurt-am-Main, 1902. Erikson, who came to the United States in 1933, has written extensively on the identity crisis and problems of growth and maturation. His two most acclaimed books are *Childhood and Society* (1950) and *Young Man Luther* (1958).

H. J. Eysenck. Born Berlin, 1916. Eysenck, a British psychologist, is a foremost critic of psychoanalytic and psychiatric theory. In a number of books he has argued that psychotherapy is no more effective in treating mental illness than other approaches, although it is a great deal more expensive and time-consuming.

Jerome D. Frank. Born New York, 1909. Frank, professor of psychiatry at Johns Hopkins and a consulting member of the Henry Phipps Psychiatric Clinic in Baltimore, has written on group therapy and comparative aspects of psychotherapy. Many of his articles and one book, *Sanity and Survival* (1967), concern the threat of nuclear war and relationships between mental health and public policy.

Viktor Frankl. Born Vienna, 1905. Frankl is professor of psychiatry and neurology at the University of Vienna. On the basis of his experiences at Auschwitz and other concentration camps, Frankl originated "logotherapy," which focuses on man's wholeness and his search for meaning and self-realization.

Anna Freud. Born Vienna, 1895. Freud's only surviving daughter and the only one of his children to become a psychoanalyst, Miss Freud has lived in London since 1938, where she has specialized in the psychoanalysis of children. She is director of the Hampstead Child Therapy Clinic. Her best-known book is *The Ego and the Mechanisms of Defense* (1937). She has been editor of the annual *The Psychoanalytic Study of the Child.*

Erich Fromm. Born Frankfurt, Germany, 1900. Regarded as one of the major revisionists in psychoanalysis, Fromm is widely known to the general public as well as to the psychoanalytic world. He has published many books on such social and political topics as authoritarianism, religion, ethics, and philosophy. Perhaps his best-known book is *Escape from Freedom* (1941). In recent years he has made his home in Mexico.

The late **Frieda Fromm-Reichmann** believed that schizophrenia could be treated through psychotherapy. For many years she was a senior staff member of Chestnut Lodge Sanitarium in Rockville, Maryland.

Edward Glover. Born Lanarkshire, Scotland, 1888. A British psychoanalyst practicing in London, Glover has been critical of training methods in psychoanalysis and other aspects of professional life. As a result, in 1944 he resigned from the British Psycho-Analytical Society. He has written on a variety of subjects, including *Freud or Jung?* (1960), and has contributed to *The Psychoanalytic Study of the Child.*

Phyllis Greenacre. Born Chicago, 1894. A faculty member of the New York Psychoanalytic Institute since 1942, Greenacre has written on the relationship between neurosis and creativity, and many other topics.

Roy R. Grinker, Sr. Born Chicago, 1900. Grinker, who has spent almost his entire career in Chicago, is a foremost exponent of the view that psychoanalysis must accommodate itself to the methodologies and findings of the behavioral sciences, especially field theory and general system theory. He has served as president of the American Academy of Psychoanalysis and, since 1950, has been editor of the *Archives of General Psychiatry.*

Martin Grotjahn. Born Berlin, 1904. Grotjahn, who emigrated to the United States in 1936, lives and practices psychoanalysis in Beverly Hills. One of the founders of the Southern California Psychoanalytic Society, Grotjahn has written numerous articles and several books.

The late **Manfred S. Guttmacher** was a leading figure in forensic or "courtroom" psychiatry.

Heinz Hartmann. Born Vienna, 1894. Hartmann, who left Vienna in 1938 for Paris, Geneva, Lausanne, and finally New York, is the foremost exponent of ego psychology. His numerous books include *Ego Psychology and the Problem of Adaptation* (1958) and *Essays on Ego Psychology: Selected Problems in Psychoanalytic Theory* (1964), a collection of his papers.

Robert G. Heath. Born Pittsburgh, 1915. On the medical faculty of Tulane University, Heath's principal research interests are in the area of biochemistry and neurophysiology, with particular reference to schizophrenia. In 1957 he reported discovery of a protein peculiar to the blood of schizophrenics, which he called taraxein.

The late **Don D. Jackson** was an authority on schizophrenia and the founder of the Mental Research Institute in Palo Alto, California.

Edith Jacobson. Born Haynau, Germany, 1897. A training analyst at the New York Psychoanalytic Institute since 1942, Jacobson has written many articles on psychoanalytic concepts. She has served on the editorial board of *The Psychoanalytic Study of the Child.*

Maxwell Jones. Born Queenstown, South Africa, 1907. Jones, superintendent of Dingleton Hospital in Melrose, Scotland, is an authority on social psychiatry and its implications for the mental hospital and society at large. His best-known book, which has had widespread influence on hospital treatment of the mentally ill, is *The Therapeutic Community* (1953).

The late **Melanie Klein,** who believed that children of a tender age could be psychoanalyzed, held that some psychoses in adult life, such as paranoia, had their roots in certain conditions that were manifested in infancy.

Nathan Kline. Born Philadelphia, 1916. Director of the Research Center of Rockland Hospital in New York, Kline is a leading figure in psychopharmacology research and, more recently, the application of computers. He has been associated with studies of lithium carbonate use in the treatment of manic-depression.

Lawrence Kolb. Born Baltimore, 1916. Coauthor of one of the most widely used textbooks in psychiatry, Kolb was educated at Johns Hopkins and received his analytic training at the Washington Psychoanalytic Institute. He was president of the American Psychiatric Association 1968–69.

The late **Ernst Kris,** one of the few lay analysts to be admitted to membership in the American Psychoanalytic Association, was a collaborator with Hartmann and Loewenstein in the development of ego psychology. He also wrote numerous papers on the role of the unconscious in creativity with special reference to art.

Lawrence Kubie. Born New York, 1896. Author of several books and articles, Kubie has been associated with the College of Physicians and Surgeons of Columbia University, Mount Sinai Hospital in New York, and, most recently, with the University of Maryland Medical School and Johns Hopkins University. For a number of years he was director of training at Sheppard and Enoch Pratt Hospital in Maryland. He has written on creativity and other topics.

Maurice Levine. Born Cincinnati, 1902. Except for brief periods in Baltimore and Chicago, Levine, an analyst since 1938, has spent his professional life in Cincinnati. He has written numerous articles on aspects of psychoanalysis and psychosomatic medicine.

Bertram D. Lewin. Born Victoria, Texas, 1896. Lewin, who received his psychoanalytic training in Berlin, has practiced in New York and Pittsburgh. He has written extensively on dreams and, with Helen Ross, is coauthor of *Psychoanalytic Education in the United States* (1960).

Rudolph Loewenstein. Born Lodz, Poland, 1898. Since his arrival in the United States in 1942, Loewenstein has been active in Jewish affairs as well as psychoanalytic organizations. He has been president of both the American Psychoanalytic Association and the International Psycho-Analytic Association. He has collaborated with Hartmann and the late Ernst Kris in studies of ego psychology.

Judd Marmor. Born London, 1910. A founder and past president of the American Academy of Psychoanalysis, Marmor, following Alexander's death in 1964, succeeded him as director of psychiatry at Cedars of Lebanon-Mount Sinai Hospital in Los Angeles. He is also a clinical professor of psychiatry at the University of California in Los Angeles. In addition to having published numerous articles on many subjects, including aspects of social psychiatry, Marmor edited *Modern Psychoanalysis* (1968).

Jules Masserman. Born Chudnov, Poland, 1905. Masserman arrived in the United States in 1908 when he was three years of age. He is the author of several textbooks and more than 300 articles. In addition to having served as president of the American Academy of Psychoanalysis and two other professional organizations, Masserman has taught psychiatry at both the University of Chicago and Northwestern University.

Rollo May. Born Ada, Ohio, 1909. A training and supervisory analyst at the William Alanson White Institute in New York, May has written at length on existential psychiatry and psychoanalysis.

Karl Menninger. Born Topeka, Kansas, 1893. Brother of the late William C. Menninger, Karl Menninger has been active in psychiatric and psychoanalytic professional enterprises. He is a prolific writer, whose numerous books include *Man Against Himself* (1938), *Love Against Hate* (1942), and *A Psychiatrist's World: The Selected Papers of Karl Menninger, M.D.* (1959).

The late **William C. Menninger,** in addition to his extensive publishing and professional activities, served formally and informally as liaison between organized psychiatry and the federal government. He had much to do with the government's recognition of, and financial provision for, psychiatry following World War II.

J. L. Moreno. Born Bucharest, 1892. Moreno is an advocate of sociometry and psychodrama as means of studying the disturbed behavior of individuals and groups. He maintains a training center and sanitarium in Beacon, New York.

Sandor Rado. Born Hungary, 1890. A practicing analyst in New York, Rado has been associated with the Columbia University Psychoanalytic Clinic for Training and Research and with the New York School of Psychiatry. He has written on psychoanalytic aspects of medicine and other subjects.

Leo Rangell. Born New York, 1913. A graduate of the University of Chicago, Rangell has been associated with the Los Angeles Psychoanalytic Institute since 1946. He has twice been president of the American Psychoanalytic Association and is active in organization affairs. His writings deal with anxiety, symptom conversion, the present and future of psychoanalysis, and related professional topics. In 1969 he was elected president of the International Psycho-Analytical Association.

Frederick C. Redlich. Born Vienna, 1910. Redlich, who left Vienna in 1938, has served as president of the Western New England Institute of Psychoanalysis and as clinical professor of psychiatry at Yale. Currently dean of the Yale Medical School, his best-known book (with A. B. Hollingshead) is *Social Class and Mental Health* (1958).

Carl R. Rogers. Born Oak Park, Illinois, 1902. A psychologist by training, Rogers is associated with "client-centered therapy," based on the belief that the psychotherapist should involve himself with the patient and his problems rather than remain indifferent or aloof. He is a resident fellow of the Western Behavioral Sciences Institute.

John Rosen. Born Brooklyn, 1902. Rosen, in his book *Direct Analysis* (1953), argues the possibility of psychoanalytic therapy for schizophrenics, not excluding those in the advanced stages of acute catatonic excitement. He practices in Philadelphia.

Joseph Sandler. Born Cape Town, South Africa, 1927. Sandler, scientific secretary of the British Psycho-Analytical Society, has published many articles on methodological problems and testing methods in psychoanalysis, including self-assessment.

Harold F. Searles. Born Hancock, New York, 1918. A training analyst in the Washington Psychoanalytic Institute, Searles has published numerous articles on schizophrenia.

Elvin V. Semrad. Born Abie, Nebraska, 1910. Since 1935 Semrad, a psychoanalyst, has lived and practiced in the Boston area, where he has been associated with the Massachusetts General Hospital and Harvard University. He has written widely on the psychotherapy of psychoses.

René Spitz. Born Vienna, 1887. Spitz has taught and practiced psychoanalysis in Budapest, Paris, New York, Geneva, and Colorado, where he is visiting professor emeritus of psychiatry in the University of Colorado Medical Center. He has worked extensively with children and is on the editorial board of *The Psychoanalytic Study of the Child.*

Leo Stone. Born Brooklyn, 1904. A faculty member of the New York Psychoanalytic Institute, Stone has also taught at Cornell and Columbia. He has written on clinical problems in psychiatry and psychoanalysis, aspects of brief psychotherapy, and other topics.

Thomas S. Szasz. Born Budapest, 1920. Professor of Psychiatry at Upstate Medical Center of the State University of New York in Syracuse, Szasz received his analytic training at the Chicago Institute for Psychoanalysis. In a number of books and articles, Szasz has suggested that mental illness is largely a "myth" invented by psychiatrists themselves to conceal their own ethical and ideological preferences. He also has been critical of the role of psychiatrists in court proceedings.

S. A. Szurek. Born Chicago, 1907. A faculty member of the San Francisco Psychoanalytic Institute, Szurek has published widely in the area of childhood schizophrenia.

The late **Robert Waelder** wrote extensively on theoretical constructs in psychoanalysis.

Robert S. Wallerstein. Born Berlin, 1921. Wallerstein received his psychiatric training at Mount Sinai Hospital in New York and his analytic training at the Topeka Psychoanalytic Institute. He is currently resident in San Francisco, and his publications deal with psychoanalytic education, treatment problems, and child analysis.

John C. Whitehorn. Born Spencer, Nebraska, 1894. Educated at Harvard, Whitehorn taught at Johns Hopkins from 1940 until his retirement in 1960. His articles deal with a variety of topics including psychiatric education and training, alienation and leadership, and clinical problems.

D. W. Winnicott. Born Plymouth, England, 1896. A past president of the British Psycho-Analytical Society, Winnicott, who practices in London, has published numerous articles on aspects of child analysis, the role of transference in psychoanalysis, and disturbances in object relationships.

Joseph Wolpe. Born Johannesburg, South Africa, 1915. Wolpe is the leading advocate of behavior therapy as a method of treating neurosis. He is attached to the Temple University School of Medicine.

Appendix II

Glossary of Psychiatric Terms

The following definitions of terms frequently used in psychiatry and psychoanalysis are taken from *A Psychiatric Glossary* (3d ed., 1969), published by the American Psychiatric Association's Committee on Public Information. I am greatly indebted to the American Psychiatric Association for permission to reprint these terms. Somewhat more extended definitions of terms used in psychoanalysis appear in *A Glossary of Psychoanalytic Terms and Concepts,* a publication of the American Psychoanalytic Association (1967). See also Leland E. Hinsie and Robert Jean Campbell, *Psychiatric Dictionary* (New York: Oxford University Press, 3d ed., 1960).

A

acting out: Expression of unconscious emotional conflicts or feelings of hostility or love in actions that the individual does not consciously know are related to such conflicts or feelings. May be harmful or, in controlled situations, therapeutic (*e.g.,* in children's play therapy).

affect: A person's emotional feeling tone. "Affect" and "emotion" are commonly used interchangeably.

affective disorder: Any mental disorder in which a disturbance of affect is predominant. This is a broad concept that includes depressive neurosis (see under *neurosis*), the major affective disorders, and psychotic depressive reaction.

aggression: In psychiatry, a forceful, physical, verbal, or symbolic attack. May be appropriate and self-protective, including healthful self-assertiveness, or inappropriate. Also may be directed outward toward the environment, as in explosive personality, or inward toward the self, as in depression.

alcoholism: Addiction to or psychological dependence on the use of alcohol to the point that it is damaging to one's physical or emotional health, interpersonal relations, or economic functioning. The inability of a person to do without drinking or to limit his drinking once he starts is presumptive evidence of alcohol addiction.

alienation: In psychiatry, the term is used variously. For example: In depersonalization phenomena, feelings of unreality or strangeness produce a sense of alienation from one's self or environment. In obsessional states (see *obsession*) where there is fear of one's emotions, avoidance of situations that arouse emotions, and continuing effort to keep feelings out of awareness, there is alienation of affect. More broadly, the term is used to denote the state of estrangement the individual feels in cultural settings that he views as foreign, unpredictable, or unacceptable.

ambivalence: The coexistence of two opposing drives, desires, feelings, or emotions toward the same person, object, or goal. These may be conscious or partly conscious; or one side of the feelings may be unconscious. Example: love and hate toward the same person.

ambulatory schizophrenia: An unofficial term for a person with schizophrenia who functions sufficiently well that he generally does not require hospitalization. If in a hospital, he is kept on open wards or he may be allowed the complete freedom of the community.

American Board of Psychiatry and Neurology (ABPN): A medical body of 12 members, four each appointed by the American Psychiatric Association, the American Neurological Association, and the American Medical Association, which examines and certifies candidates as specialists or diplomates in psychiatry, child psychiatry, neurology, and neurology with special competence in child neurology. ABPN was established in 1934.

American Psychiatric Association: The leading national professional organization in the United States for physicians who specialize in psychiatry. It also includes members from Canada, Central America, and the Caribbean Islands, and corresponding members from other countries. Founded in 1844 as the Association of Medical Superintendents of American Institutions for the Insane, the association changed its name to the American Medico-Psychological Association in 1891, and to its present name in 1921. In 1969 it had nearly 17,000 members.

amphetamines: A group of chemicals that stimulate the cerebral cortex of the brain. Often misused by adults and adolescents to control normal fatigue and to induce euphoria. Used clinically to treat hyperkinesis in some children and to control minor depressions and overeating in adults. Highly addicting.

anal character: A personality type that manifests excessive orderliness, miserliness, and obstinacy. In psychoanalysis, a pattern of behavior in an adult that is believed to originate in the anal stage of infancy. See *psychosexual development.*

anal erotism: The pleasurable part of the experience of anal function. Anal erotism appears in disguised and sublimated forms in later life. See also *psychosexual development* and *anal character.*

analysand: A patient in psychoanalytic treatment.

analysis: a common synonym for *psychoanalysis* (q.v.).

analytic psychology: The name given by Swiss psychoanalyst Carl Gustav Jung (1875–1961) to his theoretical system, which minimizes the influence of sexual factors in emotional disorders and stresses mystical religious influences.

anima: In Jungian psychology, the inner being of an individual as opposed to the outer character or *persona* that he presents to the world. Further, the anima may be the more feminine "soul" or inner self of a man; the *animus* the more masculine soul of a woman.

antidepressant: Drugs used in treating depressions.

anxiety: Apprehension, tension, or uneasiness that stems from the anticipation of danger, the source of which is largely unknown or unrecognized. Primarily of intrapsychic origin, in distinction to fear, which is the emotional response to a consciously recognized and usually external threat or danger. Anxiety and fear are accompanied by similar physiologic changes. May be regarded as pathologic when present to such extent as to interfere with effectiveness in living, achievement of desired goals or satisfactions, or reasonable emotional comfort. See also *panic.*

autism (autistic thinking): A form of thinking marked by extreme self-absorption and egocentricity, in which objective facts are obscured, distorted, or excluded in varying degrees.

autistic child: In child psychiatry, a child who responds chiefly to inner thoughts, who does not relate to his environment; his overall functioning is immature and he often appears retarded. It may be an extension of early infantile autism, a manifestation of brain damage, or a sign of childhood schizophrenia. See under *schizophrenia.*

early infantile autism (Kanner's syndrome): A syndrome beginning in infancy and characterized by self-absorption, inaccessibility, and inability to relate.

autoeroticism: Sensual self-gratification. Characteristic of, but not limited to, an early stage of emotional development. Includes satisfactions derived from genital play, masturbation, fantasy, and from oral, anal, and visual sources.

automatism: Automatic and apparently undirected behavior that is not consciously controlled.

autonomic nervous system: The part of the nervous system that innervates the cardiovascular, digestive, reproductive, and respiratory organs. It operates outside of consciousness and controls basic life-sustaining functions such as the heart rate, digestion, and breathing. It includes the sympathetic nervous system and the parasympathetic nervous system.

aversive therapy (conditioning): A treatment that suppresses undesirable behavior by associating a painful or unpleasant reaction with the behavior. Some examples are: the use of emetics or Antabuse with alcoholics, or the administration of an electric shock following the occurrence of some undesired behavior or symptom. Aversive therapy or conditioning is thought by some (but disputed by others) to be effective in the treatment of such disorders as enuresis, writer's cramp, homosexuality, fetishism, transvestitism, and alcoholism.

B

battered child syndrome: Physical injury to a child resulting from excessive beating, usually by a parent or parents and usually performed repeatedly over an extended period of time. The presence of mental illness in the parents may be presumed.

behavior disorders of childhood: a group of disorders occurring in childhood and adolescence that are less severe than psychoses but more resistant to treatment than transient situational disturbances because they are more stabilized and internalized. They are characterized by overactivity, inattentiveness, shyness, feelings of rejection, overaggressiveness, timidity, and delinquency. The child who runs away from home or who persistently lies, steals, and teases other children in a hostile fashion falls into this category.

behavior therapy: Any treatment approach designed to modify the patient's behavior directly rather than inquiring into the dynamic causation. Typically, the psychopathology is conceptualized as maladaptive behavior. The treatment techniques are adapted from laboratory investigations of learning and may use principles of classical, instrumental, and traumatic avoidance conditioning, reciprocal inhibition and desensitization, simple extinction, etc.

behavioral science(s): While, strictly speaking, physiology, neurology, endocrinology, and other biologically based sciences may be called behavioral sciences, the term is generally reserved for those sciences focused on the study of man's interpersonal relationships, values, experiences, activities, and institutions, such as psychiatry, psychology, cultural anthropology, sociology, and political science.

behaviorism: A body of psychologic theory developed by John B. Watson (1878–1958), concerned chiefly with objectively observable, tangible, and measurable data, rather than with subjective phenomena such as ideas and emotions.

birth trauma: Term used by Otto Rank (1884–1939) to relate his theories of anxiety and neurosis to the inevitable psychic shock of being born.

bisexuality: Presence of the qualities of both sexes in the same individual. In psychoanalytic theory considered to be a universal trait, so that each individual has both masculine and feminine traits and homosexual and heterosexual tendencies, latent if not overt.

blocking: A sudden obstruction and interruption in the train of thought or speech, typically in the midst of a sentence, due to unconscious factors. Although normal persons may occasionally experience blocking, it is commonly seen in a variety of mental disorders and most often in schizophrenia.

borderline state (borderline psychosis): An unofficial diagnostic term for a condition in which a person's symptoms are difficult to classify as either psychotic or nonpsychotic. The symptoms may shift quickly from one pattern to another, and often include acting out and behavior suggesting schizophrenia.

C

castration: In psychiatry, usually the fantasied loss of the penis. Also used figuratively to denote state of impotence, powerlessness, helplessness, or defeat. See also *castration complex* under *complex*.

castration anxiety: Anxiety due to fantasied danger or injuries to the genitals. May be precipitated by everyday events which have symbolic significance and appear to be threatening, such as loss of job, loss of a tooth, or an experience of ridicule or humiliation. See also *castration complex* under *complex*.

catatonic state (catatonia): A state characterized by immobility with muscular rigidity or inflexibility and at times by excitability. Often a symptom of schizophrenia.

catchment area: In psychiatry, a term borrowed from the English to delineate geographic area for which a mental health facility has responsibility. See also *community psychiatry*.

catharsis: (1) The healthful (therapeutic) release of ideas through a "talking out" of conscious material accompanied by the appropriate emotional reaction. (2) The release into awareness of repressed (*i.e.*, "forgotten") material from the unconscious.

cathexis: Attachment, conscious or unconscious, of emotional feeling and significance to an idea or object, most commonly a person.

cerebral arteriosclerosis: Hardening of the arteries of the brain resulting in an organic brain syndrome that may be either primarily neurologic in nature (*e.g.*, convulsions, aphasia, chorea, athetosis, parkinsonism, etc.), or primarily mental (*e.g.*, intellectual dulling, memory defects, emotional lability, paranoid delusions, confusion, and finally profound dementia), or a combination of both. Cerebral arteriosclerosis typically manifests itself in people older than fifty and at the present time accounts for approximately one-fifth of all first admissions to mental hospitals.

character: In psychiatry, the sum of the relatively fixed personality traits and habitual modes of response of an individual.

character analysis: Psychoanalytic treatment aimed at the character defenses.

character defense: In psychiatry, any character or personality trait which serves an unconscious defensive purpose. See also *defense mechanism*.

character disorder: A personality disorder manifested by a chronic and habitual pattern of reaction that is maladaptive in that it is relatively inflexible, limits the optimal use of potentialities, and often provokes the very counterreactions from the environment that the subject seeks to avoid. In contrast to symptoms of neurosis, character traits are typically egosyntonic. See also *personality*.

character neurosis: Similar to character disorder except that the neurotic conflicts are expressed in exaggerated but socially acceptable patterns of behavior and may not be easily recognizable as symptoms.

child analysis: Application of modified psychoanalytic methods and goals to problems of children to remove impediments to normal personality development.

cognitive: refers to the mental process of comprehension, judgment, memory, and reasoning, as opposed to emotional and volitional processes.

collective unconscious: In Jungian theory, a portion of the unconscious common to all mankind; also called "racial unconscious." See *unconscious.*

combat fatigue: Term for disabling physical and emotional reaction incident to military combat. Paradoxically, the reaction may not neccessarily include fatigue.

commitment: In psychiatry, a legal process for admitting a mentally ill person to a mental hospital, usually without his consent. The legal definition and procedure vary from state to state. Typically requires a court or judicial procedure, although not in all states, and sometimes the commitment may be entirely voluntary. A "voluntary" commitment, however, is to be distinguished from a "voluntary admission" in that in the former case the hospital has the right to detain the patient for a legally defined period of time after he has given notice that he wishes to leave.

community mental health center: In general, a community or neighborhood-based facility, or a network of component facilities, for the prevention and treatment of mental illness, ideally with emphasis on a comprehensive range of services and with convenient accessibility to the population it serves. Since 1964, regulations governing federal support for community centers have required that a center offer at least five services, namely, inpatient, outpatient, partial hospitalization, emergency services, and consultation and education for community agencies. It is also considered desirable that a center should provide diagnostic, rehabilitative, precare and aftercare services, training, research, and public education.

community psychiatry: That branch of psychiatry concerned with the provision and delivery of a coordinated program of mental health care to a specified population (usually all residents of a designated geographical area termed the *catchment area*). Implicit in the concept of community psychiatry is acceptance of continuing responsibility for all the mental health needs of the community—diagnosis, treatment, rehabilitation (tertiary prevention) and aftercare, and, equally important, early case-finding (secondary prevention), and promoting mental health and preventing psychosocial disorder (primary prevention). The organizational nucleus for such services is typically the community mental health center. The body of knowledge and theory on which the methods and techniques of community psychiatry are based is often called *social psychiatry*. See also *preventive psychiatry*.

compensation: (1) A defense mechanism, operating unconsciously, by which the individual attempts to make up for (*i.e.,* to compensate for) real or fancied deficiencies. (2) A conscious process in which the individual strives to make up for real or imagined defects of physique, performance, skills, or psychological attributes. The two types frequently merge.

compensation neurosis: An unofficial term for certain unconscious neurotic reactions in which features of secondary gain, such as a situational or financial advantage, are prominent. To be distinguished from malingering, in which there is conscious concealment or an ulterior motive to defraud. See also *hysterical neurosis, conversion type,* under *neurosis.*

complex: A group of associated ideas that have a common strong emotional tone. These are largely unconscious and significantly influence attitudes and associations. Three examples are:

> **castration complex:** A group of emotionally charged ideas that are unconscious and which refer to the fear of losing the genital organs, usually as punishment for forbidden sexual desires; includes the childhood fantasy that female genitals result from loss of a penis.
>
> **inferiority complex:** (Adler) Feelings of inferiority stemming from real or imagined physical or social inadequacies that may cause anxiety or other adverse reactions. The individual may overcompensate by excessive ambition or by the development of special skills, often in the very field in which he was originally handicapped.
>
> **Oedipus complex:** (Freud) Attachment of the child for the parent of the opposite sex, accompanied by envious and aggressive feelings toward the parent of the same sex. These feeling are largely repressed (*i.e.,* made unconscious) because of the fear of displeasure or punishment by the parent of the same sex. In its original use, the term applied only to the male.

compulsion: An insistent, repetitive, intrusive, and unwanted urge to perform an act that is contrary to the person's ordinary wishes or standards. Since it serves as a defensive substitute for still more unacceptable unconscious ideas and wishes, failure to perform the compulsive act leads to overt anxiety. Compulsions are *obsessions* that are still felt as impulses.

compulsive personality: A personality characterized by excessive adherence to rigid standards. Typically, the individual is inflexible, overconscientious, overinhibited, unable to relax, and exhibits repetitive patterns of behavior. See *obsessive compulsive personality* under *personality disorder.*

conditioning: Any process by which an individual learns—either consciously or unconsciously—to modify his behavior in the presence of a particular stimulus. Conditioning is employed clinically in behavior therapy.

classical (Pavlovian) conditioning: A conditioning process by which an individual learns to make a response mediated primarily by the autonomic nervous system (*e.g.*, salivation or pupillary constriction) in the presence of a stimulus that normally does not elicit that response (*i.e.*, a "neutral conditioned stimulus"). This is done by repeatedly exposing the individual to the neutral conditioned stimulus (*e.g.*, the sound of a bell) at the same time or soon before he is exposed to the "unconditioned stimulus" (*e.g.*, food or a bright light) that normally elicits that response in an untrained individual. When it occurs regularly in the presence of the neutral conditioned stimulus, the response is called a "conditioned reflex."

instrumental (operant) conditioning: A conditioning process by which an individual learns to make (or to avoid making) specific responses in the presence of a once-neutral stimulus. Conditioning is achieved by repeatedly presenting the individual with a rewarding (or punishing) stimulus after he has performed (or avoided performing) the particular response. The once-neutral stimulus is called a "conditioned" stimulus; and the rewarding (or punishing) stimulus is called a "reinforcing" or "unconditioned" stimulus.

traumatic avoidance: A form of instrumental conditioning in which, after a signal, a particular response must be completed in order to avoid a highly aversive stimulus. Once learned, this type of response is extremely resistant to extinction, particularly when it is difficult for the individual to find out that the traumatic consequences no longer obtain.

confidentiality: In medicine, the ethical principle that a physician may not reveal the confidences entrusted or any information gained by him in the course of medical attendance, unless he is required to do so by law or unless it becomes necessary in order to protect the welfare of the individual or of the community. See also *privilege, privileged communication.*

conflict: In psychiatry, a mental struggle that arises from the simultaneous operation of opposing impulses, drives, or external (environmental) or internal demands; termed *intrapsychic* when the conflict is between forces within the personality, *extrapsychic* when it is between the self and the environment.

confusion: In psychiatry, refers to disturbed orientation in respect to time, place, or person.

congenital: Literally, present at birth. Not synonymous with hereditary or genetic, for it may include conditions that arise during fetal development or the birth process. It does not refer to conditions that appear after birth.

conscience: The morally self-critical part of the self-encompassing standards of behavior, performance, and value judgments. Commonly equated with the conscious superego.

constitution: A person's intrinsic physical and psychological endowment; sometimes used more narrowly to indicate the physical inheritance or potential from birth.

constitutional types: Constellations of morphologic, physiologic, and psychologic traits as earlier proposed by various scholars. Galen, Kretschmer, and Sheldon proposed the following major types: *Galen*: sanguine, melancholic, choleric, and phlegmatic types; *Kretschmer*: pyknic (stocky), asthenic (slender), athletic, and dysplastic (disproportioned) types; *Sheldon*: ectomorphic (thin), mesomorphic (muscular), and endomorphic (fat) types, based on the relative preponderance of outer, middle, or inner layers of embryonic cellular tissue.

conversion: A defense mechanism, operating unconsciously, by which intrapsychic conflicts that would otherwise give rise to anxiety are, instead, given symbolic external expression. The repressed ideas or impulses, plus the psychologic defenses against them, are converted into a variety of somatic symptoms. Example: psychogenic paralysis of a limb that prevents its use for aggressive purposes.

coping mechanisms: Ways of adjusting to environmental stress without altering one's goals or purposes; includes both conscious and unconscious mechanisms.

counterphobia: The desire or seeking out of experiences that are consciously or unconsciously feared.

countertransference: The psychiatrist's conscious or unconscious emotional reaction to his patient. See also *transference*.

criminally insane: A legal term for psychotic patients who have been found not guilty of a serious crime, such as murder, rape, or arson, "by reason of insanity." See also *Currens Formula, Durham Decision, McNaghten Rule.*

crisis intervention: A type of brief treatment in which a therapist or team of therapists assist a patient and his family with an immediate problem by giving medication, altering environmental circumstances, suggesting changes in patterns of behavior, and making referrals to community agencies.

cross-cultural psychiatry: The comparative study of mental illness and mental health among different societies, nations, and cultures. The latter term is often used synonymously with *transcultural psychiatry,* the "trans" prefix denoting that the vista of the scientific observer extends beyond the scope of a single cultural unit.

Currens Formula: A ruling that a person is not responsible for a crime if, as a consequence of a mental disorder, he did not have "adequate capacity to conform his conduct to the requirements of the law." This formula is applied only in the federal (not the state) courts of Pennsylvania, Delaware, and New Jersey, the Third U.S. Circuit. See also *McNaghten Rule* and *Durham Decision.*

cybernetics: Term introduced by Norbert Wiener (1894–1964) to designate the science of control mechanisms. It covers the entire field of communication and control in machines and puts forth the hypothesis that there is some similarity between the human nervous system and electronic control devices.

cultural psychiatry: A branch of *social psychiatry* (q.v.) that concerns itself with the mentally ill in relation to their cultural environment. Symptoms of behavior regarded as quite evident psychopathology in one society may well be regarded as acceptable and normal in another society.

D

death instinct (Thanatos): In Freudian theory, the unconscious drive toward dissolution and death. Coexists with and is in opposition to the life instinct (Eros).

defense mechanism: Unconscious intrapsychic processes that are employed to seek relief from emotional conflict and freedom from anxiety. Conscious efforts are frequently made for the same reasons, but true defense mechanisms are out of awareness (unconscious). Some of the common defense mechanisms defined in this glossary are: *com-*

pensation, conversion, denial, displacement, dissociation, idealization identification, introjection, projection, rationalization, reaction formation, regression, repression, sublimation, substitution, symbolization undoing.

delusion: A false belief out of keeping with the individual's level o knowledge and his cultural group. The belief results from unconsciou needs and is maintained against logical argument and despite objective contradictory evidence. Common delusions include:

delusions of grandeur: Exaggerated ideas of one's importance o identity.

delusions of persecution: Ideas that one has been singled out fo persecution. See also *paranoia.*

delusions of reference: Incorrect assumption that certain casual o unrelated events or the behavior of others applies to oneself. Se also *paranoia.*

dementia: An old term denoting madness or insanity; now used tc denote organic loss of intellectual function.

dementia praecox: Obsolescent descriptive term for *schizophrenia*. Introduced by Morel (1860) and later popularized by Kraepelin.

denial: A defense mechanism, operating unconsciously, used to resolve emotional conflict and allay anxiety by disavowing thoughts, feelings, wishes, needs, or external reality factors that are consciously intolerable.

dependency needs: Vital needs for mothering, love, affection, shelter, protection, security, food, and warmth. May be a manifestation of regression when they reappear openly in adults.

depersonalization: Feelings of unreality or strangeness concerning either the environment or the self or both. See also *neurosis.*

depression: Psychiatrically, a morbid sadness, dejection, or melancholy. To be differentiated from grief, which is realistic and proportionate to what has been lost. A depression may be a symptom of any psychiatic disorder or may constitute its principal manifestation. Neurotic depressions are differentiated from psychotic depressions in that they do not involve loss of capacity for reality testing. The major psychotic depressions include psychotic depressive reaction and the various *major affective disorders.*

deprivation, emotional: A lack of adequate and appropriate interpersonal and/or environmental experience, usually in the early developmental years.

depth psychology: The psychology of unconscious mental processes. Also a system of psychology in which the study of such processes plays a major role, as in *psychoanalysis.*

deterioration: Worsening of a clinical condition, usually expressed as progressive impairment of function; in organic brain syndromes, for example, deterioration refers to a progressive loss of intellectual faculties without implying permanency of change. *Dementia,* in contrast, usually refers to an irreversible decline of mental functions with intellectual disintegration of such a degree as to render fragmentary or to falsify entirely the patient's relationship to his environment. *Regression,* on the other hand, implies that the decline in functioning is reversible, and is more often applied to impairment in the emotional sphere than to intellectual impairment.

determinism: In psychiatry, the postulate that nothing in the individual's emotional or mental life results from chance alone but rather from specific causes or forces known or unknown.

Diagnostic and Statistical Manual of Mental Disorders: A manual that lists and defines all of the psychiatic diagnoses recognized by the American Psychiatric Association as acceptable for use in the United States. The first edition (DSM-I) was published in 1952, and the second (DSM-II) in 1968.

displacement: A defense mechanism, operating unconsciously, in which an emotion is transferred or "displaced" from its original object to a more acceptable substitute.

dissociation: A defense mechanism, operating unconsciously, through which emotional significance and affect are separated and detached from an idea, situation, or object. Dissociation may defer or postpone experiencing some emotional impact as, for example, in selective amnesia.

dominance: (1) In psychiatry, an individual's disposition to play a prominent or controlling role in his interaction with others. (2) In neurology, the (normal) tendency of one half of the brain to be more important than the other in controlling behavior (cerebral dominance). (3) In genetics, the ability of one gene (dominant gene) to express itself in the phenotype of an individual, even though that gene is paired with another (recessive gene) that would have expressed itself in a different way.

double bind: A type of interaction, noted frequently in families with schizophrenic members, in which one person (often the mother) demands a response to a message containing mutually contradictory signals while the other (the schizophrenic son, for example) is unable either to comment on the incongruity or to escape from the situation. Example: a mother tells her son to act like a man and express his opinion and, when he does, berates him as unloving and disloyal.

double-blind study: A research procedure for testing the therapeutic effectiveness of a drug. Neither the research investigator nor the patients know whether the drug being given is the one under investigation, another drug, or a placebo until the completion of the study.

drug dependence: Habituation to, abuse of, and/or addiction to a chemical substance. Largely because of psychologic craving, the life of the drug-dependent person revolves about his need for the specific effect of one or more chemical agents on his mood or state of consciousness. The term thus includes not only addiction (which emphasizes physiologic dependence) but also drug abuse (where the pathologic craving for drugs seems unrelated to physical dependence). Alcoholism is a special type of drug dependence. Other examples are dependence on opiates; synthetic analgesics with morphinelike effects; barbiturates; other hypnotics, sedatives, and tranquilizers; cocaine; marihuana; other psychostimulants; and hallucinogens.

Durham Decision: A ruling which states that a person is not responsible for a crime if his act was the product of mental disease or defect. Currently, this formula applies only in the District of Columbia and the state of Maine. See also *McNaghten Rule* and *Currens Formula.*

dyadic: The relationship between a pair. In psychiatry, refers to the therapeutic relationship between doctor and patient as in "dyadic therapy."

dynamic psychiatry: As distinguished from descriptive psychiatry, refers to the study of emotional processes, their origins, and the mental mechanisms. Implies the study of the active, energy-laden, and changing factors in human behavior and its motivation. Dynamic principles convey the concepts of change, of evolution, and of progression or regression.

dyssocial behavior: In psychiatry, a diagnostic term for individuals who are not classifiable as antisocial personalities but who are predatory and follow more or less criminal pursuits such as racketeers, dishonest gamblers, prostitutes, and dope peddlers. Formerly called "sociopathic personalities."

E

ego: In psychoanalytic theory, one of the three major divisions in the model of the psychic apparatus, the others being the id and superego. The ego represents the sum of certain mental mechanisms, such as perception and memory, and specific defense mechanisms. The ego serves to mediate between the demands of primitive instinctual drives (the id), of internalized parental and social prohibitions (the superego), and of reality. The compromises between these forces achieved by the ego tend to resolve intrapsychic conflict and serve an adaptive and executive function. Psychiatric usage of the term should not be confused with common usage, which connotes "self-love" or "selfishness."

ego analysis: Intensive psychoanalytic study and analysis of the ways in which the ego resolves or attempts to deal with intrapsychic conflicts, especially in relation to the development of mental mechanisms and the maturation of capacity for rational thought and act. Modern psychoanalysis gives more emphasis to considerations of the defensive operations of the ego than did earlier techniques, which emphasized instinctual forces to a greater degree.

ego-dystonic: Aspects of the individual's behavior, thoughts, and attitudes that he views as repugnant or inconsistent with his total personality. See also *ego-syntonic.*

ego ideal: That part of the personality that comprises the aims and goals of the self; usually refers to the conscious or unconscious emulation of significant figures with whom the person has identified. The ego ideal emphasizes what one should be or do in contrast to what one should not be or do.

ego-syntonic: Aspects of the individual's behavior, thoughts, and attitudes that he views as acceptable and consistent with his total personality.

emotion: A feeling such as fear, anger, grief, joy, or love. As used in psychiatry, emotions may not always be conscious. Synonymous with *affect.*

emotionally disturbed: Often used to describe a person with a mental disorder.

emotional health: Often used synonymously with *mental health.*

emotional illness: Often used synonymously with *mental disorder.*

empathy: An objective and insightful awareness of the feelings, emotions, and behavior of another person, their meaning and significance; to be distinguished from sympathy, which is usually nonobjective and noncritical.

engram: A memory trace. Theoretically, a change in neural issue that accounts for persistence of memory.

entropy: In psychiatry, diminished capacity for spontaneous change such as occurs in aging.

epidemiology: In psychiatry, the study of the incidence, distribution, prevalence, and control of mental disorders in a given population. Common terms used in epidemiology are:

> **incidence:** The number of new cases of a mental disorder that occur in a given population over a set period of time, a year, for example.
>
> **endemic:** Describes a disorder that is native to or restricted to a particular area.
>
> **epidemic:** Describes a disorder or the outbreak of a disorder that affects significant numbers of persons in a given population at any time.
>
> **pandemic:** Describes a disorder that occurs over a very wide area or in many countries, or even universally.
>
> **prevalence:** The number of cases of a disorder that currently exists in a given population. **Point prevalence:** the number of cases that exist at a specific point in time. **Period prevalence:** the number of cases that exist in a defined period of time. **Lifetime prevalence:** the number of persons who have had a disorder in their lifetimes.

ethology: Study of animal behavior. Also the systematic study of the phylogenetic development of human character.

etiology: Causation, particularly with reference to disease.

euphoria: An exaggerated feeling of physical and emotional well-being not consonant with apparent stimuli or events; usually of psychologic origin but also seen in organic brain diseases, toxic, and drug-induced states.

existential psychiatry (existentialism): A school of psychiatry that has evolved out of orthodox psychoanalytic thought and incorporates the ideas of such existentialists as Kierkegaard, Heidegger, Sartre, and others. It focuses on the individual's subjective awareness of his style of existence, his intimate interaction with himself, his values, and his environment. Stress is placed on the way in which man experiences the phenomenological world about him and takes responsibility for his existence. Philosophically, the point of view is holistic and self-deterministic in contrast to biologically or culturally deterministic points of view. See also *phenomenology*.

extraversion: A state in which attention and energies are largely directed outward from the self, as opposed to inward toward the self, as in *introversion*.

F

family therapy: Treatment of more than one member of the family simultaneously in the same session. The treatment may be supportive, directive, or interpretive. The assumption is that a mental disorder in one member of a family may be a manifestation of disorder in other members and in their interrelationships and functioning as a total group.

fantasy: An imagined sequence of events or mental images, *e.g.*, daydreams. Serves to express unconscious conflicts, to gratify unconscious wishes, or to prepare for anticipated future events.

fixation: The arrest of psychosexual maturation. Depending on degree it may be either normal or pathological. See *psychosexual development*.

flight of ideas: Verbal skipping from one idea to another. The ideas appear to be continuous but are fragmentary and determined by chance associations. Sometimes seen in manic-depressive illness.

folie à deux: A condition in which two closely related persons, usually in the same family, share the same delusions.

forensic psychiatry: That branch of psychiatry dealing with the legal aspects of mental disorders.

free association: In psychoanalytic therapy, spontaneous, uncensored verbalization by the patient of whatever comes to mind.

free-floating anxiety: Severe, generalized, persisting anxiety. Often a precursor of panic.

fugue: A major state of personality dissociation characterized by amnesia; may involve actual physical flight from the customary environment.

G

general systems theory: A theoretical framework that views events from the standpoint of the "systems" involved in the event. Systems are groups of organized interacting components. The behavior of each system is determined by its own structure, by the aggregate characteristics of its component systems ("subsystems"), and by the larger systems ("suprasystems") of which it is a component. Consequently, all systems may be viewed as part of an interrelated hierarchy (*e.g.*, from subatomic particles to whole societies). The value of this theory in psychiatry lies in its emphasis on the holistic nature of personality (as compared to mechanistic, stimulus-response, and cybernetic theories, for example) and in its potential for advancing interdisciplinary understanding by integrating concepts about all of the systems, subsystems, and suprasystems that affect human behavior.

gross stress reaction: A term employed for an acute emotional reaction incident to severe environmental stress, as, for example, in military operations, industrial, domestic, or civilian disasters, and other life situations.

group process: A general term for the way a group goes about solving a common problem.

group psychotherapy: Application of psychotherapeutic techniques to a group, including utilization of interactions of members of the group.

H

halfway house: In psychiatry, a specialized residence for mental patients who do not require full hospitalization but who need an intermediate degree of protection and support before returning to fully independent community living.

hallucination: A false sensory perception in the absence of an actual external stimulus. May be induced by emotional and other factors such as drugs, alcohol, and stress. May occur in any of the senses.

hallucinogen: A chemical agent that produces hallucinations.

hypnosis: A state of increased receptivity to suggestion and direction, initially induced by the influence of another person. Often characterized by an altered state of consciousness similar to that observed in spontaneous dissociative conditions. The degree may vary from mild hypersuggestibility to a trance state with complete anesthesia.

hypnotic: Strictly speaking, any agent that induces sleep. While sedatives and narcotics in sufficient dosage may produce sleep as an incidental effect, the term "hypnotic" is appropriately reserved for drugs employed primarily to produce sleep. See also *drug dependency, tranquilizer, psychopharmacology.*

I

iatrogenic illness: An illness unwittingly precipitated, aggravated, or induced by the physician's attitude, examination, comments, or treatment.

id: In Freudian theory, that part of the personality structure which harbors the unconscious instinctive desires and strivings of the individual. See also *ego, superego.*

idealization: A mental mechanism, operating consciously or unconsciously, in which the individual overestimates an admired aspect or attribute of another person.

ideas of reference: Incorrect interpretation of casual incidents and external events as having direct reference to one's self. May reach sufficient intensity to constitute delusions.

idée fixe: Fixed idea. Loosely used to describe a compulsive drive, an obsessive idea, or a delusion.

identification: A defense mechanism, operating unconsciously, by which an individual endeavors to pattern himself after another. Identification plays a major role in the development of one's personality and specifically of one's superego. To be differentiated from imitation, which is a conscious process.

identity crisis: A loss of the sense of the sameness and historical continuity of one's self, and inability to accept or adopt the role the subject perceives as being expected of him by society; often expressed by isolation, withdrawal, extremism, rebellion, and negativity, and typically triggered by a combination of sudden increase in the strength of instinctual drives in a milieu of rapid social evolution and technological change.

imago: In Jungian psychology, an unconscious mental image, usually idealized, of an important person in the early history of the individual.

impotence: Usually refers to inability of the male to perform the sexual act, generally for psychologic reasons; more broadly used to indicate powerlessness or lack of sexual vigor.

imprinting: A relatively recent term used in ethology to refer to the process of rapid learning and behavioral patterning which occurs at critical points in very early stages of development in animals. The extent to which imprinting occurs in human learning has not been established.

individual psychology: The system of psychiatric theory, research, and therapy developed by Alfred Adler which stresses compensation and overcompensation for inferiority feelings.

information theory: A philosophical system that deals with the mathematical characteristics of communicated messages and the systems that transmit, propagate, distort, or receive them.

inhibition: In psychiatry, an unconscious defense against forbidden instinctual drives; it may interfere with or restrict specific activities or general patterns of behavior.

insanity: A vague, legal term for psychosis, now obsolete in psychiatric usage. Generally connotes: (a) a mental incompetence, (b) inability to distinguish "right from wrong," and/or (c) a condition that interferes with the individual's ability to care for himself or that constitutes a danger to himself or to others. See *Currens Formula, Durham Decision, McNaghten Rule.*

instinct: An inborn drive. The primary human instincts include self-preservation and sexuality and—for some proponents—aggression, the ego instincts, and "herd" or "social" instincts. Freud also postulated a death instinct.

intellectualization: The defense mechanism that utilizes reasoning as a defense against conscious confrontation with unconscious conflicts and their stressful emotions.

intelligence quotient (IQ): A numerical rating determined through psychological testing that indicates the approximate relationship of a person's mental age (MA) to his chronological age (CA). Expressed mathematically as $IQ = \frac{MA}{CA} \times 100$. Thus, if MA = 6 and CA = 12, then IQ = 6/12 × 100 or 50 (retarded). If MA = 12 and CA = 12, then IQ = 100 (average). If MA = 18 and CA = 12, then IQ = 150 (very superior). (Note: Since intellectual capacity is assumed to be fully developed about age fifteen, adult IQ's are computed by using a fixed arbitrary value of 15 for CA.)

intrapsychic: That which takes place within the psyche or mind.

introjection: A defense mechanism, operating unconsciously, whereby loved or hated external objects are taken within oneself symbolically. The converse of projection. May serve as a defense against conscious recognition of intolerable hostile impulses. For example, in severe depression, the individual may unconsciously direct unacceptable hatred or aggression toward himself, *i.e.*, toward the introjected object within himself. Related to the more primitive mechanism of incorporation.

introversion: Preoccupation with oneself and accompanying reduction of interest in the outside world. Roughly, the reverse of extraversion.

involutional melancholia (involutional psychosis): A major affective disorder occurring in late middle life and characterized by worry, anxiety, agitation, and severe insomnia. Feelings of guilt and somatic preoccupations are common and may be of delusional proportions.

irresistible impulse test: A formula that states that a person is not responsible for a crime if his act was compelled by an irresistible impulse. This is usually construed to mean a psychotic or an obsessive-compulsive (neurotic) impulse and not a simple reaction of rage. Currently, the irresistible impulse test is accepted in 14 states, rejected in the remaining 36.

isolation: A defense mechanism, operating unconsciously, in which an unacceptable impulse, idea, or act is separated from its original memory source, thereby removing the emotional charge associated with the original memory.

L

latent content: The hidden (unconscious) meaning of thoughts or actions, especially in dreams or fantasies. In dreams it is expressed in distorted, disguised, condensed, and symbolic form which is known as the *manifest content*.

libido: The psychic drive or energy usually associated with the sexual instinct. (Sexual is used here in the broad sense to include pleasure and love-object seeking.)

lithium therapy: The use of certain lithium salts in the treatment of manic and hypomanic states of excitement. See also manic-depressive illness.

LSD (lysergic acid diethylamide): An extremely potent drug that produces symptoms and behavior resembling certain psychoses. These symptoms may include hallucinations, delusions, and time-space distortions.

lunacy: Obsolete legal term for a major mental illness.

lunatic: Obsolete legal term for a psychotic person.

M

magical thinking: A person's conviction that thinking equates with doing. Occurs in dreams, in children and primitive peoples, and in patients under a variety of conditions. Characterized by lack of realistic relationship between cause and effect.

major affective disorders: A group of psychoses characterized by severe disorders of mood—either extreme depression or elation or both—that do not seem to be attributable entirely to precipitating life experiences. Includes involutional melancholia and the varieties of manic-depressive illness.

malingering: Deliberate simulation or exaggeration of an illness or disability that, in fact, is nonexistent or minor, in order to avoid an unpleasant situation or to obtain some type of personal gain. See also *compensation neurosis* and *secondary gain.*

-mania: Formerly used as a nonspecific term for any kind of "madness." Currently used as a suffix with any number of Greek roots to indicate a morbid preoccupation with some kind of idea or activity, and/or a compulsive need to behave in some deviant way. *Phobia* as a suffix is used in a similar way. For example, hellenomania, the tendency to use cumbersome Greek or Latin terms instead of readily understandable English words, characterizes the pseudo-erudite jargon of many fields as evidenced by the various terms (often unpreferred) listed below and elsewhere under *phobia.*

dipsomania: Compulsion to drink alcoholic beverages.

egomania: Pathological preoccupation with self.

erotomania: Pathological preoccupation with erotic fantasies or activities.

kleptomania: Compulsion to steal.

megalomania: Pathological preoccupation with delusions of power or wealth.

monomania: Pathological preoccupation with one subject.

necromania: Pathological preoccupation with dead bodies.

nymphomania: Abnormal and excessive need or desire in the female for sexual intercourse. Most nymphomaniacs, if not all, fail to achieve orgasm in the sexual act. See also *erotomania.*

pyromania: Morbid compulsion to set fires.

trichotillomania: Compulsion to pull out one's hair.

mania: A mood disorder characterized by excessive elation, hyperactivity, agitation, and accelerated thinking and speaking, sometimes manifested as flight of ideas. Mania is seen most frequently as one of the two major forms of manic-depressive illness.

maniac: Imprecise, sensational, and misleading lay term for an emotionally disturbed person. Usually implies violent behavior. Is not specifically referable to any psychiatric diagnostic category.

manic-depressive illness: A major affective disorder characterized by severe mood swings and a tendency to remission and recurrence. It is divided into the following three subgroups:

circular type: A manic-depressive illness distinguished by at least one depressive episode *and* a manic episode.

depressed type: A kind of manic-depressive illness consisting exclusively of depressive episodes characterized by severely depressed mood and by mental and motor retardation that may progress to stupor. Uneasiness, apprehension, perplexity, and agitation may also be present.

manic type: A kind of manic-depressive illness consisting exclusively of manic episodes characterized by excessive elation, irritability, talkativeness, flight of ideas, and accelerated speech and motor activity.

manifest content: The remembered content of a dream or fantasy, as opposed to latent content, which it conceals and distorts.

masculine protest: Term coined by Alfred Adler to describe a striving to escape identification with the feminine role. Applies primarily to women but may also be noted in the male.

masochism: See *sexual deviation*.

maximum security unit: A building or ward in a mental hospital or other institutional setting especially designed to prevent the escape of mental patients who have committed crimes or whose symptoms are a physical threat to the safety of others. See also *criminally insane*.

McNaghten Rule (Also M'Naghten, McNaughten, and McNaughton): The formula that holds a person not responsible for a crime if the accused "was laboring under such a defect of reason from disease of the mind as not to know the nature and quality of the act; or, if he did know it, that he did not know that he was doing what was wrong." This is the criminal responsibility formula in most states of the U.S.A.

Also see *Currens Formula, Durham Decision,* and *irresistible impulse test.*

megalomania: See *-mania.*

melancholia: See *involutional melancholia.*

mental health: A state of being, relative rather than absolute, in which a person has effected a reasonably satisfactory integration of his instinctual drives. His integration is acceptable to himself and to his social milieu as reflected in his interpersonal relationship, his level of satisfaction in living, his actual achievement, his flexibility, and the level of maturity he has attained.

mental hygiene: Measures employed to reduce the incidence of mental disorders through prevention and early treatment and to promote mental health.

mental retardation: Subnormal general intellectual functioning, which may be evident at birth or develop during childhood. Learning, social adjustment, and maturation are impaired. Emotional disturbance is often present. The degree of retardation is commonly measured in terms of IQ: borderline (68–83), mild (52–67), moderate (36–51), severe (20–35), and profound (under 20).

mescaline: An alkaloid originally derived from the peyote cactus, resembling amphetamine and adrenaline chemically; used experimentally to induce hallucinations. Used by Indians of the Southwest in religious rites.

mesmerism: Early term for hypnosis. Named after Anton Mesmer (1733–1815).

metapsychology: The branch of theoretical or speculative psychology that deals with the significance of mental processes; the nature of the mind-body interrelationship; the origin, purpose, and structure of the mind; and similar hypotheses that are beyond the realm of empirical verification.

milieu therapy: Literally, treatment by environment in a hospital setting. Physical surroundings, equipment, and staff attitudes are structured in such a way as to enhance the effectiveness of other therapies and foster the patient's rehabilitation. See also *total push therapy, therapeutic community.*

N

narcissism (narcism): From Narcissus, figure in Greek mythology who fell in love with his own reflected image. Self-love, as opposed to object-love (love of another person). In psychoanalytic theory, cathexis (investment) of the psychic representation of the self with libido (sexual interest and energy). Some degree of narcissism is considered healthy and normal, but an excess interferes with relations with others. To be distinguished from egotism, which carries the connotation of self-centeredness, selfishness, and conceit. Egotism is but one expression of narcissism. See also *cathexis, libido.*

National Association for Mental Health: Leading voluntary citizens' organization in the mental health field. Founded in 1909 by Clifford W. Beers as the National Committee for Mental Hygiene.

National Institute of Mental Health: A government bureau within the U.S. Department of Health, Education, and Welfare responsible for administering federal grant programs to advance and support mental health research, training, and service programs.

nervous breakdown: A nonmedical, nonspecific term; a euphemism for a mental disorder.

neurologist: A physician with postgraduate training and experience in the field of organic diseases of the nervous system and whose professional work focuses primarily in this area.

neurology: The branch of medical science devoted to the study, diagnosis, and treatment of organic diseases of the nervous system.

neuropsychiatry: Combination of the specialties of neurology and psychiatry.

neurosis (psychoneurosis): An emotional maladaption characterized chiefly by anxiety arising from some unresolved unconscious conflicts. This anxiety is either felt directly or controlled by various psychological mechanisms to produce other, subjectively distressing symptoms. The neuroses are usually considered less severe than the psychoses (although not always less disabling) because they manifest neither gross personality disorganization nor gross distortion or misinterpretation of external reality. The neuroses are classified according to the predominating symptoms. The common neuroses are:

anxiety neurosis: A neurosis characterized by anxious overconcern occasionally progressing to panic; frequently associated with somatic symptoms.

depersonalization neurosis: A neurosis characterized by feelings of unreality and of estrangement from the self, body, or surroundings. Different from the process of depersonalization, which may be a manifestation of normal anxiety or of another mental disorder.

depressive neurosis: A neurosis manifested by an excessive reaction of depression due to an internal conflict or to an identifiable event, such as a loss of a loved person or a cherished possession.

hypochondriacal neurosis: A neurosis characterized by preoccupation with the body and with fear of presumed diseases of various organs. Although the fears are not delusional in quality, they persist despite reassurance.

hysterical neurosis: A neurosis characterized by a sudden psychogenic loss or disorder of function in response to an emotional stress. This disorder is divided into two subtypes:

conversion type: A hysterical neurosis manifested by disorders of the special senses or the voluntary nervous system, such as blindness, deafness, anesthesia, paresthesia paralysis, and impaired muscular coordination. A patient with this disorder may show *la belle indifference* about his symptoms, which may actually provide secondary gains by winning him sympathy or relieving him of unpleasant responsibilities. See also *conversion.*

dissociative type: A hysterical neurosis manifested by alterations in the patient's state of consciousness or in his identity, producing such symptoms as amnesia, somnambulism, fugue, or multiple personality. See also *dissociation.*

neurasthenic neurosis (neurasthenia): A neurosis characterized by complaints of chronic weakness, easy fatigability, and exhaustion.

obsessive compulsive neurosis: A neurosis characterized by the persistent intrusion of unwanted thoughts, urges, or actions that the individual is unable to stop. The thoughts may consist of single words or ideas, ruminations, or trains of thought that the individual often views as nonsensical. The actions may vary from simple movements to complex rituals, such as repeated handwashing. See also *compulsion.*

phobic neurosis: A neurosis characterized by intense fear of an object or situation that the individual consciously recognizes as harmless. His apprehension may be experienced as faintness, fatigue, palpations, perspiration, nausea, tremor, and even panic. See also *phobia.*

O

object relations: The emotional bonds that exist between an individual and another person, as contrasted with his interest in, and love for, himself; usually described in terms of his capacity for loving and reacting appropriately to others.

obsession: A persistent, unwanted idea or impulse that cannot be eliminated by logic or reasoning.

obsessive compulsive neurosis: See under *neurosis.*

obsessive compulsive personality: See under *personality disorder.*

occupational psychiatry: A field of psychiatry concerned with the diagnosis and prevention of mental illness in industry and with psychiatric aspects of absenteeism, accident proneness, personnel policies, operational fatigue, vocational adjustment, retirement, and related phenomena.

occupational therapy: An adjunctive therapy that utilizes purposeful activities as a means of altering the course of illness. The patient's relationship to staff personnel and to other patients in the occupational therapy setting is often more therapeutic than the activity itself.

Oedipus complex: See under *complex.*

open hospital: Literally, a mental hospital, or section thereof, that has no locked doors or other forms of physical restraint.

orthopsychiatry: An approach to the study and treatment of human behavior that involves the collaborative effort of psychiatry, psychology, psychiatric social work, and other behavioral, medical, and social sciences in the study and treatment of human behavior in the clinical setting. Emphasis is placed on preventive techniques to promote healthy emotional growth and development, particularly of children.

P

panic: In psychiatry, an attack of acute, intense, and overwhelming anxiety, accompanied by a considerable degree of personality disorganization. See *anxiety.*

paranoia: See under *paranoid states.*

paranoid: An adjective applied to individuals who are oversuspicious, some of whom may also harbor grandiose or persecutory delusions, or ideas of reference.

paranoid personality: See under *personality disorder.*

paranoid states: Psychotic disorders in which a delusion, generally persecutory or grandiose, is the essential abnormality and accounts for disturbances in mood, behavior, and thinking (including hallucinations) that may be present. Its two major subdivisions are:

involutional paranoid state (involutional paraphrenia): A paranoid psychosis characterized by delusion formation that begins in the involutional period. Distinguished from schizophrenia, paranoid type, by the absence of a schizophrenic thought disorder.

paranoia: An extremely rare condition characterized by the gradual development of an intricate, complex, and elaborate paranoid system based on (and often proceeding logically from) misinterpretation of an actual event. Frequently the individual considers himself endowed with unique and superior ability. In spite of a chronic course, this condition does not seem to interfere with the rest of the individual's thinking and personality. To be distinguished from schizophrenia, paranoid type, and involutional paranoid state.

parapraxis: A faulty act, blunder or lapse of memory such as a slip of the tongue or misplacement of an article. According to Freud, these acts are caused by unconscious motives.

parapsychology: The study of metapsychic (psi) phenomena, *i.e.,* events caused or perceived without the ordinary use of physical actions or senses. Example: predicting outcome of throw of dice.

partial hospitalization: A psychiatric treatment program for patients who require hospitalization but not on a full-time basis. For example:

day hospital: A special facility or an arrangement within a hospital setting that enables the patient to come to the hospital for treatment during the day and return home at night.

night hospital: A hospital or hospital service for patients who are able to work or otherwise function in the community during the day but who require specialized treatment and supervision in a hospital setting after working hours.

weekend hospital: A hospital setting providing a treatment program over weekends. The patient resumes his usual work and activities outside the hospital during the week.

passive-aggressive personality: See under *personality disorders.*

passive-dependent personality: A disorder manifested by marked indecisiveness, emotional dependency, and lack of self-confidence. For diagnostic purposes, once considered to be a subtype of passive-aggressive personality. See under *personality disorders.*

pastoral counseling: The use of psychological principles by clergymen in interviews with parishioners who seek help with emotional problems.

penis envy: Literally, envy by the female of the penis of the male.

More generally, the female wish for male attributes, position, or advantages. Believed by many to be a significant factor in female character development.

perception: The mental mechanism by which the nature and meaning of sensory stimuli are recognized and interpreted by comparing them with stimuli associated with past experiences.

persona: A Jungian term for the personality "mask" or façade that each person presents to the outside world. Distinguished from the person's inner being or *anima.*

personality: The characteristic way in which a person behaves; the deeply ingrained pattern of behavior that each person evolves, both consciously and unconsciously, as his style of life or way of being in adapting to his environment. See *character disorder, personality disorders.*

personality disorders: A group of mental disorders characterized by deeply ingrained maladaptive patterns of behavior, generally life-long in duration and consequently often recognizable by the time of adolescence or earlier. Affecting primarily the personality of the individual, they are different in quality from neurosis and phychosis.

antisocial personality: A personality disorder characterized by a basic lack of socialization and by behavior patterns that bring the individual repeatedly into conflict with society. People with this disorder are incapable of significant loyalty to individuals, groups, or social values and are grossly selfish, callous, irresponsible, impulsive, and unable to feel guilt or to learn from experience and punishment. Frustration tolerance is low. Such individuals tend to blame others or offer plausible rationalizations for their behavior.

asthenic personality: A personality disorder characterized by easy fatigability, low energy level, lack of enthusiasm, marked incapacity for enjoyment, and oversensitivity to physical and emotional stress.

cyclothymic personality (affective personality): A personality disorder characterized by recurring and alternating periods of depression and elation not readily attributable to external circumstances.

explosive personality: A personality disorder characterized by gross outbursts of rage or of verbal or physical aggressiveness. Outbursts are strikingly different from the individual's usual behavior, and he may be regretful and repentant for them. See also *aggression.*

hysterical personality (histrionic personality disorder): A personality disorder characterized by excitability, emotional instability, overreactivity, and self-dramatization that is attention-seeking and often seductive, whether or not the individual is aware of its purpose. Often individuals with this disorder are immature, self-centered, vain, and unusually dependent on others.

inadequate personality: A personality disorder characterized by ineffectual responses to emotional, social, intellectual, and physical demands. While the individual seems neither physically nor mentally deficient, he does manifest inadaptability, ineptness, poor judgment, social instability, and lack of physical and emotional stamina.

obsessive compulsive personality (anankastic personality): A personality disorder characterized by excessive concern with conformity and adherence to standards of conscience. Individuals with this disorder may be rigid, overinhibited, overconscientious, overdutiful, indecisive, perfectionistic, and unable to relax easily.

paranoid personality: A personality disorder characterized by hypersensitivity, rigidity, unwarranted suspicion, jealousy, envy, excessive self-importance, and a tendency to blame others and ascribe evil motives to them.

passive-aggressive personality: A personality disorder characterized by aggressive behavior manifested in passive ways, such as obstructionism, pouting, procrastination, intentional inefficiency, or stubbornness. The aggression often arises from resentment at failing to find gratification in a relationship with an individual or institution upon which the individual is overdependent.

schizoid personality: A personality disorder manifested by shyness, oversensitivity, seclusiveness, frequent daydreaming, avoidance of close or competitive relationships, and often eccentricity. Individuals with this condition often react to disturbing experiences and conflicts with apparent detachment and are often unable to express hostility and ordinary aggressive feelings.

phenomenology: The study of occurrences or happenings in their own right, rather than from the point of view of inferred causes; specifically, the theory that behavior is determined not by external reality as it can be described objectively in physical terms but rather by the way in which the subject perceives that reality at any moment. See *existentialism.*

phenothiazine derivatives: A group of psychotropic drugs that, chemically, have in common the phenothiazine nucleus but that differ from one another through variations in chemical structure. As a group of drugs, the phenothiazines are also known as *major tranquilizers* posessing marked antianxiety and antipsychotic properties. See *psycho-pharmacology* and the other terms listed there.

phobia: An obsessive, persistent, unrealistic intense fear of an object or ituation. The fear is believed to arise through a process of displacing an internal (unconscious) conflict to an external object symbolically elated to the conflict. (See also *displacement.*) Some of the common phobias are:

acrophobia: Fear of heights.

agoraphobia: Fear of open places.

ailurophobia: Fear of cats.

algophobia: Fear of pain.

claustrophobia: Fear of closed spaces.

erythrophobia: Fear of blushing; sometimes used to refer to the blushing itself.

mysophobia: Fear of dirt and germs.

panphobia: Fear of everything.

xenophobia: Fear of strangers.

phylogenetic: Pertaining to the evolutionary or racial history of the species.

placebo: Originally, an inactive substance such as a "bread pill" given to "placate" a patient who demands medication that is not necessary. Useful in research and practice because of its potential psychological effect, which may be neutral, therapeutic, or noxious depending on suggestion by the therapist or experimenter and the patient's own expectations, faith, fear, apprehension, or hostility. In British usage a placebo is sometimes called a "dummy."

play therapy: A treatment technique utilizing the child's play as a medium for expression and communication between patient and therapist.

pleasure principle: The psychoanalytic concept that man instinctually seeks to avoid pain and discomfort and strives for gratification and pleasure. In personality development theory the pleasure principle antedates and subsequently comes in conflict with the *reality principle.*

preconscious: Referring to thoughts that are not in immediate awareness but that can be recalled by conscious effort.

prefrontal lobotomy: A type of psychosurgery.

pregenital: In psychoanalysis, refers to the period of early childhood before the genitals have begun to exert the predominant influence in the organization or patterning of sexual behavior. Oral and anal influences predominate during this period. See also *anal erotism* and *oral phase* under *psychosexual development.*

preventive psychiatry (prevention): In traditional medical usage, the prevention or prophylaxis of a disorder. The modern trend, particularly in community psychiatry, is to broaden the meaning of prevention to encompass also the amelioration, control, and limitation of disease. Prevention is often categorized as follows:

> **primary prevention:** Measures to prevent a mental disorder (*e.g.,* preventing general paralysis with adequate doses of penicillin in treating syphilis).
>
> **secondary prevention:** Measures to limit a disease process (*e.g.,* through early case finding and treatment).
>
> **tertiary prevention:** Measures to reduce impairment or disability following a disorder (*e.g.,* through rehabilitation programs).

primary gain: The relief from emotional conflict and the freedom from anxiety achieved by a defense mechanism. The concept is that mental states, both normal and pathological, develop defensively in largely unconscious attempts to cope with or to resolve unconscious conflicts. All mental mechanisms operate in the service of the primary gain, and the need for such gain may be thought of as responsible for the initiation of an emotional illness. To be distinguished from *secondary gain.*

primary process: In psychoanalytic theory, the generally unorganized mental activity characteristic of unconscious mental life. Seen in less disguised form in infancy and in dreams. It is marked by the free discharge of energy and excitation without regard to the demands of environment, reality, or logic. See also *secondary process.*

privilege: The legal right of a patient, always established by statute, to prevent his physician from testifying about information gleaned in the course of his treatment by the physician. Thus, a legal affirmation of the ethical principle of confidentiality. Many states have privileged communication laws.

> **privileged communication:** A legal term for information that a patient discloses to his physician while the latter attends him in a professional capacity. The information is termed "privileged" because in some states by law, and universally according to medical ethics, the physician is not allowed to divulge such information with-

out the patient's consent. Also, the medical record of a patient is regarded as a privileged communication in jurisdictions where privilege is established by law, and in any case, as a confidential communication where it is not.

process schizophrenia: See under *schizophrenia.*

projection: A defense mechanism, operating unconsciously, whereby that which is emotionally unacceptable in the self is unconsciously rejected and attributed (projected) to others.

projective tests: Psychological tests used as a diagnostic tool in which the test material is so unstructured that any response will reflect a projection of some aspect of the subject's underlying personality and psychopathology. Among the most common projective tests are the Rorschach (inkblot) and the thematic apperception test (TAT).

psychedelic: A term applied to any of several drugs that may induce hallucinations and psychotic states, including the production of bizarre distortion of time, sound, color, etc. Among the more commonly used psychedelics are LSD, marihuana, mescaline, morning-glory seeds, psilocybin.

psychiatrist: A doctor of medicine who specializes in psychiatry.

psychiatry: The medical science that deals with the origin, diagnosis, prevention, and treatment of mental disorders.

psychic energizer: A popular term for drugs that stimulate or elevate the mood of a depressed patient.

psychoanalysis: A psychologic theory of human development and behavior, a method of research, and a system of psychotherapy, originally developed by Sigmund Freud. Through analysis of free associations and interpretation of dreams, emotions and behavior are traced to the influence of repressed instinctual drives and defenses against them in the unconscious. Psychoanalytic treatment seeks to eliminate or diminish the undesirable effects of unconscious conflicts by making the patient aware of their existence, origin, and inappropriate expression in current emotions and behavior.

psychoanalyst: A psychiatrist who has had additional training in psychoanalysis and who employs the techniques of psychoanalytic therapy.

psychobiology: The science of the human being as an integrated unit. Specifically, it views the individual not as having a psychological and a biological set of functions, but rather as functioning as an integrated unit. Generally associated with Adolf Meyer, who introduced the term in the United States in 1915.

psychodrama: A technique of group psychotherapy in which individuals dramatize their emotional problems.

psychodynamics: The systematized knowledge and theory of human behavior and its motivation, the study of which depends largely upon the functional significance of emotion. Psychodynamics recognizes the role of unconscious motivation in human behavior. It is a predictive science, based on the assumption that a person's total makeup and probable reactions at any given moment are the product of past interactions between his specific genetic endowment and the environment in which he has lived from conception onward.

psychogenesis: Production or causation of a symptom or illness by mental or psychic factors as opposed to organic ones.

psychologist, clinical: A psychologist with a graduate degree, usually a PhD, and with additional supervised training and experience in a clinical setting, who specializes in the evaluation and psychological treatment of mental disorders. Frequently clinical psychologists work in medical settings in collaboration with psychiatrists and other physicians.

psychology: An academic discipline, a profession, and a science dealing with the study of mental processes and behavior in man and animals. See also *psychiatry*.

psychopathic personality: An informal term for *antisocial personality*. Afflicted individuals are referred to casually as "psychopaths."

psychopathology: The study of the significant causes and processes in the development of mental illness. Also the manifestations of mental illness.

psychopharmacology: The study of the mental and behavioral effects of certain drugs. Some of the many facets of psychopharmacology are described in this glossary under the following terms: *antidepressant, psychedelic, psychic energizer, tranquilizer.*

psychophysiologic disorders: A group of disorders characterized by physical symptoms that are caused by emotional factors and that involve a single organ system, usually under autonomic nervous system control. Symptoms are caused by physiological changes that normally accompany certain emotional states, but in these disorders the changes are more intense and sustained. Frequently called "psychosomatic disorders." These disorders are usually named and classified according to the organ system involved (*e.g.*, musculo-skeletal, respiratory).

psychosexual development: In psychoanalysis, a term encompassing the various stages of libidinal maturation from infancy to adulthood. The way in which a child experiences these stages significantly influences his basic personality characteristics in later life. The stages are:

oral phase: The earliest of the stages of infantile psychosexual development, lasting from birth to twelve months or longer. Usually subdivided into two stages: the **oral erotic,** relating to the pleasurable experience of sucking; and the **oral sadistic,** associated with aggressive biting. Both oral erotism and sadism continue into adult life in disguised and sublimated forms.

anal phase: The period of pregenital psychosexual development, usually from one to three years, in which the child has particular interest and concern with the process of defecation and the sensations connected with the anus. The pleasurable part of the experience is termed *anal erotism.* See also *anal character.*

phallic phase: The period from about two and a half to six years during which sexual interest, curiosity, and pleasurable experience center about the penis, and in girls, to a lesser extent, the clitoris.

latency period: The period from about five to seven years to adolescence when there is an apparent cessation of psychosexual development.

genital phase: The culminating stage of development in which a person achieves a genuinely affectionate, mature relationship with a sex partner.

psychosis: A major mental disorder of organic or emotional origin in which the individual's ability to think, respond emotionally, remember, communicate, interpret reality, and behave appropriately is sufficiently impaired so as to interfere grossly with his capacity to meet the ordinary demands of life. Often characterized by regressive behavior, inappropriate mood, diminished impulse control, and such abnormal mental content as delusions and hallucinations. The term is applicable to conditions having a wide range of severity and duration. See also *schizophrenia, manic-depressive illness, reactive depression, involutional melancholia.*

psychosomatic: Adjective to denote the constant and inseparable interaction of the *psyche* (mind) and the *soma* (body). Most commonly used to refer to illnesses in which the manifestations are primarily physical with at least a partial emotional etiology. See also *psychophysiologic disorders.*

psychosurgery: Treatment of chronic, severe, and intractable psychiatric disorders by surgical removal or interruption of certain areas or pathways in the brain, especially in the prefrontal lobes.

psychotherapy: The generic term for any type of treatment that is based primarily upon verbal or nonverbal communication with the patient as distinguished from the use of drugs, surgery, or physical measures such as electroconvulsive treatment. The basic treatment method used by psychiatrists either alone or in conjunction with other forms of treatment. See also *psychoanalysis, group therapy.*

R

rapport: In psychiatry, the conscious feeling of harmonious accord, mutual responsiveness, and sympathy that contributes to the patient's confidence in the therapist and willingness to work cooperatively with him. To be distinguished from *transference,* which is unconscious.

rationalization: A defense mechanism, operating unconsciously, in which the individual attempts to justify or make consciously tolerable, by plausible means, feelings, behavior and motives that would otherwise be intolerable. Not to be confused with conscious evasion or dissimulation. See also *projection.*

reaction formation: A defense mechanism, operating unconsciously, wherein attitudes and behavior are adopted that are the opposites of impulses the individual harbors either consciously or unconsciously (*e.g.,* excessive moral zeal may be a reaction to strong but repressed asocial impulses).

reactive depression: An informal term for *depressive neurosis.*

reactive schizophrenia: See under *schizophrenia.*

reality principle: In psychoanalytic theory, the concept that the pleasure principle, which represents the claims of instinctual wishes, is normally modified by the inescapable demands and requirements of the external world. In fact, the reality principle may still work in behalf of the pleasure principle; but it reflects compromises in the nature of the gratification and allows for the postponement of gratification to a more appropriate time. The reality principle usually becomes more prominent in the course of development but may be weak in certain psychiatric illnesses and undergo strengthening during treatment.

recall: The process of bringing a memory into consciousness. In psychiatry, recall is often used to refer to the recollection of facts or events in the immediate past.

reciprocal inhibition and desensitization: A term for a widely used form of behavior therapy. The patient is made comfortable in relaxed, pleasant, supportive surroundings and is then exposed, usually by imagery, to gradually increasing amounts of anxiety-provoking stimuli. The feeling of comfort associated with the situation allows the patient to tolerate increasing amounts of these stimuli and may eventually entirely remove their ability to arouse anxiety.

reference, delusion of (idea of): See *ideas of reference.*

regression: The partial or symbolic return to more infantile patterns of reacting. Manifested in a wide variety of circumstances such as normal sleep, play, severe physical illness, and in many psychiatric disorders.

rehabilitation: The methods and techniques used in a program that seeks to achieve maximal functional and optimal adjustment for the identified patient, and to prevent relapses or recurrences of his condition (because of the latter, sometimes termed *tertiary prevention*). The focus in rehabilitation is on the patient's assets and recoverable functions, rather than on the liabilities engendered by his pathology or the complications of disuse and social deterioration which formerly were often mistakenly considered to be part of the underlying disease process. Includes individual and group psychotherapy, directed socialization, vocational retraining, education. See *community psychiatry.*

REM sleep: One of two kinds of sleep. The term designates the "deep sleep" periods during which the sleeper makes coordinated rapid eye movements (REM's) resembling purposeful fixation shifts, as might be seen in the waking state. REM sleep is also called "dreaming sleep" since there appears to be an intimate relationship with dreaming activity, as if the dreamer were watching the visual imagery of his dream. *NREM* sleep is the term given to the longer period of sleep that begins as the subject passes from wakefulness into a light sleep with *no rapid eye movements* (NREM's). REM sleep interrupts NREM sleep about once in every ninety minutes and lasts for about twenty minutes. REM sleep is believed to account for one-fifth to one-fourth of the total sleep time. Between the two forms of sleep, there are distinct differences in the EEG patterns and in the oculomotor, cardiovascular, respiratory, muscular, and other bodily activities.

remission: Abatement of an illness.

repetition compulsion: In psychoanalytic theory the impulse to reenact earlier emotional experiences. Considered by Freud more fundamental than the pleasure principle. According to Ernest Jones: "The blind impulse to repeat earlier experiences and situations quite irrespective of any advantage that doing so might bring from a pleasure-pain point of view."

repression: A defense mechanism, operating unconsciously, that banishes unacceptable ideas, affects, or impulses from consciousness or that keeps out of consciousness what has never been conscious. Although not subject to voluntary recall, the repressed material may emerge in disguised form. Sometimes used as a generic term for all defense mechanisms. Often confused with the conscious mechanism of *suppression.*

resident: An MD who has completed his internship and who is in graduate training to qualify as a specialist in a particular field of medicine, such as psychiatry. The American Board of Psychiatry and Neurology requires three years of psychiatric residency training in an approved hospital or clinic, together with two years of practice in the specialty of psychiatry, to qualify for examinations.

resistance: In psychiatry, the individual's conscious or unconscious psychological defense against bringing repressed (unconscious) thoughts to light.

retardation: Slowing down of mental and physical activity. Most frequently seen in severe depressions, which are sometimes spoken of as retarded depressions. Also a synonym for *mental retardation.*

S

schizoid personality: See under *personality disorders.*

schizophrenia: A large group of disorders, usually of psychotic proportion, manifested by characteristic disturbances of thought, mood, and behavior. Thought disturbances are marked by alterations of concept formation that may lead to misinterpretation of reality and sometimes to delusions and hallucinations. Mood changes include ambivalence, constriction, inappropriateness, and loss of empathy with others. Behavior may be withdrawn, regressive, and bizarre. Currently recognized types of schizophrenia are:

acute schizophrenic episode: A condition characterized by the acute onset of schizophrenic symptoms, often associated with confusion, perplexity, ideas of reference, emotional turmoil, excitement, depression, fear, or dreamlike dissociation. This term is *not* applicable to acute episodes of the other types of schizophrenia described here.

catatonic type: A schizophrenic disorder manifested in either or both of two ways: (1) by excessive and sometimes violent motor activity and excitement ("excited subtype") or (2) by generalized inhibition manifested as stupor, mutism, negativism, or waxy flexibility ("withdrawn subtype").

childhood schizophrenia: Schizophrenia appearing before puberty. It is frequently manifested by autism and withdrawn behavior; failure to develop an identity separate from the mother's; and general unevenness, gross immaturity, and inadequacy in development.

chronic undifferentiated type: A condition manifested by definite signs of schizophrenic thought, affect, and behavior that are of a sufficiently mixed or indefinite type that they defy classification into one of the other types of schizophrenia.

hebephrenic type: A schizophrenic disorder characterized by disorganized thinking, shallow and inappropriate affect, inappropriate giggling, silly and regressive behavior and mannerisms, and frequent hypochondriacal complaints. Delusions and hallucinations are usually bizarre and not well organized.

latent type: A condition manifested by clear symptoms of schizophrenia but no history of psychotic schizophrenic episodes. Sometimes designated as incipient, prepsychotic, pseudoneurotic, pseudopsychopathic, or borderline schizophrenia.

paranoid type: A schizophrenic disorder characterized primarily by the presence of persecutory or grandiose delusions, often associated with hallucinations.

process schizophrenia: Unofficial term for schizophrenia attributed more to organic factors than to environmental ones; typically begins gradually, continues chronically, and progresses (either rapidly or slowly) to an irreversible psychosis. See also *reactive schizophrenia,* to which this condition is contrasted.

reactive schizophrenia: Unofficial term for schizophrenia attributed primarily to strong predisposing and/or precipitating environmental factors; usually of rapid onset and brief duration, with the affected individual appearing well both before and after the schizophrenic episode. Differentiating this condition from *process schizophrenia* is generally considered more important in Europe than in this country.

residual type: A condition manifested by individuals with signs of schizophrenia who, following a psychotic schizophrenic episode, are no longer psychotic.

screen memory: A consciously tolerable memory that serves as a cover or "screen" for another associated memory that would be disturbing and emotionally painful if recalled.

secondary gain: The external gain that is derived from any illness, such as personal attention and service, monetary gains, disability benefits, and release from unpleasant responsibility. See also *primary gain.*

secondary process: In psychoanalytic theory, mental activity and thinking characteristic of the ego and influenced by the demands of the environment. Characterized by organization, systematization, intellectualization, and similar processes leading to logical thought and action in adult life. See also *primary process.*

sedative: A broad term applied to any agent that quiets or calms or allays excitement. While narcotics, hypnotics, and other classes of drugs have calming properties, the term is generally restricted to drugs that are not primarily used to achieve analgesia or sleep. See also *psychopharmacology.*

senile dementia: A chronic organic brain syndrome associated with generalized atrophy of the brain due to aging. In addition to the organic symptoms present, self-centeredness, difficulty assimilating new experiences, and childish emotionality are usually prominent. Deterioration may range from minimal to severe.

sensory deprivation: Term for experience of being cut off from usual external stimuli and the opportunity for perception. May occur experimentally or accidentally in various ways such as through loss of hearing or eyesight, by becoming marooned, by solitary confinement, by assignment to a remote service post, or by traveling in space. May lead to disorganized thinking, depression, panic, delusions, and hallucinations.

separation anxiety: The fear and apprehension noted in infants when removed from their mothers (or surrogates) or when approached by strangers. Most marked from sixth to tenth month. In later life, similar reaction may be caused by separation from significant persons or familiar surroundings.

sexual deviation: The direction of sexual interest toward objects other than persons of the opposite sex, toward sexual acts not associated with coitus, or toward coitus performed under bizarre circumstances. Examples are:

bestiality: Sexual relations between human and animal.

exhibitionism: Psychiatrically, body exposure, usually of the male genitals to females.

fetishism: A sexual deviation characterized by attachment of special meaning to an inanimate object (or fetish) which serves, usually unconsciously, as a substitute for the original object or person. The fetish is essential for completion of orgasm. Rare in females.

homosexuality: Sexual attraction or relationship between members of the same sex. **Overt homosexuality:** Homosexuality that is consciously recognized or practiced. **Latent homosexuality:** A condition characterized by unconscious homosexual desires.

masochism: Pleasure derived from physical or psychological pain inflicted either by oneself or by others. When it is consciously sought as a part of the sexual act or as a prerequisite to sexual gratification, it is classifiable as a sexual deviation. It is the converse of *sadism,* and the two tend to coexist in the same individual.

pederasty: Homosexual intercourse between man and boy by anus.

pedophilia: In psychiatry, a sexual deviation involving the use of children for sexual purposes.

sadism: Pleasure derived from inflicting physical or psychological pain or abuse on others. The sexual significance of sadistic wishes or behavior may be conscious or unconscious. When necessary for sexual gratification, classifiable as a sexual deviation.

sodomy: Anal intercourse. Legally, the term may include other types of perversion such as bestiality.

transvestitism (transvestism): Sexual pleasure derived from dressing or masquerading in the clothing of the opposite sex. The sexual origins of transvestitism may be unconscious. There is a strong wish to appear as and to be accepted as a member of the opposite sex.

voyeurism: Sexually motivated and often compulsive interest in watching or looking at others, particularly at genitals. Roughly synonymous with "peeping Tom." Found predominantly in males.

shell shock: Obsolete term used in World War I to designate a wide variety of psychotic and neurotic disorders presumably due to combat experience. See *conversion, combat fatigue, hysterical neurosis.*

shock treatment: A form of psychiatric treatment in which electric current, insulin, carbon dioxide, or Indoklon is administered to the patient and results in a loss of consciousness or a convulsive or comatose reaction to alter favorably the course of the illness. Some common types of shock therapy are:

carbon dioxide therapy: A form of inhalation treatment in which carbon dioxide gas is administered to the point of unconsciousness in order to cause emotional abreactions and alleviation of anxiety.

electroconvulsive treatment (ECT): Use of electric current to induce unconsciousness and/or convulsive seizures. Most effective in the treatment of depression. Introduced by Cerletti and Bini in 1938. Modifications are electronarcosis, producing sleeplike states, and electrostimulation, which avoids convulsions.

Indoklon therapy: A form of shock treatment in which a convulsive seizure is produced by intravenous injection or inhalation of the drug Indoklon.

insulin coma therapy (ICT): A treatment primarily for schizophrenia in which insulin is injected in large enough doses to produce profound hypoglycemia (low blood sugar) resulting in coma. First used by Manfred Sakel in 1933. Its use in the United States has decreased since the introduction of tranquilizers.

Metrazol shock therapy: A form of shock treatment, now rarely used, in which a convulsive seizure is produced by intravenous injection of Metrazol (known as Cardiazol in Europe). Introduced by L. von Meduna in 1935.

subcoma insulin treatment: A treatment in which insulin is administered to induce drowsiness or somnolence short of coma. Used to alleviate anxiety, stimulate appetite, and induce a feeling of well-being.

sibling: Term for a full brother or sister.

sibling rivalry: The competition between siblings for the love of a parent or for other recognition or gain.

social control: The way in which society or any of its subgroups, various institutions, organizations, and agencies exert influence upon the individual, or groups of individuals, to conform to the expectations and requirements of that society or subgroup. Control may be coercive (as by means of the law) or persuasive (through such devices as suggestion, blame, praise, reward, and recognition). See also *sociology*.

social psychiatry: The field of psychiatry concerned with the cultural, ecologic, and sociologic factors that engender, precipitate, intensify, prolong, or otherwise complicate maladaptive patterns of behavior and their treatment; sometimes used synonymously with *community psychiatry,* although some limit the latter term to practical or clinical applications of social psychiatry. Important in social psychiatry is the ecological approach to maladaptive behavior, which is viewed not only as a deviation of an individual but also as a reflection of deviation in the social systems in which he lives.

social work: The use of community resources and of the conscious adaptive capacities of individuals and groups to better the adjustment of an individual to his environment and to improve the quality and functioning of an individual's external environment.

social worker, psychiatric: A social worker with specialized psychiatric training leading to a graduate degree (MSW or DSW) in social work. Such a worker may utilize all social work techniques such as casework, group work, and community organization in a psychiatric or mental health setting.

socialization: The process by which society integrates the individual and the way in which the individual learns to become a functioning member of that society. See *sociology.*

sociology: The study of the development and governing principles of social organization and the group behavior of men, in contrast to the individual behavior of man. Overlaps to some extent with cultural anthropology. Related concepts are defined elsewhere under the following terms: *alienation, social control, socialization.*

sociopath: An unofficial term for antisocial personality (q.v. under *personality disorders*).

sublimation: A defense mechanism, operating unconsciously, by which instinctual drives, consciously unacceptable, are diverted into personally and socially acceptable channels.

substitution: A defense mechanism, operating unconsciously, by that an unattainable or unacceptable goal, emotion, or object is replaced by one that is more attainable or acceptable. Comparable to displacement.

superego: In psychoanalytic theory, that part of the personality associated with ethics, standards, and self-criticism. It is formed by the infant's identification with important and esteemed persons in his early life, particularly parents. The supposed or actual wishes of these significant persons are taken over as part of the child's own personal standards to help form the "conscience." In late life they may become anachronistic and self-punitive, especially in neurotic persons. See also *ego, id.*

supportive psychotherapy: A technique of psychotherapy that aims to reinforce a patient's defense and to help him suppress disturbing psychological material. Supportive psychotherapy utilizes such measures as inspiration, reassurance, suggestion, persuasion, counseling, and reeducation. It avoids probing the patient's emotional conflicts in depth.

suppression: The conscious effort to control and conceal unacceptable impulses, thoughts, feelings, or acts.

surrogate: One who takes the place of another; a substitute person. In psychiatry, usually refers to an authority figure who replaces a parent in the emotional feelings of the patient (*e.g.*, father-surrogate, mother-surrogate).

symbiosis: In psychiatry, denotes a mutually reinforcing relationship between two disturbed persons who are dependent on each other.

symbolization: An unconscious mental process operating by association and based on similarity and abstract representation whereby one object or idea comes to stand for another through some part, quality, or aspect which the two have in common. The symbol carries in more or less disguised form the emotional feelings vested in the initial object or idea.

T

thematic apperception test (TAT): A projective test consisting of a series of drawings suggesting life situations, which may be variously interpreted depending on the mood and personality of the subject.

therapeutic community: A term of British origin, now widely used, for a specially structured mental hospital milieu that encourages patients to function within the range of social norms. Special educational techniques are used to overcome the patients' dependency needs, to encourage them to assume personal responsibility, and to speed their social rehabilitation.

total push therapy: In a hospital setting, the energetic simultaneous application of all available psychiatric therapies to the treatment of a patient, first described by Abraham Myerson (1881–1948). Myerson emphasized physical activity, recreation, praise, blame, reward, punishment, and involvement in care of clothing and personal hygiene.

toxic psychosis: A psychosis resulting from the toxic effect of chemicals and drugs, including those produced in the body.

trance: A state of diminished activity and consciousness resembling sleep. Seen in hypnosis, hysteria, and ecstatic religious states.

tranquilizer: A drug that decreases anxiety and agitation, usually without causing drowsiness. Divided into two groups:

major tranquilizers: Drugs such as *phenothiazines* which produce relief from symptoms of psychosis.

minor tranquilizers: Drugs that are used predominantly to diminish neurotic anxiety.

transactional analysis: A psychodynamic approach that attempts to understand the interplay between therapist and patient—and ultimately between the patient and exernal reality—in terms of role theory, beginning with an exposure of current, well-defined, explicit roles, and ultimately evoking a recognition of implicit emotional roles and a repetition of earlier interactions that trace the genesis of current behavior.

transcultural psychiatry: See *cross-cultural psychiatry.*

tranference: The unconscious "transfer" to others of feelings and attitudes that were originally associated with important figures (parents, siblings, etc.) in one's early life. The transference relationship follows roughly the pattern of its prototype. The psychiatrist utilizes this phenomenon as a therapeutic tool to help the patient understand his emotional problems and their origin. In the patient-physician relationship the transference may be negative (hostile) or positive (affectionate). See also *countertransference.*

U

unconditioned reflex (UCR): An inborn physiologic reflex response to a stimulus; *e.g.*, salivation at the sight of food.

unconscious: In Freudian theory, that part of the mind or mental functioning of which the content is only rarely subject to awareness. It is a repository for data that have never been conscious (primary repression), or that may have become conscious briefly and later repressed (secondary repression).

underachiever: Term used in psychiatry for a person who manifestly does not function up to his capacity.

undoing: A primitive defense mechanism, operating unconsciously, in which something unacceptable and already done is symbolically acted out in reverse, usually repetitiously, in the hope of "undoing" it and thus relieving anxiety.

W

working through: Active exploration of a problem by patient and therapist until a satisfactory solution has been found or until a symptom has been traced to its unconscious sources.

Acknowledgments

The dedication of the book to the John Simon Guggenheim Memorial Foundation and its president, Gordon N. Ray, expresses my appreciation for the Foundation's financial support in 1965–66. For other assistance and encouragement I wish to thank the following: the graduate division of Stanford University, especially Albert H. Bowker, former dean of the graduate school and now chancellor of the City University of New York; Robert Rosenzweig, associate dean of the Stanford Graduate School; Mina Rees, provost of the graduate division of the City University of New York; Dean Harold M. Proshansky, former associate dean Hyman Kublin and assistant dean Marilyn Mikulsky of the graduate division of the City University of New York; Walter E. Barton, MD, medical director, and Robert L. Robinson, public information officer, of the American Psychiatric Association; the office staff of the American Psychoanalytic Association; and Preston Cutler, associate director of the Center for Advanced Study in the Behavioral Sciences. Without the cooperation and, in some instances, the advice of more than 200 psychiatrists and psychoanalysts whom I have thought it best not to identify by name, this book could not have been written; my gratitude to them is profound.

My thanks also go to the following research assistants: Jule Mozley Kringel, Ronald Newman, Carol Vitz, Thomas Reilly, Penny Handler, Bharti Parekh, and Felice Swados. Kathryn Holbrook, Ted Cooper, and Jack Nadler were indispensable as statisticians. The entire manuscript was typed by Barbara Givan, sometime *au pair* girl, secretary, and office manager, whose skill in making literary order out of typing chaos is equaled only by her capacity for hard work amid the distractions of jackhammers, power failures, student unrest, garbage strikes, mail delays, and other features of daily life in a large urban university. Despite all this, she not only functioned successfully as Girl Friday;

she frequently raised the question in my mind whether Robinson Crusoe could not be dispensed with altogether.

The entire Rogow family contributed in ways that are too numerous as well as too personal to be enumerated here. To Pat, Jenny, Sarah, and Jeanne ("Bu") go my gratitude and love.

Discussions with friends were helpful in clarifying and occasionally modifying my own ideas about the role of psychiatrists and psychoanalysts in American society. I especially want to thank the following: Eliot Asinof, Penelope Balogh, Samuel Bloom, Esther Cole, Hilary Hogarth Cranswick, Jeanne Friedman, Albert Haas, Jr., Eleanor Haas, Harold D. Lasswell, Hugh L'Etang, Max Levin, Sandra Levinson, Jeanne and Norman MacKenzie, Laidily McBride, Emily Mumford, Mina Post Peyser, Borden and Jeanne Polson, Harlan Robinson, Nevitt Sanford, Lenore and Robert Schwartz, Joan Simon, Harvey and Bette Swados, Petra Toelle, and Helene Veltfort.

I am grateful to my editor, Harvey Ginsberg, of G. P. Putnam's Sons, for giving the manuscript his close personal attention. Not least among my satisfactions in seeing the book published is the working relationship we were able to establish. Such a relationship with my friend and agent, James Oliver Brown, has long been a source of gratification.

Finally, I should mention that portions of the book were delivered as lectures in the Benjamin F. Shambaugh Memorial Lecture series at the University of Iowa, 1966–67. I wish to thank the university and its Department of Political Science for the opportunity to present this material to a critical but always friendly audience. A Unitarian-Universalist Billings Lectureship at North Texas universities in 1968 enabled me to further develop some themes and interpretations. I also am grateful to the Yale University School of Medicine, the Downstate Medical Center of the State University of New York, and the University of Oklahoma Medical School for lecture invitations. Many of the psychiatrists, psychoanalysts, and psychologists present at these lectures contributed greatly to my understanding of their professional interests and problems.

No one mentioned or unnamed merits blame for errors, misconceptions, erroneous interpretations, and other flaws that may appear in these pages. For some writing ventures the rule of *caveat emptor* may be appropriate, but to this book, since I alone am responsible for its contents, the principle of *caveat actor* necessarily applies.

ARNOLD A. ROGOW

New York City
June 15, 1969

Notes

Preface

1. Clyde Kluckhohn and Henry A. Murray (eds.), *Personality in Nature, Society, and Culture* (New York: Knopf, 1965), 59.

2. Morris Parloff, Norman Goldstein, and Boris Iflund, "Communication of Values and Therapeutic Change," *Archives of General Psychiatry,* 2 (March, 1960), 302. See also Parloff, Iflund, and Goldstein, "Communication of 'Therapy Values' Between Therapist and Schizophrenic Patients," *Journal of Nervous and Mental Disease,* 130, 3 (March, 1958), 193–99; Georgene H. Seward, "The Relations Between Psychoanalytic School and Value Problems in Therapy," *American Journal of Psychoanalysis,* 22, 2 (1962), 138–52; David Rosenthal, "Changes in Some Moral Values Following Psychotherapy," *Journal of Consultative Psychology,* 19 (1955), 431–37; Danuta Ehrlich and Daniel N. Weiner, "The Measurement of Values in Psychotherapeutic Settings," *Journal of General Psychology,* 64 (1961), 359–72; Anselm Strauss *et al., Psychiatric Ideologies and Institutions* (New York: Free Press of Glencoe, 1964); Werner Wolff, *Contemporary Psychotherapists Examine Themselves* (Springfield, Ill.: Thomas, 1956); Charlotte Buhler, *Values in Psychotherapy* (New York: Free Press of Glencoe, 1962); Perry London, *The Modes and Morals of Psychotherapy* (New York: Holt, Rinehart, and Winston, 1964); Sol W. Ginsburg, *A Psychiatrist's Views on Social Issues* (New York: Columbia, 1963); Seymour L. Halleck, "Psychiatry and the Status Quo," *Archives of General Psychiatry,* 19 (September, 1968), 257–65.

It is unfortunate that very little effort has been made to compare the values of psychiatrists and analysts with those of their patients and other professionals. An outstanding example of systematic values analysis in psychiatry is Robert Rubenstein and Harold D. Lasswell, *The Sharing of Power in a Psychiatric Hospital* (New Haven: Yale University Press, 1966), in which the value positions of staff and patients of the Yale Psychiatric Institute are compared. The value categories used are: power, enlightenment, wealth, well-being, skill, affection, respect, and rectitude.

Designed by Lasswell for the purpose of comparative study irrespective of whether the objects of study are individuals or entire groups, the eight value categories are best understood by reference to the larger map of which they are part. This map is concerned with a fundamental characteristic of man, namely, that he is in perpetual interaction with other men and with the physical environment. In this interaction individuals or groups of men seek value outcomes ("preferred events"). The overriding postulate is "maximization," or, to phrase it in a somewhat more sophisticated form, "optimization." The latter term implies that a commitment to one preferred outcome would have yielded at least *some* gratification. This is "opportunity" cost.

The generalized social process model, then, is "man" striving to optimalize "values" ("preferred outcomes") through "institutions" using "resources."

In examining an individual the problem is to describe his personality system, which is composed of the relatively stable patterns of interaction that he displays in reference to himself and others during the various time periods of his career. The "personality system" is composed of the primary ego references ("I," "me") and the secondary ego references ("he," "you," "they") which are included in the "self": the "value demands" and "expectations" for the self as a whole or its components (family, profession, etc.). The patterns are his values and practices. Value priorities either conform with or deviate from a group's priorities; and the practices conform to or deviate from the practices of a group. Since the individual has been exposed to various social environments, his personality has developed according to the net value expectations and realizations that have occurred in the past.

The study of an individual for the purpose of ascertaining his value priorities calls for several kinds of data: direct statements (explicit declarations of positive or negative preference or volition); indirect statements (such as presentation of the self as receiving value indulgences or deprivations, and as imposing indulgences or deprivations on others).

As in any study of an individual, it is necessary to distinguish between "conscious" and "unconscious" value orientations. The unconscious orientations, in turn, are "superego" or "id" patterns. The unconscious patterns may add intensity to some conscious value objectives (such as the demand to live up to professional obligations); or they may be in conflict with them (as when the demand to act like a white Protestant, acquired in childhood, is aroused by a Catholic, or Jewish, or Negro patient). The unconscious component may be with or without influence or behavioral expression.

Power in value terms is defined as a demand to play a role in important decisions. It is easy to recognize when it is explicitly articulated in reference to conventional political (or near-political) institutions in the community (municipal, state, national, international government; political parties; pressure groups; professional associations). It is more subtle in intimate circles. In the extreme form—the demand to impose one's will on others—the demand may be largely unconscious, having been repressed, suppressed, or rejected in the course of growth.

Enlightenment is the demand to know. It is manifested in the desire to contribute to knowledge and to obtain knowledge from others. Enlightenment not only includes demands in regard to knowledge: it covers news about the social environment where choices and decisions are made.

Wealth is control over the services or resources, and is positively exhibited in the demand to accumulate a fortune.

Well-being refers to safety, health, and comfort. It includes (negatively) the demand to escape anxiety or (positively) to achieve euphoria.

Skill is opportunity to acquire and exercise manual, intellectual, or social skills. It includes occupational, professional, and artistic techniques.

Affection is opportunity to give and receive love and loyalty. (Negatively, indifference.)

Respect is opportunity to give and receive recognition. (Negatively, contempt.)

Rectitude is opportunity to act responsively in terms of religious and ethical criteria. (Negatively, guilt.)

While no effort has been made in the present study to interpret the value preferences of the psychiatrists and the analysts in terms of these eight categories, there is every reason to think that interactions between therapists and patients lend themselves to such interpretation. Indeed, all of the eight value categories are involved, directly or indirectly, in psychiatric practice whatever the locale. For some nonpsychiatric applications of these value categories see Harold D. Lasswell, *Power and Personality* (New York, Norton, 1948); and Arnold A. Rogow and Harold D. Lasswell, *Power, Corruption, and Rectitude* (Englewood Cliffs, New Jersey: Prentice-Hall, 1963).

3. Letter to Sir Frederick Pollock, May 26, 1919, quoted in Max Lerner (ed.), *The Mind and Faith of Justice Holmes* (Boston: Little, Brown and Co., 1946), 444.

Chapter I

1. The monthly column in *McCall's,* which was originally written by psychiatrist Theodore Isaac Rubin, is called "A Psychiatrist's Notebook." Rubin, author of the novels *David and Lisa,* subsequently made into a movie, and *The 29th Summer,* has also written such popular works as *The Winner's Notebook, The Thin Book by a Formerly Fat Psychiatrist,* and *The Angry Book.* The *Cosmopolitan* column, contributed by psychiatrist Renatus Hartogs, is titled "Analyst's Couch." In 1969 the *McCall's* psychiatric columnist was Gerald Caplan.

2. New York: Houghton Mifflin Co., 1966.

3. *Encounter,* February, 1967, 91. Nabokov, of course, as he made clear in *Lolita,* has never been friendly to psychiatry. Reviewers of the Freud-Bullitt book, almost all of whom were hostile, included psychiatrist Robert Coles (*New Republic,* January 28, 1967); psychoanalysts Erik H. Erikson (*New York Review of Books,* February 9, 1967), Henry Lowenfeld (*Psychoanalytic Quarterly,* April, 1967), and Thomas Szasz (*National Review,* March 21, 1967); historians Richard Hofstadter (*New York Review of Books,* February 9, 1967), Arthur Link (*Harper's,* April, 1967), and Barbara Tuchman (*Atlantic Monthly,* February, 1967). George Steiner reviewed the book for the *New Yorker* of January 21, 1967, and *Encounter* published reviews by Philip Rieff and Marcus Cumliffe. For a somewhat more sympathetic treatment of *Thomas Woodrow Wilson,* see the present author's article "Reviewing Reviews" in *Medical Opinion & Review,* June, 1967.

4. Quoted from George Steiner, *Language and Silence* (London: Faber, 1967), in Nicolas Krasso, "Words, Words, Words," *New Statesman,* October 20, 1967.

5. Abby Rand, "Davos: Yesterday and Today," New York *Times* Sunday travel section, October 15, 1967.

6. Review of E. S. Turner, *Taking the Cure* (London: Michael Joseph, 1967), in the *Economist,* September 30, 1967.

7. Wylie Sypher in *Book Week,* September 25, 1966.

8. Alfred Kazin, "The Language of Pundits," in Charles Rolo (ed.), *Psychiatry in American Life* (New York: Delta, 1966), 193–207. For further evidence of the decline of psychoanalysis in intellectual circles, see Donald M. Kaplan, "Psychoanalysis: The Decline of a Golden Craft," *Harper's,* February, 1967, 41–46; Alasdair MacIntyre, "The Psycho-analysts: The Future of an Illusion?" *Encounter,* May, 1965, 38–43.

9. Portrayals of psychiatrists in fiction are discussed in Charles Winick, "The Psychiatrist in Fiction," *Journal of Nervous and Mental Disease,* 136, 1 (January, 1963), 43–57; Marjorie C. Meehan, "Psychiatrists Portrayed in Fiction," *Journal of the American Medical Association,* 188, 3 (April 20, 1964), 255–58. Paul Rom, "Psychiatry in Modern Novels," *International*

Journal of Social Psychiatry, 11, 1 (Winter, 1965), 70–77. The psychiatrist in cartoons is dealt with in Henry A. Davidson, "The Image of the Psychiatrist," *American Journal of Psychiatry,* 121, 4 (October, 1964), 329–34. For a discussion of jokes about psychiatrists, see Arnold R. Beisser, "Transference and Countertransference in the Psychiatric Joke," *American Journal of Psychiatry,* 17, 1 (January, 1963), 78–82. According to Rom, the *Comprehensive Fiction Index* for 1945–60 lists under "psychiatrist" fifty-five novels. The best-known novels since 1940 in which psychiatrists figure prominently are undoubtedly Graham Greene's *The Ministry of Fear* (1943), Henry Bellerman's *King's Row* (1941), Arthur Koestler's *Arrival and Departure* (1944), and Leo Rosten's *Captain Newman, M.D.* (1961). A psychiatrist is a central figure in T. S. Eliot's *The Cocktail Party* (1950).

10. Quoted in the New York *Times,* March 29, 1969. See also the New York *Times* for March 13, 20, and 21, 1969. Another example among many is the trial of Duane Pope, who killed three employees during a bank robbery in Big Springs, Nebraska, June, 1965. Following psychiatric testimony that Pope was suffering from schizophrenia, Dr. Groves B. Smith, a psychiatrist attached to the Menard (Illinois) State Penitentiary, stated that, in his opinion, there was no evidence either of schizophrenia or of "uncontrollable impulses" in the defendant. Asked how, employing the same data as other psychiatrists, he could disagree so sharply with them, Smith explained that differences were possible because "their philosophy is based on theories of psychoanalysis which I have not accepted." He added, "It represents a difference in our training." New York *Times,* November 30, 1965. See also "Psychiatry Said to Hinder Justice," in the New York *Times,* May 23, 1966, and "Don't Play 'Dr. Fixit' Even if Judge Asks, Psychiatrists Told," in *Medical Tribune,* January 18, 1963. For discussion of international legal and psychiatric issues, see Jay Katz, Joseph Goldstein, and Alan M. Dershowitz, *Psychoanalysis, Psychiatry, and Law* (New York: Free Press, 1967); Seymour L. Halleck, *Psychiatry and the Dilemmas of Crime* (New York: Harper & Row, 1967); Thomas S. Szasz, *Psychiatric Justice* (New York: Macmillan Co., 1965); and Manfred Guttmacher, *The Role of Psychiatry in Law* (Springfield, Ill.: Charles C. Thomas, 1968).

11. Adolf Meyer was Zelda Fitzgerald's analyst, according to John Dos Passos, *The Best Times* (New York: New American Library, 1966), 209. See also Frank Conroy, *Stop-time* (New York: Viking, 1967), 6.

12. Andrew Boyle, *Montagu Norman: A Biography* (London: Cassell, 1967).

13. Quoted by Peter Quennell in his review of Leonard Woolf, *Downhill All the Way: An Autobiography of the Years 1919–1939* (New York: Harcourt, Brace & World, 1967), in *New York Times Book Review,* October 29, 1967.

14. O. H. Mowrer, "Changing Conceptions of the Unconscious," *Journal of Nervous and Mental Disease,* 129, 3 (September, 1959), 222–34.

15. Abram Kardiner, Aaron Karush, and Lionel Ovesey, "A Methodological Study of Freudian Theory," *International Journal of Psychiatry,* 2, 5 (September, 1966), 576, 580. Reprinted from *Journal of Nervous and Mental Disease,* 129, 1 (July, 1959). Kardiner presumably is referring to Erik H. Erikson's study of Sioux childhood in *Childhood and Society* (New York: Norton, 1950), 98–141.

16. Theodore Lidz, "Adolf Meyer and American Psychiatry," *American Journal of Psychiatry,* 123, 3 (September, 1966), 330–31. See also his "Psycho-

analytic Theories of Development and Maldevelopment: Some Recapitulations," *American Journal of Psychoanalysis,* 27, 2 (1967), 115–26.

17. Ernest R. Hilgard in *International Journal of Psychiatry,* 2, 5 (September, 1966), 549–50.

18. Roy R. Grinker, Sr., "Conceptual Progress in Psychoanalysis," in Judd Marmor (ed.), *Modern Psychoanalysis: New Directions and Perspectives* (New York: Basic Books, 1968), 19–43.

19. "Psychiatry Rides Madly in All Directions," *Archives of General Psychiatry,* 10, 3 (March, 1964), 228–34.

20. Lawrence S. Kubie, "Missing and Wanted: Heterodoxy in Psychiatry and Psychoanalysis," *Journal of Nervous and Mental Disease,* 137, 4 (October, 1963), 311.

21. A review of psychological studies using only one subject demonstrated that over a twenty-five-year period (1939–63) "a total of 246 reports of studies with one subject appeared in the leading American journals of psychology." W. F. Dukes, "N = 1," *Psychological Bulletin,* 64, 1, 74–79. Summarized in *American Journal of Orthopsychiatry,* 37, 1 (January, 1967), 171.

22. Meyer Maskin, "Adaptations of Psychoanalytic Technique in Specific Disorders," in Jules H. Masserman (ed.), *Science and Psychoanalysis,* Vol. III. *Psychoanalysis and Human Values* (New York: Grune & Stratton, 1960), 321–52.

23. The Schreber case is analyzed by Freud in "A Case of Paranoia (Dementia Paranoides) (1911)," *Collected Papers,* III (London: Hogarth Press, 1949), 387–70. Others analyzed by Freud sight unseen, so to speak, include Moses, Michelangelo, Leonardo da Vinci, and, assuming he was in fact coauthor with William Bullitt of one of 1966's most controversial books, Woodrow Wilson.

24. Burton S. Glick in *Medical Opinion & Review,* January, 1966, 117.

25. "Cream puff psychiatry" is Paul Hoch's phrase; the remainder of the statement is from Milton Greenblatt, "A New Image to Gladden Our Hearts," *American Journal of Psychiatry,* 123, 2 (August, 1966), 199.

26. Allen Wheelis, "To Be a God," *Commentary,* August, 1963. Reprinted in *The Illusionless Man* (New York: Norton, 1966), 147–87. And again: ". . . ten patients a day now, make more money, pay more taxes, buy more stocks and better clothes, worry about practice, reputation, Russians, cholesterol . . . the same old things. Is this the way to live? Is there a choice?" (155).

27. A small number of psychiatrists, of whom the leading spokesmen are Thomas S. Szasz and Joost A. M. Meerloo, have questioned whether the so-called drug revolution has already gone too far; they refer to the tranquilizers, antidepressants, and other mood-changing drugs as "chemical straitjackets."

28. A foremost representative of this position, British psychologist H. J. Eysenck, has put the percentage of spontaneous recoveries at two-thirds. See his trilogy: *Uses and Abuses of Psychology, Sense and Nonsense in Psychology,* and *Fact and Fiction in Psychology* (London: Penguin, 1965).

29. The major figure in behavior is Joseph Wolpe, who asserts, in flat contradiction to the psychoanalysts, that "there is no scientific evidence for

the Freudian conception of neurosis as the result of a repressed complex. Contrary to the popular psychoanalytic conception, a neurosis is just a habit. . . . Get rid of the symptoms and you have eliminated the neurosis." Quoted in Morton M. Hunt, "A Neurosis Is 'Just' a Bad Habit," *New York Times Magazine,* June 4, 1967.

30. Samuel A. Stouffer, "Indices of Psychological Illness," in Paul F. Lazarsfeld and Morris Rosenberg (eds.), *The Language of Social Research* (New York: The Free Press of Glencoe, 1955), 63–65. Reprinted from Stouffer's *Measurement and Prediction, Studies in Social Psychology in World War II,* 4 (Princeton, N.J.: Princeton University Press, 1950), 473–77.

31. Celia S. Deschin, "The Future Direction of Social Work," *American Journal of Orthopsychiatry,* 38, 1 (January, 1968), 9–17.

32. New York *Times,* October 21, 1965. According to M. Brewster Smith as quoted in the *Times,* a partial explanation for the lack of correlation was the "over-concern" of psychiatrists for "adjustment and mental health."

33. Quoted from Israel Zwerling, *The Mental Health Potential of Urban Life for Children and Youth,* in Celia S. Deschin, *op. cit.* Critical studies of psychiatric methodologies may be found in Arnold P. Goldstein and Sanford J. Dean (eds.), *The Investigation of Psychotherapy: Commentaries and Readings* (New York: Wiley, 1966). See also Seymour L. Halleck and Milton H. Miller, "The Psychiatric Consultation: Questionable Social Precedents of Some Current Practices," *American Journal of Psychiatry,* 120, 2 (August, 1963), 164–69; and G. N. Raines and J. H. Rohrer, "The Operational Matrix of Psychiatric Practice: I. Consistency and Variability of Interview Impressions of Different Psychiatrists," *American Journal of Psychiatry,* 111, 10 (April, 1955), 721–33.

34. Robert A. Harper, *Psychoanalysis and Psychotherapy: 36 Systems* (Englewood Cliffs, N.J.: Prentice-Hall, 1959). Nosology problems in psychiatry—that is, problems of illness classification and nomenclature—have bedeviled the profession from the beginning, and even today there is little terminological precision. Thus, what one psychiatrist may label involutional melancholia may be called by another reactive depression and by a third paranoid schizophrenia. Karl Menninger has suggested that certain "dangerous words," especially those that frighten patients and their families and encourage feelings of hopelessness, be dropped altogether. "I avoid using words like schizophrenia," he wrote in 1964, "just as I avoid using words like 'wop' and 'nigger.'" *Saturday Evening Post,* April 25, 1964, 12 ff.

35. This point of view is common in the medical profession, where psychiatry and especially psychoanalysis have always been viewed with suspicion. See, for example, Seymour L. Halleck and Milton H. Miller, "Medical Criticisms of Psychiatry," *Psychiatry Digest,* December, 1966, 25–38. See also the editorial "Psychiatry and Progress" in *Medical Tribune,* September 5, 1966. *Medical Tribune,* which is circulated to all doctors in the United States, does not have a psychiatrist on its nine-man board of editors. For that matter, *The Great Doctors,* by Henry Sigerist, himself a physician and an eminent historian of medicine, deals with fifty doctors but no psychiatrists, not even Freud.

36. Roy R. Grinker, Sr., has long stressed the relevance to psychiatry of general system theory, the sophisticated use of statistics, laboratory techniques of experimentation, and controlled and rigorous clinical procedures. See his

"Conceptual Progress in Psychoanalysis," in Judd Marmor (ed.), *op. cit.*, and "'Open-System' Psychiatry," *American Journal of Psychoanalysis* (Fourteenth Karen Horney Lecture), 26, 2 (1966), 115–28. Psychiatric interest in the social sciences is reflected in the full-time or part-time presence in psychiatry departments of sociologists, anthropologists, and, in a few instances, political scientists. Training and research programs, involving departments of psychiatry and political science, are also under way. For a review of past experience and present prospects of such collaboration, see the present author's "Psychiatry, History, and Political Science: Notes on an Emergent Synthesis," in Marmor (ed.), *op. cit.*, 663–91.

37. Kenneth M. Colby, formerly a training analyst in the San Francisco Psychoanalytic Institute, is a pioneer in computerized psychiatry. Computers are already in use at the Institute of Living in Hartford, Connecticut, and at Rockland State Hospital, New York, where two computer languages, "Novel" and "Scribe," have been devised by George Simpson, director of research, and his associates.

38. Bruno M. Bettelheim, in "Review of Committee on Social Issues: Psychiatric Aspects of the Prevention of Nuclear War," *Bulletin of the Atomic Scientists,* 21, 6 (June, 1965), 55–56.

39. Frank Reissman and S. M. Miller, "Social Change Versus the 'Psychiatric World View,'" *American Journal of Orthopsychiatry,* 34, 1 (January, 1964), 29–38.

40. Robert Coles in *Atlantic Monthly,* July, 1961.

41. Robert Coles in a review of Tarsis' *Ward 7,* in *Dissent,* May–June, 1966, 320–23. *Ward 7* was published in the United States by E. P. Dutton; *One Flew Over the Cuckoo's Nest* by Viking Press.

42. The "series of striking similarities" was explored in the New York *Times,* March 13, 1969. In the *Times* of March 19, psychologist Martin M. Schorr explained that he had borrowed from James A. Brussel's *Casebook of a Crime Psychiatrist* (New York: Bernard Geis, 1968), solely in order to describe the "paranoid mechanism" and make his own diagnosis "more readable." The initial reaction of Brussel and his publisher was to sue for damages.

43. Thomas S. Szasz, *Law, Liberty, and Psychiatry* (New York: Macmillan Co., 1963), 15.

44. Thomas S. Szasz, *Psychiatric Justice* (New York: Macmillan Co., 1965).

45. Thomas S. Szasz, "Mental Illness Is a Myth," *New York Times Magazine,* June 12, 1966, 92. See also *The Myth of Mental Illness* (New York: Hoeber–Harper, 1961).

46. Paul Lowinger, "Psychiatrists Against Psychiatry," *American Journal of Psychiatry,* 123, 4 (October, 1966), 490–94.

47. Lowinger, *ibid.* See also Milton H. Miller and Seymour L. Halleck, "The Critics of Psychiatry: A Review of Contemporary Critical Attitudes," *American Journal of Psychiatry,* 119, 8 (February, 1963), 705–12; and Leo Rangell, "Psychoanalysis—A Current Look," *Journal of the American Psychoanalytic Association,* 15, 2 (April, 1967), 423–31.

48. Quoted in Ernest Jones, *The Life and Works of Sigmund Freud,* II, 57. James apparently addressed his remark to Jones following Freud's lectures at Clark University in 1909.

Chapter II

1. *Psychiatric News,* March, 1967.

2. Based on information supplied by the American Medical Association to Nora Piore and Sondra Sokal of the Urban Medical Economics Research Project.

3. See *Psychiatric Aspects of School Desegregation,* 37, May, 1957; *Sex and the College Student,* 60, November, 1965; and *Psychiatric Aspects of the Prevention of Nuclear War,* 57, September, 1954.

4. Urban Medical Economics Research Project, *Physicians in New York City,* March, 1967.

5. American Medical Association, *Distribution of Physicians, Hospitals, and Hospital Beds in the U.S., 1966* (Chicago: American Medical Association, 1967), 12.

6. Charles K. Kanno and Raymond M. Glasscote, *Private Psychiatric Hospitals: A National Survey,* a publication of the Joint Information Service of the American Psychiatric Association and the National Association of Mental Health (Washington, 1966).

7. *Psychiatric News,* September, 1967. See also American Medical Association, *op. cit.* The *Psychiatric News* study showed that departments of psychiatry employ more full-time PhD's than other departments.

8. American Medical Association, *op. cit.* Approximately 50 psychiatrists are attached to a variety of government agencies including the Peace Corps and the Arms Control and Disarmament Agency.

9. Bertram D. Lewin and Helen Ross, *Psychoanalytic Education in the United States* (New York: Norton, 1960); John A. P. Millet, "Psychoanalysis in the United States," in Franz Alexander, Samuel Eisenstein, and Martin Grotjahn (eds.), *Psychoanalytic Pioneers* (New York: Basic Books, 1966), 546–96; C. P. Oberndorf, *A History of Psychoanalysis in America* (New York: Grune & Stratton, 1953).

10. Millet, *op. cit.,* 560–63.

11. American Psychoanalytic Association *Newsletter,* 1, 1 (February, 1967); and Leo Loomie in *Bulletin of the American Psychonalytic Association,* 24, 1 (April, 1968), quoted in *Journal of the American Psychoanalytic Association,* 16, 2 (April, 1968), 340.

12. Leon Salzman in *Newsletter* of the American Academy of Psychoanalysis, 11, 2 (October, 1967), 14.

13. Millet, *op. cit.,* 560.

14. Robert P. Knight in Foreword to Robert R. Holt and Lester Luborsky, *Personality Patterns of Psychiatrists* (New York: Basic Books, 1958), vii.

15. Lewin and Ross, *op. cit.,* 91–100.

16. F. G. Ebaugh in *American Journal of Psychiatry,* 114, 6 (December, 1957), 560.

17. American Psychoanalytic Association, "Minimal Standards for the Training of Physicians in Psychoanalysis," *Journal of the American Psychoanalytic Association,* 4, 4 (October, 1956), 714–21.

18. *Ibid.,* 12.

19. According to information supplied by Osler L. Peterson, Department of Preventive Medicine, Harvard University Medical School.

20. Daniel H. Funkenstein, "The Problem of Increasing the Number of Psychiatrists," *American Journal of Psychiatry,* 121, 9 (March, 1965), 855–56.

21. *Ibid.*

22. Osler L. Peterson, Fremont J. Lyden, H. Jack Geiger, and Theodore Colton, "Appraisal of Medical Students' Abilities as Related to Training and Careers After Graduation," *New England Journal of Medicine,* 269, 21 (November 28, 1963), 1174–82.

23. D. C. Gilbert and D. J. Levinson in *Journal of Abnormal and Social Psychology,* 53 (1956), 263; G. M. Carstairs and A. Heron, "The Social Environment of Mental Hospital Patients: A Measure of Staff Attitudes," in M. Greenblatt, D. J. Levinson, and R. W. Williams (eds.), *The Patient and the Mental Hospital* (Glencoe, Ill.: The Free Press, 1957), 219–27. The latter reference is to a British study.

24. *Medical Tribune* (May 22, 1961), 21.

25. See footnote 19.

26. E. S. C. Ford, "Being and Becoming a Psychotherapist: The Search for Identity," *American Journal of Psychotherapy,* 17, 3 (July, 1963), 482.

27. A. Eisendorfer, "The Selection of Candidates Applying for Psychoanalytic Training," *Psychoanalytic Quarterly,* 28, 3 (July, 1959), 374–78.

28. Seymour L. Halleck and Sherwyn M. Woods, "Emotional Problems of Psychiatric Residents," *Psychiatry,* 25, 4 (November, 1962), 345.

29. *Ibid.,* 344. See also Robert R. Holt, "Personality Growth in Psychiatric Residents," *Archives of Neurology and Psychiatry,* 81, 2 (February, 1959), 214.

30. Allen Wheelis, "To Be a God," in *The Illusionless Man* (New York: Norton, 1966), 140–85. The tendency of some psychiatrists and psychoanalysts to view themselves as all-powerful is also dealt with in Myron R. Sharaf and Daniel J. Levinson, "The Quest for Omnipotence in Professional Training," *Psychiatry,* 27, 2 (May, 1964), 135–49. See also Bertram D. Lewin, "Education or the Quest for Omniscience," *Journal of the American Psychoanalytic Association,* 6, 3 (July, 1958), 389–412; and Judd Marmor, "The Feeling of Superiority: An Occupational Hazard in the Practice of Psychiatry," *American Journal of Psychiatry,* 110, 5 (November, 1953), 370–76.

31. Sharaf and Levinson, *ibid.,* 144. See also Ralph R. Greenson, "The Selection of Candidates for Psychoanalytic Training," *Journal of the American Psychoanalytic Association,* 9, 1 (January, 1961), 135–45.

32. Henriette R. Klein, *Psychoanalysts in Training—Selection and Evaluation* (New York: Department of Psychiatry, Columbia College of Physicians and Surgeons, 1965).

Chapter III

1. Sigmund Freud, *Civilization and Its Discontents* (London: Hogarth Press, 1930), 23.

2. In general, these findings are consistent with those of a Minnesota study reporting an increase in Protestants, especially Unitarians, and a decrease in Catholics and Jews, when the religion of psychiatrists is compared with that of their parents. Only 36 psychiatrists, or 60 percent of the Minnesota sample, declared that "they were currently active in their church affiliation. . . ." Carl P. Malmquist, "Psychiatry in a Midwestern Metropolitan Community," *Mental Hygiene,* 48, 1 (January, 1964), 55–65.

3. A study of Catholic psychiatrists and analysts lends support to the hypothesis that "psychoanalysis, especially of the classical Freudian brand, can and does serve people as a functional substitute for traditional religion." Ex-Catholics, it also appeared, were often less analytic and Freudian than other apostate religionists. John J. Lally, "Interrelationships of Statuses in Status-Sets: The Case of Catholic Psychiatrists" (unpublished PhD dissertation, Columbia University, Department of Sociology, 1968).

4. Arthur W. McMahon and Miles F. Shore, "Some Psychological Reactions to Working with the Poor," *Archives of General Psychiatry,* 18, 5 (May, 1968), 562–68.

5. See, for example, Robert E. Gould, "Dr. Strangeclass: Or How I Stopped Worrying About the Theory and Began Treating the Blue-Collar Worker," *American Journal of Orthopsychiatry,* 37, 1 (January, 1967), 78–86; June Jackson Christmas, "Sociopsychiatric Treatment of Disadvantaged Psychotic Adults," *ibid.,* 93–100; Morton Chethik, Elizabeth Fleming, Morris F. Mayer, and John N. McCoy, "A Quest for Identity: Treatment of Disturbed Negro Children in a Predominantly White Treatment Center," *ibid.,* 71–77; Leon A. Rosenberg and Harriet P. Trader, "Treatment of the Deprived Child in a Community Mental Health Center," *ibid.,* 87–92; Philip S. Wagner, "Psychiatry for Everyman," *Psychiatry,* 30, 1 (February, 1967), 79–90.

6. Joe Yamamoto, "Racial Factors in Patient Selection," *American Journal of Psychiatry,* 124, 5 (November, 1967), 636. Since the total patient group included only five persons of Oriental extraction, it was not possible to make any statistically significant judgment about their "popularity" status.

7. For a report on the topics dealt with by the black psychiatrists see *Medical Tribune,* May 29, 1969, including its editorial "Racism and Psychiatry."

8. *Psychiatric News,* August, 1967. In 1966 the National Center for Health Statistics, projecting from a sample of households containing 34,000 persons, reported that almost 1,000,000 people visit psychiatrists each year, averaging 4.7 visits each. The percentage of population consulting psychiatrists increased substantially with income and educational level. *Psychiatric News,* June, 1966.

9. Cf. Daniel J. Levinson, John Merrifield, and Kenneth Berg, "Becoming a Patient," *Archives of General Psychiatry,* 17, 4 (October, 1967), 385–406; Douglas H. Frayn, "A Relationship Between Rated Ability and Personality in Psychotherapists," *American Journal of Psychiatry,* 124, 9 (March, 1968), 1236–37; Jerome D. Frank, "The Influence of Patients' and Therapists' Expectations on the Outcome of Psychotherapy," *British Journal of Medical Psychology,* 41, Part 4 (December, 1968), 349–56.

10. George L. Engel, "Research in Psychoanalysis," *Journal of the American Psychoanalytic Association,* 16, 2 (April, 1968), 203. See also C. E. Schorer *et al.,* "Improvement Without Treatment," *Diseases of the Nervous System,* 29, 2 (February, 1968), 100–4.

11. *Psychiatric News,* March, 1968. The range was from 9 percent for male schizophrenics to 46 percent for males with depressive symptoms.

12. Fredric Wertham in Werner Wolff, *Contemporary Psychotherapists Examine Themselves* (Springfield, Ill.: Charles C. Thomas, 1956), 39.

13. H. Schjelderup, quoted in Nevitt Sanford, "Personality: Its Place in

Psychology," in Sigmund Koch (ed.), *Psychology: A Study of a Science,* 5 (New York: McGraw-Hill, 1963), 491–92.

14. *Psychiatric News,* December, 1966, quoting a press release "for a psychiatric facility in one of our large Eastern cities." In an editorial comment *Psychiatric News* noted, in tongue-in-cheek style, that if this statement were true, "the typical patient will have made himself an investment that puts Xerox and Syntex to shame."

Chapter IV

1. Theodor Reik, *Listening with the Third Ear* (New York: Farrar, Straus, 1948), quoted in Joseph M. Natterson, "Theodor Reik," in Franz Alexander, Samuel Eisenstein, and Martin Grotjahn (eds.), *Psychoanalytic Pioneers* (New York: Basic Books, 1966), 249.

2. On career satisfactions and problems, see also John MacIver and Frederick C. Redlich, "Patterns of Psychiatric Practice," *American Journal of Psychiatry,* 115, 8 (February, 1959), 692–97; and Benjamin Pasamanick and Salomon Rettig, "Status and Work Satisfaction of Psychiatrists," *Archives of Neurology and Psychiatry,* 81, 3 (March, 1959), 399–402.

3. *Medical Economics,* June 26, 1967, December 11, 1967, and March 4, 1968.

4. The following account of what constitutes "Basic Psychiatric Literature" is based on a study of 178 three-year training programs conducted in 1965 by Joan Woods and Shervert H. Frazier. Portions of the study, which was summarized in a monograph released in May, 1966, were published in the *American Journal of Psychiatry,* 124, 2 (August, 1967), 217–24.

5. Freud's books are: *The Basic Writings of Sigmund Freud*; *Collected Papers* (5 vols.); *The Ego and the Id; A General Introduction to Psychoanalysis; The Interpretation of Dreams; New Introductory Lectures on Psychoanalysis; An Outline of Psychoanalysis; The Problem of Anxiety; Three Contributions to the Theory of Sex.*

6. "Mourning and Melancholia" (1917), in *Collected Papers,* 4:8, 152–70; also in *Standard Edition,* 19, 183–87.

7. In *Collected Papers,* 5:30, 316–57.

8. David F. Musto and Boris M. Astrachan, "Strange Encounter: The Use of Study Groups with Graduate Students in History," *Psychiatry,* 31, 3 (August, 1968), 265.

Chapter V

1. William A. Glaser, "Doctors in Politics," *American Journal of Sociology,* 64, 3 (November, 1960), 230–45. As Glaser notes, this was not always the case. Five physicians signed the Declaration of Independence, of whom the best known, of course, was Benjamin Rush.

2. Cited from "The Doctor as Citizen," *Medical Economics,* 33 (May, 1956), 143, in Glaser, *ibid.,* 235.

3. Stanley Lesse, "Politics and Mail Order Psychiatry" (editorial), *American Journal of Psychotherapy,* 18, 4 (October, 1964), 559–60.

4. See "Diagnosis by Mail" (Editor's Notebook), *American Journal of Psychiatry,* 124, 10 (April, 1968), 1446–48.

5. In 1966, the vote for the antiwar resolution was 1,096 for, 197 against, representing a total of 46 percent of American Orthopsychiatric Association membership. The vote for the 1968 resolution calling for American withdrawal from Vietnam was 1,074 in favor, 348 against. At the 1967 annual meeting in Washington, about 500 American Orthopsychiatric Association members picketed the White House. A petition signed by 5,000 members, asking President Johnson to stop the bombing of North Vietnam, was presented to an official of the Department of Health, Education, and Welfare.

6. Quoted from *Medical Tribune* in *Psychiatric News,* April, 1968.

7. Quoted in *Psychiatric News,* December, 1968.

8. *Psychiatric News,* June, 1968.

9. *Medical Tribune,* October 31, 1968.

10. The test of attitudes toward the UN was based on an Elmo Roper survey of public opinion about the UN in "American Attitudes on World Organizations," *Public Opinion Quarterly,* 17, 4 (1953–54), 405–42. The six possible responses in the Roper survey and the percentile scores of the psychiatrists and analysts were as follows:

	Psychiatrists (144)	*Analysts* (34)
a. We shouldn't get tied up in any *more* alliances or joint commitments with other countries and we should aim at getting out of as many as we can as soon as we can.	2.8%	0.0%
b. We should continue to work along with the United Nations just about as we have been, gradually trying to make it better as time goes on.	20.8%	2.9%
c. We should immediately get behind *strengthening* the United Nations and do everything necessary to give it more power and authority than it has—enough to actually keep even a strong nation from starting a war.	38.2%	73.5%
d. In addition to continuing with the United Nations, we should also unite with the friendly democratic countries into one government in which each member nation would in effect become a state, somewhat like the different states in this country.	4.2%	0.0%
e. We should start now working toward transforming the United Nations into a real world government of *all* nations of the world, in which every nation would in effect become a state, somewhat like the different states in this country.	27.1%	20.6%
f. Some of these ideas are good, but we won't get any of them working in time to prevent war, so we'd better not rely on them.	6.9%	2.9%

11. See, for example, Myron R. Sharaf, Patricia Schneider, and David Kantor, "Psychiatric Interest and Its Correlates Among Medical Students," *Psychiatry,* 31, 2 (May, 1968), 157.

12. In an effort to determine what effects public events have on private lives, the American Psychoanalytic Association in 1968 sponsored a study of the Presidential election. The study, which is focused on the reactions to the election of patients and nonpatients, was directed by a number of analysts and political scientists in California and New York. Publication of the results is expected.

13. For explorations of health/personality-policy cases, see Hugh L'Etang, "The Health of Statesmen," *The Practitioner,* January, 1958, and his forthcoming book-length study of illness in high office; Arnold A. Rogow, *James Forrestal: A Study of Personality, Politics, and Policy* (New York: Macmillan Co., 1964); "Disability in High Office," *Medical Opinion & Review,* April, 1966; "Private Illness and Public Policy: The Cases of James Forrestal and John Winant," *American Journal of Psychiatry,* 125, 8 (February, 1969), 1093–97. Studies primarily focused on personality dynamics and motivations but which also deal with health factors include Alexander and Juliette George, *Woodrow Wilson and Colonel House: A Personality Study* (New York: John Day, 1956); Lewis J. Edinger, *Kurt Schumacher: A Study in Personality and Political Behavior* (Stanford: Stanford University Press, 1965); Victor Wolfenstein, *The Revolutionary Personality: Lenin, Trotsky, Gandhi* (Princeton: Princeton University Press, 1967); William H. Blanchard, *Rousseau and the Spirit of Revolt* (Ann Arbor: University of Michigan Press, 1967).

14. Books and articles dealing with these topics are too numerous to be listed here. For a partial bibliography, see Arnold A. Rogow, "Psychiatry, History, and Political Science: Notes on an Emergent Synthesis," in Judd Marmor (ed.), *Modern Psychoanalysis: New Directions and Perspectives* (New York: Basic Books, 1968), 663–91. A work focused on the implications for politics of Freudian theory is Paul Roazen, *Freud: Political and Social Thought* (New York: Knopf, 1968).

15. Quoted in Howard P. Rome, "Psychiatry and Foreign Affairs," *American Journal of Psychiatry,* 125, 6 (December, 1968), 726.

16. Quoted in Bryant Wedge, "Training for a Psychiatry of International Relations," *American Journal of Psychiatry,* 125, 6 (December, 1968), 731. See also Wedge, "Psychiatry and International Affairs," *Science,* 157 (July 21, 1967); Robert A. Clark, "Psychiatrists and Psychoanalysts on War," *American Journal of Psychotherapy,* 19, 4 (October, 1965), 540–58; Isidore Ziferstein, "Psychological Habituation to War: A Sociopsychological Case Study," *American Journal of Orthopsychiatry,* April, 1967; Ira L. Mintz, "Unconscious Motives in the Making of War," *Medical Opinion & Review,* April, 1968.

17. See his *Sanity & Survival: Psychological Aspects of War and Peace,* with a Preface by Senator J. William Fulbright (New York: Random House, 1968).

18. Advocating such an appointment, psychiatrist Harry Klein has argued that no one would deny an ordinary person the "right and benefit of a thorough diagnostic study" if he "exhibited a pattern of distorting reality, of operating through deception, and of not only admitting he might have started World War III but also continuing policies to achieve it. . . . Our President deserves no less an advantage. He as well as our country and the international community might have been spared our present agony." Letter in *Psychiatric News,* January, 1968.

19. See Chapter II.

20. Howard P. Rome, *op. cit.* The article was the lead one in the issue.

21. American Psychiatric Association committees and task forces created between 1966 and 1968 deal with such issues as foreign affairs, poverty, aggression, and violence.

22. The first program of this type was established in 1967 by the City University of New York. Administered jointly by the Department of Psychiatry of the Mount Sinai School of Medicine and the PhD program in political science of the City University's Graduate Center, the program is designed to provide political science graduate students with teaching and research training in the psychodynamics of political behavior.

23. Psychiatry, as the editorial noted, is not alone in moving toward an explicit concern with social problems. Since 1968, similar moves and urgings away from neutrality have been under way in the American Political Science Association, Modern Language Association, American Historical Association, and other professional organizations. While these developments were inspired by opposition to the Vietnam War and misgivings about President Johnson's leadership, they are not likely to disappear with an end to the war and a change of leadership.

Chapter VI

1. Lawrence K. Frank, *Society as the Patient: Essays on Culture and Personality* (New Brunswick, N.J.: Rutgers University Press, 1948).

2. Most of the statistics that follow are taken from *The U.S. Book of Facts, Statistics & Information for 1969* (officially published by the government as *Statistical Abstracts of the United States*) or *The World Almanac* for 1968.

3. According to Theodore Lidz, there are a "million or so illegal abortions" each year. Lidz, *The Person* (New York: Basic Books, 1968), 404. See also Lucy Freeman, *The Abortionist* (Garden City, N.Y.: Doubleday, 1962).

4. New York *Times,* April 9, 1967.

5. New York *Times,* January 7, 1967.

6. New York *Times,* December 10, 1968.

7. Joseph Downing, "Something's Happening," in *Medical Opinion & Review,* September, 1967, 100–6.

8. Joel Fort, "The AMA Lies About Pot," *Ramparts,* August 24, 1968, 12–16.

9. A. B. Hollingshead and F. C. Redlich, *Social Class and Mental Illness* (New York: Wiley, 1958); Jerome K. Myers and Lee L. Bean, in collaboration with Max P. Pepper, *A Decade Later* (New York: Wiley, 1968). See also Robert E. L. Faris and H. Warren Dunham, *Mental Disorders in Urban Areas* (Chicago: University of Chicago Press, 1939; Phoenix Books Edition, 1965); Leo Srole *et al., Mental Health in the Metropolis* (New York: McGraw-Hill, 1962); M. Harvey Brenner *et al.,* "Economic Conditions and Mental Hospitalization for Functional Psychosis," *Journal of Nervous and Mental Disease,* 145, 5 (November, 1967), 371–84; and M. Harvey Brenner, "Economic Change and Mental Hospitalization: New York State, 1910–1960," *Sozialpsychiatric* (Berlin: Springer-Verlag), 2, 4 (1967), 180–88.

10. *Medical Tribune,* July 30, 1962.

11. Quoted from *Time* magazine in *Psychiatric News,* September, 1968.

12. New York *Times,* September 23, 1968.

13. Mental illness as a cause of fatal automobile accidents is dealt with in the New York *Times,* December 24, 1965. For relationships between "nervous tensions" and fertility, see the report of a symposium on population control at the 1966 AAAS meeting in Washington, reported in the New York *Times,* December 28, 1966.

14. New York *Times,* March 9, 1968.

15. In Edward Bond's *Early Morning,* which opened at the Royal Court Theatre, London, in April, 1968.

16. In Rolf Hochhuth's *Soldiers,* as presented at the Royal Alexandra, Toronto, in March, 1968.

17. Norman S. Litowitz and Kenneth M. Newman, as quoted in the San Francisco *Chronicle,* July 19, 1967.

18. New York: Popular Library edition, 1962, 208–9.

19. R. D. Laing, *The Politics of Experience* (London: Penguin, 1967), 24. See also his *The Divided Self: A Study of Sanity and Madness* (London: Tavistock, 1960).

20. See, for example, Michel Foucault, *Madness and Civilization* (New York: Pantheon Books [Random House], 1965); George Rosen, *Madness in Society* (Chicago: University of Chicago Press, 1968).

21. Quoted in Paul Roazen, *Freud: Political and Social Thought* (New York: Knopf, 1968), 200.

22. *Ibid.*

23. Harold I. Lief in *Newsletter* of the American Academy of Psychoanalysis, April, 1968.

24. A pioneering organization in the field is the Mental Research Institute of Palo Alto, California. Under the direction of the late Don D. Jackson, the Mental Research Institute was among the first institutes to develop a training course for family therapists and, on the research side, to demonstrate that disturbed family relations could be important in the etiology of schizophrenia.

25. For a résumé of Karen Horney's views on marriage, see Harold Kelman, "Karen Horney on Feminine Psychology," *American Journal of Psychoanalysis,* 27, 2 (1967), 163–83.

26. These remarks were made before the films *The Graduate* and *Petulia* were shown, both of which deal with some of the themes discussed, and before the appearance on CBS Playhouse of Reginald Rose's *Dear Friends,* described as "a contemporary drama of four marriages." The plot summaries of the four, well worth reproducing here, were as follows:

> He is 44; she, 40. He had tried to be a writer and had failed. The climactic work of his career was a play which appeared on Broadway and closed after one week. Yet he has adjusted reasonably well to business. He makes perhaps $30,000 per year. Lois, a housewife, had visions of being an actress, then gave it up in favor of marriage and children. Both exceedingly decent and intelligent . . . separated now for three months because both are discontented, unhappy, unfulfilled. Michael has asked for a divorce. Lois has not agreed. Their separation is civilized.
>
> He is 42; she, 39. They have been married for 16 years and have a daughter.

Douglas earns approximately $25,000 per year. Their money needs to stretch beyond its endurance. Douglas is soft, gentle, humorous, home-loving. At home, endearing and unreal . . . at the office, a tyrant and very real. Sally, warm, gossipy, effusive, lacking in insight, has a yearning for romance, excitement, a need for social involvement. She is appealing, vulnerable and perhaps pathetic. One wonders how she fills her days. And nights.

He is 38; she, 31. He is an accountant, she, a housewife who writes children's books. He earns $15,000 per year. Her books bring in perhaps $3,000. They have been married for 10 years, have three children. Lenny is sharp, driving, ambitious, bright but sometimes crude. Charlotte is all-knowing without knowing, ready to argue, frustrating and frustrated, in competition with her husband. Lenny is constantly inconstant. A brittle but lively couple. Their outward relationship is a sham.

He is 46; she, 47. He is editor of a trade paper and ashamed of it. She is part owner of a shop in Greenwich Village. Their combined earnings total perhaps $17,500. They have been married for 21 years, no children. They have dabbled in Zen, strange Japanese diets . . . have somehow refused to grow up, although they give all the outward appearance of having done so. Leisure time is spent in near-desperate effort to remain youthful, they appear to be enormously affectionate.

New York *Times,* December 6, 1967.

27. A 1962 study of value orientations found that a sample of thirty psychotherapists, few if any of whom were psychiatrists, was less orthodox than samples of student nurses, religious fundamentalists, Jesuit priests, suburbanites, college undergraduates, and medical students. See Paul Verden and Archer L. Michael, "Cultural Unorthodoxy Among a Group of American Psychotherapists," paper read before the California Psychological Association, December 15, 1962.

28. The debate as to whether or not there has been a sexual revolution, initiated by the Kinsey reports of 1948 and 1953, shows no signs of abating. While many believe that sexual permissiveness and indulgence have significantly increased during the past twenty years, others are less certain that there has been any important change in sexual behavior as distinct from attitudes toward such behavior and more open discussions of sex, increasing nudity and availability of pornographic or suggestive material, more use of four-letter words, and so forth. There is also much argument about whether all or most aspects of the alleged sexual revolution are healthy developments, and here, again, psychiatrists are of several minds. For a discussion of some facets and implications of the sexual revolution, see Arnold A. Rogow and Harold D. Lesswell, *Sex, Culture, and Politics* (New York: Thomas Y. Crowell, 1970).

29. Quoted in the New York *Times,* May 14, 1967.

30. The Oberlin figure is based on a study of 1,071 women students at the college in 1968. Of the 40 percent, reported the study, one in thirteen had become pregnant, and more than 80 percent of these pregnancies had been terminated by abortion. New York *Times,* June 16, 1968.

31. Robert R. Bell, "Parent-Child Conflict in Sexual Values," *Journal of Social Issues,* 22, 2 (April, 1966), 34–44.

32. Thus, the president of Wellesley College, Dr. Ruth M. Adams, recommended in 1966 that students be given birth control information although

not contraceptive devices. The latter, said Dr. Adams, was a matter for the "student's private physician rather than the college." New York *Times,* March 22, 1966.

33. Quoted in the New York *Times,* May 20, 1967.

34. New York *Times,* August 27, 1968. *Fortune* magazine, in December, 1968, estimated that 750,000 college students "now identify with the New Left." New York *Times,* December 30, 1968.

35. Membership figures are taken from a New York *Times* summary (January 25, 1968) of an article by sociologist Seymour Martin Lipset of Harvard University. According to Lipset, two-thirds to three-quarters of students in 1966 and 1967 supported the war in Vietnam, and a plurality favored the Republican Party.

36. Herbert Jacobs, a member of the journalism department of the University of California, Berkeley, has pointed out that television and press reports of student demonstrations at Berkeley consistently doubled or trebeled the actual number present. This phenomenon, termed by Jacobs "crowdmanship," is, says Clark Kerr, a "game played by the sponsor, the police and the media alike. They all have an interest in raising the score. Thus a demonstration becomes bigger and more violent than it really was. A sit-in becomes a riot, then a rebellion and finally the 'revolution' at Berkeley." Clark Kerr in the *New York Times Magazine,* June 4, 1967. In an inquiry following the student demonstrations in France, May–June, 1968, the influential Paris newspaper *Le Monde* found that neither the students nor their spokesmen had read Marcuse, that "outside the sociology cadres at Nantes few had ever heard of him." According to George Steiner, the chief intellectual influences mentioned by the French students were Jarry, Sade, Lautreamont, Trotsky, Fanon, Kierkegaard, and, above all, Artaud, originator of the "theater of cruelty." See Steiner's "Books Behind the Barricades," the *Sunday Times* (London), July 28, 1968. Nevertheless, Marcuse continues to be regarded, in the words of the New York *Times* of October 6, 1968, as the "idol of the New Left and of restive college students from Berkeley to Bologna. . . ."

37. Anne H. and Irvin Ehrenpreis (ed.), *Boswell's Life of Samuel Johnson* (New York: Washington Square Press, 1965), 335.

38. There can be little doubt that student demonstrations, exaggerated by the mass media and exploited by conservatives in appeals to middle-class voters, played a role in the Gaullist electoral victory in France of July, 1968, and in the November, 1968, triumph of Richard Nixon. In West Germany, as was pointed out by novelist Günter Grass and playwright Rolf Hochhuth in September, 1968, student emphasis on revolutionary action tends, according to Hochhuth, "to frighten the middle class and throw votes to the National Democrats (the neo-Nazi party)." New York *Times,* September 29, 1968.

39. Seymour L. Halleck, "Psychiatric Treatment of the Alienated College Student," *American Journal of Psychiatry,* 124, 5 (November, 1967), 642–50. While Halleck is speaking of alienated college students who are not identical with hippies, much of what he says about their behavior is applicable to the hippie population, many of whom are school drop-outs. A generally similar point of view is presented by Jules H. Masserman, in "The Beatnik: Up-Down-, and Off-" *Archives of General Psychiatry,* 16, 3 (March, 1967), 262–67. Masserman's term for hippies is "off-beatniks." For an account of the prob-

lems involved in the psychiatric treatment of hippies, see Kay Tooley, "A Developmental Problem of Late Adolescence: A Case Report," *Psychiatry,* 32, 1 (February, 1968), 69–83.

40. During the summer of 1966 about 10 percent of the total student body at the University of California "engaged in projects such as these: tutoring Negro children in West Oakland; volunteer teaching in Watts; running a camp in the San Bernardino Mountains for disadvantaged children; serving as 'Amigos Anonymous' in villages in Mexico; cleaning up freeways and parks as a beautification project around Berkeley; teaching in San Quentin prison; running summer schools for the children of migratory workers in the San Joaquin and Sacramento Valleys; helping to construct an orphanage in Baja, California; working with delinquents in Riverside; providing free dental care to disadvantaged familes in Northern California; 'adopting' two orphanages in South Vietnam." Clark Kerr, *op. cit.*

41. Quoted in the New York *Times,* May 5, 1968.

42. Kenneth Keniston, *Young Radicals* (New York: Harcourt, Brace & World, 1968). See also Keniston, *The Uncommitted* (New York: Dell, 1967); *Journal of Social Issues,* 23, 3 (July, 1967); David L. Westby and Richard G. Braungart, "Class and Politics in the Family Backgrounds of Student Political Activists," *American Sociological Review,* 31, 5 (October, 1966), 690–92.

43. Benjamin B. Wolman, quoted in the New York *Times,* October 19, 1967.

44. Quoted in *Psychiatric News,* May, 1967. A similar point of view was featured in an advertisement for *Forbes* magazine in 1967 that pictured a long-haired boy, somewhat resembling John Lennon, over the caption: "The heir to American business." According to the ad, "The children who are bored with the world will soon be Congressmen. The girls in go-go cages will soon climb out and join the PTA."

45. A Harvard University study suggests that the incidence of psychiatric disorder among drop-outs is four times higher than among the general undergraduate population. However, psychiatric drop-outs have the same rate of return, attainment of honors, and graduation as those who drop out for other reasons. Armand M. Nicholi, Jr., "Harvard Dropouts: Some Psychiatric Findings," *American Journal of Psychiatry,* 124, 5 (November, 1967), 651–58. Personality and family patterns among drop-out students are reported in Edgar A. Levenson, Nathan Stockhamer, and Arthur H. Feiner, "Family Transactions in the Etiology of Dropping Out of College," *Contemporary Psychoanalysis,* 3, 2 (Spring, 1967), 134–57.

46. Quoted from *Look* magazine in *Psychiatric News,* July, 1967.

47. *American Journal of Psychiatry,* 124, 10 (April, 1968), 1450.

48. In January, 1966, Professor Max Siegel, an associate dean of students at Brooklyn College, reported that college admission officers were "skeptical" of students applying for admission who had undergone psychoanalysis or psychotherapy. A survey by *Psychiatric News,* inspired by Dean Siegel's remarks, found that such students, in general, were not automatically rejected, although cases of rejection were not unknown. The sample of psychiatrists polled by *Psychiatric News* disagreed on the importance of inquiries about mental health histories and on whether such information should be required of admission applicants. See *Psychiatric News,* February, 1967, and

March, 1967. In June, 1968, psychiatrist Daniel Funkenstein of Harvard stated that reports of psychiatrists on applicants seeking admission to Harvard who were under psychiatric treatment were "too long, too detailed, and too full of such things as the student's repressed fantasies" to be of much use. *Psychiatric News,* June, 1968. They continue to be required, however.

49. Mrs. Catherine Meline in the New York *Times,* November 12, 1967.

Chapter VII

1. André Malraux, *Anti-Memoirs* (New York: Holt, Rinehart and Winston, 1968), 4–5. Malraux is referring to Freud's 1909 paper "Notes Upon a Case of Obsessional Neurosis," commonly referred to as the "Case of the 'Rat Man.'" The paper is reprinted in *Collected Papers,* III (London: Hogarth Press, 1949), 293–383.

2. Interest in the future, reflected in the birth of such organizations as the World Future Society and its Journal, *The Futurist,* not to mention a number of seminars and "think tanks" on the future, has given rise in psychiatry to a variety of activities and published articles. In September, 1968, APA President Lawrence C. Kolb announced that there would be a special conference on "the Association's role in the evolution of a national program to provide adequate health services in this country in the decade ahead." *Psychiatric News,* September, 1968. For representative articles on the future by psychiatrists, see Edward H. Knight, "Psychotherapy—Quo Vadis?" *Psychiatry Digest,* August, 1968, 8–14; Lothar B. Kalinowsky, "Thoughts About the Future of Psychiatry," *American Journal of Psychiatry,* 121, 8 (February, 1965), 820–23; Leo H. Bartemeier *et al.,* "The Future of Psychiatry: Report of the Joint Commission on Mental Illness and Health," *American Journal of Psychiatry,* 118, 11 (May, 1962), 973–81; Bertram D. Lewin, "The Past and Future of Psychiatry," *Psychiatric Communications* (Western Psychiatric Institute and Clinic, University of Pittsburgh), 9, 1 (1967), 1–12. For a nonprofessional comment see Selig Greenberg, "Frontiers Beyond Freud," *The Progressive,* March, 1967, 22–25.

3. William Sargant, *The Unquiet Mind* (London: Heinemann, 1967).

4. Economist and philosopher Burnham P. Beckwith, in *The Futurist,* 2, 5 (October, 1968), 105.

5. For a survey of current developments in computerized psychiatry, see *Computers in Psychiatry, Supplement to the American Journal of Psychiatry,* 125, 7 (January, 1969).

6. *Walden Two,* first published in 1948, has been praised for its "behavioral engineering" approach to interpersonal and organizational problems, and condemned as a subtle work of propaganda for a totalitarian social system. Its author, Edgar Pierce Professor of Psychology at Harvard, is not known to be an enthusiast for psychiatry, and he is even less enamored of psychoanalysis.

7. *Psychiatric News,* March, 1967.

8. According to psychiatrist Joseph English, assistant director for Health Affairs in the Office of Economic Opportunity, quoted in *SK&F Psychiatric Reporter,* March–April, 1968, 2.

9. New York *Times,* April 3, 1969, and *Medical Tribune,* April 21, 1969. The study of a random sample of 1,034 Manhattan children was carried out

by the Department of Psychiatry of the New York University School of Medicine. According to Thomas S. Langner, one of the investigators, as quoted in the *Times,* "The disturbed 12 percent are the kind of kids that [Lee Harvey] Oswald and [Sirhan] Sirhan were. They have the worst potential in the country."

10. Stonewall B. Stickney, "Schools Are Our Community Mental Health Centers." *American Journal of Psychiatry,* 124, 10 (April, 1968), 1407–14.

11. *Wall Street Journal,* September 30, 1968.

12. "Orientation or Training: An Urgent Issue for Child Psychiatry" (Editor's Notebook), *American Journal of Psychiatry,* 124, 10 (April, 1968), 1450–51.

13. John K. Galbraith, *The Affluent Society* (Boston: Houghton Mifflin Co., 1958).

14. Charles K. Kanno and Raymond M. Glasscote, *Private Psychiatric Hospitals,* a publication of the Joint Information Service of the American Psychiatric Association and the National Association of Mental Health (Washington, 1966). See also *Psychiatric News,* April, 1968.

15. George W. Albee, "Give Us a Place to Stand and We Will Move the Earth," *Clinical Psychologist,* 20 (1966–67).

16. New York *Times,* March 24, 1969.

17. New York *Times,* February 12, 1969; *Psychiatric News,* March, 1969.

18. *Psychiatric News,* March, 1969. The study was conducted by the Joint Information Service of the American Psychiatric Association and the National Association for Mental Health.

19. For Kolb's views on these and other issues in psychiatry and psychoanalysis, see the interview with him in *Psychiatric News,* March, 1969. The literature on community mental health problems and their solution is extensive and growing rapidly. Two important sources of information are "Community Psychiatry," *Supplement to the American Journal of Psychiatry,* 124, 4 (October, 1967), 1–76; and GAP, *The Dimensions of Community Psychiatry,* Report No. 69 (April, 1968), 877–908. For the European experience with community mental health problems, see United States Department of Health, Education, and Welfare, Public Health Service, *Community Mental Health Services in Northern Europe,* 1965. The report deals with Great Britain, the Netherlands, Denmark, and Sweden.

20. At the end of 1968, 33 states had passed community mental health services legislation, but only 5 of these had provided for the full range of services called for in federal regulations. The essential services frequently not authorized were emergency services, inpatient services, and partial hospitalization. *Psychiatric News,* March, 1969. Altogether, there were an estimated 333 community mental health centers in full or partial operation in 1968.

21. On the halfway house experience in Europe, see Roger Mesmer, "European Psychiatry: Observations Concerning the Care of the Aged, Mentally Ill and Retarded," *Pennsylvania Psychiatric Quarterly,* 7, 1 (Spring, 1967), 47–62. For an interview with Elly Jansen, a young Dutch girl who is a crusader for halfway "hostels," see *Psychiatric News,* February, 1969. Since 1959, largely at Miss Jansen's instigation, some fifteen such "hostels" have been established in England, each one catering to the special

needs or problems of discharged mental patients (*e.g.*, alcoholism, schizophrenia, etc.). See also Max Silverstein, *Psychiatric Aftercare: Planning for Community Mental Health Service* (Philadephia: University of Pennsylvania Press, 1968).

22. These references to training programs are based on accounts in *SK&F Psychiatric Reporter* for May–June, September–October, and November–December, 1968. Se also E. Fuller Torrey, "The Case for the Indigenous Therapist," *Archives of General Psychiatry,* 20, 3 (March, 1969), 365–73. The term "indigenous therapist" refers to a person sanctioned by society to act as a psychotherapist without having been given training similar to that of a psychiatrist.

23. *Medical Tribune,* January 18, 1963.

24. Carl Malmquist, "A Critique of the Education of the Child Psychiatrist," *International Journal of Psychiatry,* 6, 4 (October, 1968), 302.

25. For the essentials of poetry therapy see Eli Greifer, *Principles of Poetry Therapy* (New York: Poetry Therapy Center, 1963); music therapy is discussed in Florence Tyson, "Therapeutic Elements in Out-Patient Music Therapy," *Psychiatric Quarterly,* 39:2 (April, 1965), 315–27; and "Music Therapy Practice in the Community," *Psychiatric Quarterly Supplement,* Part 1, 1966. For cinematic therapy see "Cinemafreud," in *SK&F Psychiatric Reporter,* September–October, 1968.

26. Edwin F. Alston, "Psycho-Analytic Psychotherapy Conducted by Correspondence," *International Journal of Psycho-Analysis,* 38, Part 1 (1957), 32–50.

27. An account of a Neurotics Anonymous meeting in Philadelphia is given in *SK&F Psychiatric Reporter,* November–December, 1967.

28. R. D. Laing, *The Politics of Experience* (Harmondsworth, Middlesex, England: Penguin Books, 1967), 41–45.

29. Cf. John Seeley, *The Americanization of the Unconscious* (New York: International Science Press, 1967).

30. Quoted in New York *Times,* April 17, 1968.

31. Philip Rieff, *The Triumph of the Therapeutic* (New York: Harper & Row, 1966), 21. The line quoted from Freud appears in his *New Introductory Lectures in Psychoanalysis,* reprinted in *The Standard Edition of the Complete Psychological Works of Sigmund Freud,* ed. James Strachey (London: Hogarth Press, 1953–), XXII, 80.

32. Harold I. Lief, "Presidential Message," *Newsletter of the American Academy of Psychoanalysis,* 11, 2 (October, 1967), 1–3.

33. Robert L. Spitzer and Jean Endicott, "Diagno II: Further Developments in a Computer Program for Psychiatric Diagnosis," in *Computers in Psychiatry, Supplement to the American Journal of Psychiatry,* 125, 7 (January, 1969), 20.

34. "The Program and the Patient," in *SK&F Psychiatric Reporter,* May–June, 1967, 3–6; see also Richard Stillman, Walton T. Roth, Kenneth Mark Colby, and C. Peter Rosenbaum, "An On-Line Computer System for Initial Psychiatric Inventory," in *Computers in Psychiatry,* 8–11; Mervin Rosenberg, Bernard C. Glueck, Jr., and Charles F. Stroebel, "The Computer and the Clinical Decision Process," *American Journal of Psychiatry,* 124, 5 (November, 1967), 595–99; Bernard C. Glueck, Jr., and Marvin Reznikoff,

"Comparison of Computer-Derived Personality Profile aand Projective Psychological Test Findings," *American Journal of Psychiatry,* 121, 12 (June, 1965), 1156–61.

35. *Psychiatric News,* January, 1969. The study was conducted at Camarillo State Hospital in California.

36. Geoffrey C. Knight, in *Psychiatric News,* May, 1968.

37. A comprehensive survey of biochemical research with relevance to psychiatry appears in Arnold J. Mandell and Charles E. Spooner, "Psychochemical Research Studies in Man," *Science,* 162 (December 27, 1968). See also Janet M. Anders *et al.,* "Chromosome Findings in Chronic Psychotic Patients," *British Journal of Psychiatry,* 114, 514 (September, 1968), 1167–75; "The Case of the Active Metabolite," *SK&F Psychiatric Reporter,* May–June, 1967. The cerebrospinal fluid test is reported in the New York *Times,* May 5, 1968; the lactate ion study in *Psychiatric News,* February, 1969. For a detailed summary of what is known and not known about the origins of schizophrenia, see Roy R. Grinker, Sr., "An Essay on Schizophrenia and Science," *Archives of General Psychiatry,* 20, 1 (January, 1969), 1–24.

38. Roy R. Grinker, Sr., "Psychiatry Rides Madly in All Directions," *Archives of General Psychiatry,* 10, 3 (March, 1964), 228–37.

39. For a presentation of this view see R. D. Laing, "Family and Social Contexts in Relation to the Origin of Pschizophrenia," in John Romano (ed.), *The Origins of Pschizophrenia* (The Hague: Exerpta Medica Foundation, 1967). A comprehensive survey of psychiatric theories bearing on schizophrenia is Don D. Jackson (ed.), *The Etiology of Schizophrenia* (New York: Basic Books, 1960). See also Robert E. Kantor and William G. Herron, *Reactive and Process Schizophrenia* (Palo Alto, Calif.: Science and Behavior Books, 1966).

40. As noted earlier, the leading figure in behavior is Joseph Wolpe. See his *Psychotherapy by Reciprocal Inhibition* (Stanford: Stanford University Press, 1958). The relationship of behavioral conditioning to learning theory has been intensely explored by Albert Bandura, especially in his *Principles of Behavioral Modification* (New York: Holt, Rinehart and Winston, 1965). See also his "Social-Learning Model of Deviant Behavior," in P. London and D. L. Rosenhan (eds.), *Abnormal Psychology* (New York: Holt, Rinehart and Winston, 1965).

41. The Esalen-type institutes and programs include Kairos in Rancho Santa Fe between Los Angeles and San Diego; the Tahoe Institute at Zepher Cove, Nevada; the Topanga Human Development Center in Los Angeles. There are close ties between Esalen (and its offspring) and the American Association for Humanistic Psychology (AAHP), one of the founders of which was Abraham Maslow.

42. Quoted in the New York *Times,* February 9, 1969.

43. Psychoanalysts and psychoanalytically oriented psychiatrists who have treated schizophrenics include Frieda Fromm-Reichmann, Harry Stack Sullivan, Otto Will, and John N. Rosen. Rosen's "psychoanalysis of psychotics" is discussed at length in his book *Direct Analysis: Selected Papers* (New York: Grune and Stratton, 1953). On the relationship between attitudes of hospital personnel and recovery of patients, see A. H. Stanton and M. S. Schwartz, *The Mental Hospital* (New York: Basic Books, 1954); J. F. Bateman and H. W. Dunham, "The State Mental Hospital as a

Specialized Community Experience," *American Journal of Psychiatry,* 105, 6 (December, 1948), 445; M. Greenblatt, D. J. Levinson, and R. H. Williams, *The Patient and the Mental Hospital* (Glencoe, Ill.: Free Press, 1957); and Erving Goffman, *Asylums* (New York: Doubleday, 1961).

44. Allen Wheelis, *The Illusionless Man* (New York: Norton, 1966), 155; William C. Menninger, *A Psychiatrist for a Troubled World* (New York: Viking, 1967).

45. Alfred North Whitehead in *The Organization of Thought,* quoted in Robert K. Merton, *Social Theory and Social Structure* (Glencoe, Ill.: Free Press, 1957), 3; Sigmund Freud, *Civilization and Its Discontents* (London: Hogarth Press, 1949) (first published in 1930), 144.

Bibliography

BOOKS

Adorno, T. W., *et al., The Authoritarian Personality*. New York, Harper & Row, 1950.
Alexander, Franz, and Selesnik, Sheldon T., *The History of Psychiatry*. New York, Harper & Row, 1966.
Alexander, Franz; Eisenstein, Samuel; and Grotjahn, Martin, eds., *Psychoanalytic Pioneers*. New York, Basic Books, 1966.
American Medical Association, *Distribution of Physicians, Hospitals, and Hospital Beds in the U.S., 1966*. Chicago, American Medical Association, 1967.
American Psychiatric Association, *A Psychiatric Glossary*, 3d ed., 1969.
Arieti, Silvano, ed., *American Handbook of Psychiatry*. New York, Basic Books, 1959–1966. 3 vols.
Bandura, Albert, *Principles of Behavioral Modification*. New York, Holt, Rinehart and Winston, 1965.
Binger, Carl, *Revolutionary Doctor: Benjamin Rush, 1746–1813*. New York, Norton, 1966.
Bishop, George, *The Psychiatrist*. Los Angeles, Sherbourne, 1968.
Blanchard, William H., *Rousseau and the Spirit of Revolt*. Ann Arbor, University of Michigan Press, 1967.
Boyle, Andrew, *Montagu Norman: A Biography*. London, Cassell, 1967.
Brand, Millen, *Savage Sleep*. New York, Crown, 1968.
Brenner, Charles, *An Elementary Textbook of Psychoanalysis*. New York, International Universities Press, 1955.
Buhler, Charlotte, *Values in Psychotherapy*. New York, Free Press of Glencoe, 1962.
Conroy, Frank, *Stop-time*. New York, Viking, 1967.
Davidson, Henry A., *Opportunities in a Psychiatric Career*. New York, Universal Vocational Guidance Manual, 1964.
Dos Passos, John, *The Best Times*. New York, New American Library, 1966.
Dumont, Matthew, *The Absurd Healer*. New York, Science House, 1968.
Durrell, Lawrence, *Tunc*. New York, E. P. Dutton, 1968.
Edinger, Lewis J., *Kurt Schumacher: A Study in Personality and Political Behavior*. Stanford, Stanford University Press, 1965.
Ehrenpreis, Anne H. and Irvin, eds., *Boswell's Life of Samuel Johnson*. New York, Washington Square Press, 1965.
Erikson, Erik H., *Childhood and Society*. New York, Norton, 1950.
———, *Identity: Youth and Crisis*. New York, Norton, 1968.
———, *Insight and Responsibility*. New York, Norton, 1964.
Eysenck, H. J., *Fact and Fiction in Psychology*. London, Penguin, 1965.
———, *Sense and Nonsense in Psychology*. London, Penguin, 1965.
———, *Uses and Abuses of Psychology*. London, Penguin, 1965.
Faris, Robert E. L., and Dunham, H. Warren, *Mental Disorders in Urban Areas*. Chicago, University of Chicago Press, 1939; Phoenix Books Edition, 1965.
Foucault, Michel, *Madness and Civilization*. New York, Pantheon Books, 1965.
Frank, Jerome D., *Sanity and Survival: Psychological Aspects of War and Peace*. New York, Random House, 1968.
Frank, Lawrence K., *Society as the Patient: Essays on Culture and Personality*. New Brunswick, N.J., Rutgers University Press, 1948.

Frazier, Shervert H., and Carr, Arthur C., *Introduction to Psychopathology*. New York, Macmillan, 1964.

Freeman, Lucy, *The Abortionist*. Garden City, N.Y., Doubleday, 1962.

Freeman, Walter, *The Psychiatrist: Personalities and Patterns*. New York, Grune & Stratton, 1968.

Freud, Anna, *The Ego and the Mechanisms of Defense*. New York, International Universities Press, 1946.

Freud, Sigmund, "Analysis of a Phobia in a Five-Year-Old Boy" (1909), *Collected Papers*, III. London, Hogarth Press, 1949.

———, "Analysis: Terminable and Interminable" (1937), *Collected Papers*, V. London, Hogarth Press, 1949.

———, "A Case of Paranoia (Dementia Paranoides)" (1911), *Collected Papers*, III. London, Hogarth Press, 1949.

———, *Civilization and Its Discontents* (1930). London, Hogarth Press, 1930.

———, "Morning and Melancholia" (1917), *Standard Edition*, 19. London, Hogarth Press, 1960.

———, "Notes upon a Case of Obsessional Neurosis" (1909), *Collected Papers*, III. London, Hogarth Press, 1949.

———, *An Outline of Psychoanalysis* (1940). New York, Norton, 1963.

Freud, Sigmund, and Bullitt, William, *Thomas Woodrow Wilson*. New York, Houghton Mifflin Co., 1966.

Galbraith, John K., *The Affluent Society*. Boston, Houghton Mifflin, 1958.

George, Alexander and Juliette, *Woodrow Wilson and Colonel House: A Personality Study*. New York, John Day, 1956.

Ginsburg, Sol W., *A Psychiatrist's Views on Social Issues*. New York, Columbia, 1963.

Goffman, Erving, *Asylums*. Garden City, N.Y., Doubleday, 1961.

Goldstein, Arnold P., and Dean, Sanford J., eds., *The Investigation of Psychotherapy: Commentaries and Readings*. New York, Wiley, 1966.

Green, Hannah, *I Never Promised You a Rose Garden*. New York, Holt, Rinehart and Winston, 1964.

Greenblatt, M.; Levinson, D. J.; and Williams, R. H., eds., *The Patient and the Mental Hospital*. Glencoe, Ill., Free Press, 1957.

Greenson, Ralph R., *The Technique and Practice of Psychoanalysis*. New York, International Universities Press, 1967.

Greifer, Eli, *Principles of Poetry Therapy*. New York, Poetry Therapy Center, 1963.

Group for the Advancement of Psychiatry, *The Dimensions of Community Psychiatry*, 69. April, 1968.

———, *Psychiatric Aspects of School Desegregation*, 37. May, 1957.

———, *Psychiatric Aspect of the Prevention of Nuclear War*, 57. September, 1954.

———, *Sex and the College Student*, 60. November, 1965.

Gurin, Gerald; Veroff, Joseph; and Feld, Sheila, *Americans View Their Mental Health*. New York, Basic Books, 1960.

Guttmacher, Manfred, *The Role of Psychiatry in Law*. Springfield, Ill., Charles C. Thomas, 1968.

Halleck, Seymour L., *Psychiatry and the Dilemmas of Crime*. New York, Harper & Row, 1967.

Harper, Robert A., *Psychoanalysis and Psychotherapy: 36 Systems*. Englewood Cliffs, N.J., Prentice-Hall, 1959.

Hartmann, Heinz, *Essays on Ego Psychology*. New York, International Universities Press, 1964.

Healy, William; Bronner, Augusta F.; and Bowers, Anna Mae, *The Structure and Meaning of Psychoanalysis*. New York, Knopf, 1930.

Hollingshead, A. B., and Redlich, F. C., *Social Class and Mental Illness*. New York, Wiley, 1958.

Holt, Robert R., and Luborsky, Lester, *Personality Patterns of Psychiatrists*. New York, Basic Books, 1958.

Horney, Karen, *New Ways in Psychoanalysis*. New York, Norton, 1939.

Jackson, Don D., ed., *The Etiology of Schizophrenia*. New York, Basic Books, 1960.

———, *Communication, Family, and Marriage,* Human Communication, 1. Palo Alto, Calif., Science and Behavior Books, 1968.

Jacob, Leah, *The Psychiatrist's Wife*. New York, Signet Books, 1966.

Jones, Ernest, *The Life and Works of Sigmund Freud,* II. London, Hogarth Press, 1955.

Jones, Kathleen, and Sidebotham, B., *Mental Hospitals at Work*. London, Routledge and Kegan Paul, 1962.

Kanno, Charles K., and Glasscote, Raymond M., *Private Psychiatric Hospitals: A National Survey*. Joint Information Service of the American Psychiatric Association and the National Association of Mental Health. Washington, 1966.

Kantor, Robert E., and Herron, William G., *Reactive and Process Schizophrenia*. Palo Alto, Calif., Science and Behavior Books, 1966.

Katz, Jay; Goldstein, Joseph; and Dershowitz, Alan M., *Psychoanalysis, Psychiatry, and Law*. New York, Free Press, 1967.

Keniston, Kenneth, *The Uncommitted*. New York, Dell, 1967.

———, *Young Radicals*. New York, Harcourt, Brace & World, 1968.

Kesey, Ken, *One Flew over the Cuckoo's Nest*. New York, Viking, 1962.

Kiev, Ari, ed., *Psychiatry in the Communist World*. New York, Science House, 1968.

Klein, Henriette R., *Psychoanalysts in Training—Selection and Evaluation*. New York, Department of Psychiatry, Columbia College of Physicians and Surgeons, 1965.

Kluckhohn, Clyde, and Murray, Henry A., eds., *Personality in Nature, Society, and Culture*. New York, Knopf, 1965.

Koch, Sigmund, ed., *Psychology: A Study of a Science,* 5. New York, McGraw-Hill, 1963.

Laing, R. D., *The Divided Self: A Study of Sanity and Madness*. London, Tavistock, 1960.

———, *The Politics of Experience*. London, Penguin, 1967.

Lasswell, Harold D., *Power and Personality*. New York, Norton, 1948.

———, *Psychopathology and Politics* (1930). New York, Viking, Compass Books Edition, 1960.

———, *World Politics and Personal Insecurity*. New York, McGraw-Hill, 1935.

Lazarsfeld, Paul F., and Rosenberg, Morris, *The Language of Social Research*. New York, Free Press, 1955.

Leonard, George B., *Education and Ecstasy*. New York, Delacorte, 1968.

L'Etang, Hugh, *The Pathology of Leadership*. London, Heinemann Medical Books, 1969.

Lewin, Bertram D., and Ross, Helen, *Psychoanalytic Education in the United States*. New York, Norton, 1960.

Lidz, Theodore, *The Person: His Development Throughout the Life Cycle*. New York, Basic Books, 1968.

Loewenstein, Rudolph M.; Newman, Lottie M.; Schur, Max; and Solnit, Albert J., eds., *Psychoanalysis—A General Psychology* (*Essays in Honor of Heinz Hartmann*). New York, International Universities Press, 1966.

London, P., and Rosenhan, D. L., eds., *Abnormal Psychology*. New York, Holt, Rinehart and Winston, 1965.

London, Perry, *The Modes and Morals of Psychotherapy*. New York, Holt, Rinehart and Winston, 1964.

Malraux, André, *Anti-Memoirs*. New York, Holt, Rinehart and Winston, 1968.

Marmor, Judd, ed., *Modern Psychoanalysis: New Directions and Perspectives*. New York, Basic Books, 1968.

Masserman, Jules H., ed., *Childhood and Adolescence: Scientific Proceedings of the American Academy of Psychoanalysis*. New York, Grune & Stratton, 1969.

———, *Science and Psychoanalysis, III: Psychoanalysis and Human Values*. New York, Grune & Stratton, 1960.

Menninger, Karl, *The Crime of Punishment*. New York, Viking, 1969.

———, *A Psychiatrist's World*. New York, Viking, 1959.

Menninger, William C., *A Psychiatrist for a Troubled World*. New York, Viking, 1967.

Mittler, Peter, *The Mental Health Service*. London, Fabian Research Series 252, 1966.

Moore, Burness E., and Fine, Bernard D., eds., *A Glossary of Psychoanalytic Terms and Concepts*. New York, American Psychoanalytic Association, 1967.

Mullahy, Patrick, ed., *The Contribution of Harry Stack Sullivan*. New York, Heritage House, 1952.

Myers, Jerome K., and Bean, Lee L., with Pepper, Max P., *A Decade Later*. New York, Wiley, 1968.

Myers, Jerome K., and Roberts, Bertram H., *Family and Class Dynamics in Mental Illness*. New York, Wiley, 1959.

Oberndorf, C. P., *A History of Psychoanalysis in America*. New York, Grune & Stratton, 1953.

Percy, Walker, *The Moviegoer*. New York, Popular Library, 1962.

Reiff, Philip, *Freud: The Mind of the Moralist*. New York, Viking, 1959.

———, *The Triumph of the Therapeutic*. New York, Harper & Row, 1966.

Reik, Theodor, *Listening with the Third Ear*. New York, Farrar, Straus, 1948.

Roazen, Paul, *Freud: Political and Social Thought*. New York, Knopf, 1968.

Rogow, Arnold A., *James Forrestal: A Study of Personality, Politics and Policy*. New York, Macmillan, 1964.

———, ed., *Politics, Personality and Social Science in the Twentieth Century: Essays in Honor of Harold D. Lasswell*. Chicago, University of Chicago Press, 1969.

———, and Lasswell, Harold D., *Power, Corruption, and Rectitude*. Englewood Cliffs, N.J., Prentice-Hall, 1963.

———, *Sex, Culture, and Politics*. New York, Thomas Y. Crowell, 1970.

Rolo, Charles, ed., *Psychiatry in American Lives*. New York, Delta, 1966.

Romano, John, ed., *The Origins of Schizophrenia*. The Hague, Excerpta Medica Foundation, 1967.

Rose, Arnold, M., ed., *Mental Health and Mental Disorder*. New York, Norton, 1955.

Rosen, George, *Madness in Society*. Chicago, University of Chicago Press, 1968.

Rosen, John N., *Direct Analysis: Selected Papers*. New York, Grune & Stratton, 1953.

Rubenstein, Robert, and Lasswell, Harold D., *The Sharing of Power in a Psychiatric Hospital*. New Haven, Yale University Press, 1966.

Rycroft, Charles, *Psychoanalysis Is Observed*. New York, Coward-McCann, 1966.

Sahakian, William S., ed., *Psychotherapy and Counseling*. Chicago, Rand McNally, 1969.

Sargant, William, *The Unquiet Mind*. London, Heinemann, 1967.

Schutz, William C., *Joy: Expanding Human Awareness*. New York, Grove Press, 1967.

Seeley, John, *The Americanization of the Unconscious*. New York, International Science Press, 1967.

Sigerist, Henry, *The Great Doctors*. Garden City, N.Y., Doubleday, 1933.

Silverstein, Max, *Psychiatric Aftercare: Planning for Community Mental Health Service*. Philadelphia, University of Pennsylvania Press, 1968.

Skinner, B. F., *Walden Two*. New York, Macmillan, 1961.

Srole, Leo, *et al.*, *Mental Health in the Metropolis*. New York, McGraw-Hill, 1962.

Stanton, A. H., and Schwartz, M. S., *The Mental Hospital*. New York, Basic Books, 1954.

Stouffer, Samuel A., *Measurement and Prediction, Studies in Social Psychology in World War II*, 4. Princeton, N.J., Princeton University Press, 1950.

Strauss, Anselm, *et al.*, *Psychiatric Ideologies and Institutions*. New York, Free Press of Glencoe, 1964.

Sullivan, Harry Stack, *Conceptions of Modern Psychiatry*. Washington, William Alanson White Psychiatric Foundation, 1947.

———, *The Psychiatric Interview.* New York, Norton, 1954.
Szasz, Thomas S., *Law, Liberty and Psychiatry.* New York, Macmillan, 1963.
———, *The Myth of Mental Illness.* New York, Hoeber-Harper, 1961.
———, *Psychiatric Justice.* New York, Macmillan, 1965.
Tarsis, Valeriĭ, *Ward 7.* New York, E. P. Dutton, 1965.
Telfer, David, *The Caretakers.* New York, Signet Books, 1959.
Urban Medical Economics Research Project, *Physicians in New York City* (March, 1967).
The U. S. Book of Facts, Statistics and Information for 1969.
Ward, M. J., *The Snake Pit.* New York, Signet Books, 1956.
Wheelis, Allen, *The Illusionless Man.* New York, Norton, 1966.
Whitehead, Alfred North, *The Organization of Thought,* quoted in *Social Theory and Social Structure,* by Robert K. Merton. Glencoe, Ill.: Free Press, 1957.
Wolfenstein, Victor, *The Revolutionary Personality: Lenin, Trotsky, Gandhi.* Princeton, N.J., Princeton University Press, 1967.
Wolff, Werner, *Contemporary Psychotherapists Examine Themselves.* Springfield, Ill., Charles C. Thomas, 1956.
Wolpe, Joseph, *Psychotherapy by Reciprocal Inhibition.* Stanford, Stanford University Press, 1958.
The World Almanac, 1969.
Zilboorg, Gregory, *A History of Medical Psychology.* New York, Norton, 1941.

ARTICLES CITED

Alston, Edwin F., "Psycho-Analytic Psychotherapy Conducted by Correspondence," *International Journal of Psycho-Analysis,* 38, Part 1 (1957), 32–50.
American Psychoanalytic Association, "Minimal Standards for the Training of Physicians in Psychoanalysis." *Journal of the American Psychoanalytic Association,* 4 (October, 1956), 714–21.
American Psychoanalytic Association, *Newsletter,* 1 (February, 1967).
Anders, Janet M., *et al.,* "Chromosome Findings in Chronic Psychotic Patients." *British Journal of Psychiatry,* 14 (September, 1968), 1167–75.
Bandura, Albert, "Social-Learning Model of Deviant Behavior," in P. London and D. L. Rosenhan, eds., *Abnormal Psychology,* New York, Holt, Rinehart and Winston, 1965.
Bartemeier, Leo H., *et al.,* "The Future of Psychiatry: Report of the Joint Commission on Mental Illness and Health." *American Journal of Psychiatry,* 118 (May, 1962), 973–81.
Bateman, J. F., and Dunham, H. W., "The State Mental Hospitals as a Specialized Community Experience." *American Journal of Psychiatry,* 105 (December, 1948), 445.
Beckwith, Burnham P., in *The Futurist,* 2 (October, 1968), 105.
Beisser, Arnold R., "Transference and Countertransference in the Psychiatric Joke." *American Journal of Psychiatry,* 17 (January, 1963), 78–82.
Bell, Robert R., "Parent-Child Conflict in Sexual Values." *Journal of Social Issues,* 22 (April, 1966), 34–44.
Bettelheim, Bruno M., "Review of Committee on Social Issues: Psychiatric Aspects of the Prevention of Nuclear War." *Bulletin of the Atomic Scientists,* 21 (June, 1965), 55–56.
Brenner, M. Harvey, "Economic Change and Mental Hospitalization: New York State, 1910–1960." *Sozialpsychiatrie,* 2 (1967), 180–88.
Brenner, M. Harvey, *et al.,* "Economic Conditions and Mental Hospitalization for Functional Psychosis." *Journal of Nervous and Mental Disease,* 145 (November, 1967), 371–84.
Brown, G. W., and Wing, J. K., "A Comparative Clinical and Social Survey of Three Mental Hospitals." *Sociological Review Monograph,* 5 (1962).
Carstairs, G. M., and Heron, A., "The Social Environment of Mental Hospital

Patients: A Measure of Staff Attitudes," in M. Greenblatt, D. J. Levinson, and R. W. Williams, eds., *The Patient and the Mental Hospital.* Glencoe, Ill., Free Press, 1957.

Chethik, Morton; Fleming, Elizabeth; Mayer, Morris F.; and McCoy, John N., "A Quest for Identity: Treatment of Disturbed Negro Children in a Predominantly White Treatment Center." *American Journal of Orthopsychiatry,* 37 (January, 1967), 71–77.

Christmas, June Jackson, "Sociopsychiatric Treatment of Disadvantaged Psychotic Adults." *American Journal of Orthopsychiatry,* 37 (January, 1967), 93–100.

Clark, Robert A., "Psychiatrists and Psychoanalysts on War." *American Journal of Psychotherapy,* 19 (October, 1965), 540–58.

Coles, Robert, "Young Psychiatrist Looks at His Profession." *Atlantic Monthly* (July, 1961), 108–11.

———, Review of *Thomas Woodrow Wilson,* by Sigmund Freud and William Bullitt. *New Republic* (January 28, 1967), 27–30.

———, Review of *Ward 7* by Valeriĭ Tarsis. *Dissent* (May–June, 1966), 320–23.

Committee on Public Information of the American Psychoanalytic Association, *American Psychoanalytic Association Newsletter* (September, 1967).

"Community Psychiatry," *Supplement to the American Journal of Psychiatry,* 124 (October, 1967), 1–76.

"Computers in Psychiatry," *Supplement to the American Journal of Psychiatry,* 125 (January, 1969).

Cunliffe, Marcus, Review of *Thomas Woodrow Wilson,* by Sigmund Freud and William Bullitt. *Encounter* (July, 1967), 86–89.

Davidson, Henry A., "The Image of the Psychiatrist." *American Journal of Psychiatry,* 121 (October, 1964), 329–34.

Deschin, Celia S., "The Future Direction of Social Work," *American Journal of Orthopsychiatry,* 38 (January, 1968), 9–17.

"Diagnosis by Mail" (Editor's Notebook). *American Journal of Psychiatry,* 124 (April, 1968), 1446–48.

Downing, Joseph, "Something's Happening." *Medical Opinion & Review* (September, 1967), 100–6.

Dukes, W. F., "N = 1." *Psychological Bulletin,* 64, 74–79. Summarized in *American Journal of Orthopsychiatry,* 37 (January, 1967), 171.

Ebaugh, F. G., "Some Current Economic and Social Problems in Residency Training." *American Journal of Psychiatry,* 114 (December, 1957), 560.

Ehrlich, Danuta, and Weiner, Daniel N., "The Measurement of Values in Psychotherapeutic Settings." *Journal of General Psychology,* 64 (1961), 359–72.

Eisendorfer, A., "The Selection of Candidates Applying for Psychoanalytic Training." *Psychoanalytic Quarterly,* 28 (July, 1959), 374–78.

Engel, George L., "Research in Psychoanalysis." *Journal of the American Psychoanalytic Association,* 16 (April, 1968), 203.

Erikson, Erik H., Review of *Thomas Woodrow Wilson,* by Sigmund Freud and William Bullitt. *New York Review of Books* (February 9, 1967), 3–5.

Ford, E. S. C., "Being and Becoming a Psychotherapist: The Search for Identity." *American Journal of Psychotherapy,* 17 (July, 1963), 482.

Fort, Joel, "The AMA Lies About Pot." *Ramparts* (August 24, 1968), 12–16.

Frank, Jerome D., "The Influence of Patients' and Therapists' Expectations on the Outcome of Psychotherapy." *British Journal of Medical Psychology,* 41 (December, 1968), 349–56.

Frayn, Douglas H., "A Relationship Between Rated Ability and Personality in Psychotherapists." *American Journal of Psychiatry,* 124 (March, 1968), 1236–37.

Freeman, Walter, "Psychiatrists Who Kill Themselves: A Study of Suicide." *American Journal of Psychiatry,* 124 (December, 1967), 846–47.

Funkenstein, Daniel H., "The Problem of Increasing the Number of Psychiatrists." *American Journal of Psychiatry,* 121 (March, 1965), 855–56.

Gilbert, D. C., and Levinson, D. J., "Ideology, Personality, and Institutional Policy in the Mental Hospital." *Journal of Abnormal and Social Psychology,* 53 (November, 1956), 263.

Glaser, William A., "Doctors in Politics." *American Journal of Sociology,* 63 (November, 1960), 230–45.

Glick, Burton S., "Narcissism in Psychiatry." *Medical Opinion & Review* (January, 1966), 117.

Glueck, Jr., Bernard C., and Reznikoff, Marvin, "Comparison of Computer-Derived Personality Profile and Projective Psychological Test Findings." *American Journal of Psychiatry,* 121 (June, 1965), 1156–61.

Gould, Robert E., "Dr. Strangeclass: Or How I Stopped Worrying About the Theory and Began Treating the Blue-Collar Worker." *American Journal of Orthopsychiatry,* 37 (January, 1967), 78–86.

Greenberg, Selig, "Frontiers Beyond Freud." *The Progressive* (March, 1967), 22–25.

Greenblatt, Milton, "A New Image to Gladden Our Hearts." *American Journal of Psychiatry,* 123 (August, 1966), 199.

Greenson, Ralph R., "The Selection of Candidates for Psychoanalytic Training." *Journal of the American Psychoanalytic Association,* 9 (January, 1961), 135–45.

Grinker, Roy R., Sr., "An Essay on Schizophrenia and Science." *Archives of General Psychiatry,* 20 (January, 1969), 1–24.

———, "Conceptual Progress in Psychoanalysis," in Judd Marmor, ed., *Modern Psychoanalysis: New Directions and Perspectives.* New York, Basic Books, 1968.

———, " 'Open-System' Psychiatry." *American Journal of Psychoanalysis* (Fourteenth Karen Horney Lecture), 26 (1966), 115–28.

———, "Psychiatry Rides Madly in All Directions." *Archives of General Psychiatry,* 10 (March, 1964), 228–237.

Halleck, Seymour L., "Psychiatric Treatment of the Alienated College Student." *American Journal of Psychiatry,* 124 (November, 1967), 642–50.

———, "Psychiatry and Status Quo." *Archives of General Psychiatry,* 19 (September, 1968), 257–65.

Halleck, Seymour L., and Miller, Milton H., "Medical Criticisms of Psychiatry." *Psychiatry Digest* (December, 1966), 25–38.

———, "The Psychiatric Consultation: Questionable Social Precedents of Some Current Practices." *American Journal of Psychiatry,* 120 (August, 1963), 164–69.

Halleck, Seymour L., and Woods, Sherwyn M., "Emotional Problems of Psychiatric Residents." *Psychiatry,* 25 (November, 1962), 345.

Harris, Susan, Letter to the Editor. *New York Times Magazine* (December 10, 1967), 22, 39.

Hilgard, Ernest R., "Revision: From Inside or Outside?" *International Journal of Psychiatry,* 2 (September, 1966), 549–50.

Hofstadter, Richard, *Review of Thomas Woodrow Wilson,* by Sigmund Freud and William Bullitt. *New York Review of Books* (February 9, 1967), 6–8.

Holt, Robert R., "Ego Autonomy Re-Evaluated." *International Journal of Psychiatry,* 3 (June, 1967), 481–503. Reprinted from *International Journal of Psychoanalysis.*

———, "Personality Growth in Psychiatric Residents." *Archives of Neurology and Psychiatry,* 81 (February, 1959), 214.

Hunt, Morton M., "A Neurosis Is 'Just' a Bad Habit." *New York Times Magazine* (June 4, 1967), 38–39.

Jencks, Christopher, "Is It All Dr. Spock's Fault?" *New York Times Magazine* (March 3, 1968), 27.

Kahn, Melvin, "Students for McCarthy—What United Them." *Transaction* (July–August, 1968), 30.

Kahn, R. L.; Pollock, M.; and Fink, M., "Sociopsychologic Aspects of Psychiatric Treatment in a Voluntary Mental Hospital." *Archives of General Psychiatry,* 1 (December, 1959), 565–74.

Kalinowsky, Lothar B., "Thoughts About the Future of Psychiatry." *American Journal of Psychiatry,* 121 (February, 1965), 820–23.

Kaplan, Donald M., "Psychoanalysis: The Decline of a Golden Craft." *Harper's* (February, 1967), 41–46.

Kardiner, Abram; Karush, Aaron; and Ovesey, Lionel, "A Methodological Study of Freudian Theory." *International Journal of Psychiatry,* 2 (September, 1966), 576–80. Reprinted from *Journal of Nervous and Mental Disease,* 129 (July, 1959).

Kazin, Alfred, "The Language of Pundits," in Charles Rolo, ed., *Psychiatry in American Life.* New York, Delta, 1966.

Kelman, Harold, "Karen Horney on Feminine Psychology." *American Journal of Psychoanalysis,* 27 (1967), 163–83.

Keniston, Kenneth, "The Sources of Student Dissent." *Journal of Social Issues,* 23 (July, 1967), 108–37.

Kerr, Clark, "Clark Kerr Calls It the Exaggerated Generation." *New York Times Magazine* (June 4, 1967), 28–29.

Klein, George S., "Psychoanalysis: Ego Psychology." *International Encyclopedia of the Social Sciences,* 13. New York, Macmillan and the Free Press, 1968.

Klerman, Gerald F.; Sharaf, Milton R.; Holzman, Mathilda; and Levinson, Daniel J., "Sociopsychological Characteristics of Resident Psychiatrists and Their Use of Drug Therapy." *American Journal of Psychiatry,* 117 (August, 1960), 111–17.

Klinger, Eric, and Gee, Helen Hofer, "The Study of Applicants, 1957–1958." *Journal of Medical Education,* 34 (April, 1959), 432–35. Cited in *Psychoanalytic Education in the United States,* by Bertram D. Lewin and Helen Ross. New York, Norton, 1960.

Knight, Edward H., "Psychotherapy—Quo Vadis?" *Psychiatry Digest* (August, 1968), 8–14.

Knight, Robert P., "Foreword," in Robert R. Holt and Lester Luborsky, *Personality Patterns of Psychiatrists.* New York, Basic Books, 1958.

Kubie, Lawrence S., "Missing and Wanted: Heterodoxy in Psychiatry and Psychoanalysis." *Journal of Nervous and Mental Disease,* 137 (October, 1963), 311.

Laing, R. D., "Family and Social Context in Relation to the Origin of Schizophrenia," in John Romano, ed., *The Origins of Schizophrenia.* The Hague, Excerpta Medica Foundation, 1967.

Lehrman, Nathaniel S., "Anti-Therapeutic and Anti-Democratic Aspects of Freudian Dynamic Psychiatry." *Journal of Individual Psychology,* 19 (November, 1963), 167–81.

Lesse, Stanley, "Politics and Mail Order Psychiatry." *American Journal of Psychotherapy,* 18 (October, 1964), 559–60.

L'Etang, Hugh, "The Health of Statesmen and Affairs of Nations." *The Practitioner,* 180 (January, 1958), 113–18.

Levenson, Edgar A.; Stockhamer, Nathan; and Feiner, Arthur H., "Family Transactions in the Etiology of Dropping Out of College." *Contemporary Psychoanalysis,* 3 (Spring, 1967), 134–57.

Levinson, Daniel J.; Merrifield, John; and Berg, Kenneth, "Becoming a Patient." *Archives of General Psychiatry,* 17 (October, 1967), 385–406.

Lewin, Bertram D., "Education or the Quest for Omniscience." *Journal of the American Psychoanalytic Association,* 6 (July, 1958), 389–412.

———, "The Past and Future of Psychiatry." *Psychiatric Communications,* 9 (1967), 1–12.

Lidz, Theodore, "Adolf Meyer and American Psychiatry." *American Journal of Psychiatry,* 123 (September, 1966), 330–31.

———, "Presidential Message." *Newsletter of the American Academy of Psychoanalysis,* 11 (October, 1967), 1–3.

———, "Psychoanalytic Theories of Development and Maldevelopment: Some Recapitulations." *American Journal of Psychoanalysis,* 27 (1967), 115–26.

Link, Arthur, Review of *Thomas Woodrow Wilson,* by Sigmund Freud and William Bullitt. *Harper's* (April, 1967), 85–88.

Loomie, Leo, *Bulletin of the American Psychoanalytic Association,* 16 (April, 1968), 340–41.

Lowenfeld, Henry, Review of *Thomas Woodrow Wilson,* by Sigmund Freud and William Bullitt. *Psychoanalytic Quarterly,* 36 (April, 1967), 271–79.

Lowinger, Paul, "Psychiatrists Against Psychiatry." *American Journal of Psychiatry,* 123 (October, 1966), 490–94.

MacIntyre, Alasdair, "The Psycho-analysts: The Future of an Illusion?" *Encounter* (May, 1965), 38–43.

MacIver, John, and Redlich, Frederick C., "Patterns of Psychiatric Practice." *American Journal of Psychiatry,* 115 (February, 1959), 692–97.

Malmquist, Carl P., "A Critique of the Education of the Child Psychiatrist." *International Journal of Psychiatry,* 6 (October, 1968), 302.

———, "Psychiatry in a Midwestern Metropolitan Community." *Mental Hygiene,* 48 (January, 1964), 55–65.

Mandell, Arnold J., and Spooner, Charles E., "Psycho-chemical Research Studies in Man." *Science,* 162 (December 27, 1968), 1142–52.

Marmor, Judd, "The Feeling of Superiority: An Occupational Hazard in the Practice of Psychiatry." *American Journal of Psychiatry,* 110 (November, 1953), 370–76.

Maskin, Meyer, "Adaptations of Psychoanalytic Technique in Specific Disorders," in Jules H. Masserman, ed., *Science and Psychoanalysis,* III: *Psychoanalysis and Human Values.* New York, Grune & Stratton, 1960.

Masserman, Jules, "The Beatnik: Up-, Down-, and Off-." *Archives of General Psychiatry,* 16 (March, 1967), 262–67.

McMahon, Arthur W., and Shore, Miles F., "Some Psychological Reactions to Working with the Poor." *Archives of General Psychiatry,* 18 (May, 1968), 562–68.

Meehan, Marjorie C., "Psychiatrists Portrayed in Fiction." *Journal of the American Medical Association,* 188 (April 20, 1964), 255–58.

Menninger, Karl, "Speaking Out." *Saturday Evening Post* (April 25, 1964), 12 ff.

Mesmer, Roger, "European Psychiatry: Observations Concerning the Care of the Aged, Mentally Ill and Retarded." *Pennsylvania Psychiatric Quarterly,* 7 (Spring, 1967), 47–62.

Miller, Milton, and Halleck, Seymour L., "The Critics of Psychiatry: A Review of Contemporary Critical Attitudes." *American Journal of Psychiatry,* 119 (February, 1963), 705–15.

Millet, John A. P., "Psychoanalysis in the United States," in Franz Alexander, Samuel Eisenstein, and Martin Grotjahn, eds., *Psychoanalytic Pioneers.* New York, Basic Books, 1966.

Mintz, Ira L., "Unconscious Motives in the Making of War." *Medical Opinion & Review* (April, 1968), 88–95.

Mowrer, O. H., "Changing Conceptions of the Unconscious." *Journal of Nervous and Mental Diseases,* 129 (September, 1959), 222–34.

Musto, David F., and Astrachan, Boris M., "Strange Encounter: The Use of Study Groups with Graduate Students in History." *Psychiatry,* 31 (August, 1968), 265.

Nabokov, Vladimir, Review of *Thomas Woodrow Wilson,* by Sigmund Freud and William Bullitt. *Encounter* (February, 1967), 91.

Natterson, Joseph M., "Theodor Reik," in Franz Alexander, Samuel Eisenstein, and Martin Grotjahn, eds., *Psychoanalytic Pioneers.* New York, Basic Books, 1966.

Natterson, Joseph, and Grotjahn, Martin, "Responsive Action in Psychotherapy." *American Journal of Psychiatry,* 122 (August, 1965), 140–43.

Nicholi, Armand M., Jr., "Harvard Dropouts: Some Psychiatric Findings." *American Journal of Psychiatry,* 124 (November, 1967), 651–58.

"Orientation or Training: An Urgent Issue for Child Psychiatry" (Editor's Notebook). *American Journal of Psychiatry,* 124 (April, 1968), 1450–51.

Parloff, Morris; Iflund, Boris; and Goldstein, Norman, "Communication of 'Therapy Values' Between Therapist and Schizophrenic Patients." *Journal of Nervous and Mental Diseases,* 130 (March, 1958), 193–99.

———, "Communication of Values and Therapeutic Change." *Archives of General Psychiatry,* 2 (March, 1960), 302.

Pasamanick, Benjamin, and Rettig, Solomon, "Status and Work Satisfaction of

Psychiatrists." *Archives of Neurology and Psychiatry,* 81 (March, 1959), 399–402.

Peterson, Osler L.; Lyden, Fremont J.; Geiger, H. Jack; and Colton, Theodore, "Appraisal of Medical Students' Abilities as Related to Training and Careers After Graduation." *New England Journal of Medicine,* 269 (November 28, 1963), 1174–82.

Quennell, Peter, Review of *Downhill All the Way: An Autobiography of the Years 1919–1939,* by Leonard Woolf. *New York Times Book Review* (October 29, 1967), 5.

Rabkin, Richard, "Is the Unconscious Necessary?" *American Journal of Psychiatry,* 125 (September, 1968), 313–20.

Raines, G. N., and Rohrer, J. H., "The Operational Matrix of Psychiatric Practice: I. Consistency and Variability of Interview Impressions of Different Psychiatrists." *American Journal of Psychiatry,* 111 (April, 1955), 721–33.

Rand, Abby, "Davos: Yesterday and Today." *New York Times* Sunday travel section (October 15, 1967), 10.

Rangell, Leo, "Psychoanalysis—A Current Look." *Journal of the American Psychoanalytic Association,* 15 (April, 1967), 423–31.

Reiff, Philip, Review of *Thomas Woodrow Wilson,* by Sigmund Freud and William Bullitt. *Encounter* (April, 1967), 84–89.

Reissman, Frank, and Miller, S. M., "Social Change Versus the 'Psychiatric World View.'" *American Journal of Orthopsychiatry,* 34 (January, 1964), 29–38.

Rogow, Arnold A., "Disability in High Office." *Medical Opinion & Review,* 1 (April, 1966), 16–19.

———, "Private Illness and Public Policy: The Cases of James Forrestal and John Winant." *American Journal of Psychiatry,* 125 (February, 1969), 1093–97.

———, "Psychiatry, History, and Political Science: Notes on an Emergent Synthesis," in Judd Marmor, ed., *Modern Psychoanalysis: New Directions and Perspectives.* New York, Basic Books, 1968.

———, "Reviewing Reviews." *Medical Opinion & Review* (June, 1967), 34–38.

———, "Toward a Psychiatry of Politics," in *Politics, Personality and Social Science in the Twentieth Century: Essays in Honor of Harold D. Lasswell.* Chicago, University of Chicago Press, 1969.

Rom, Paul, "Psychiatry in Modern Novels." *International Journal of Social Psychiatry,* 11 (Winter, 1965), 70–77.

Romano, John, "Twenty-five Years of University Department Chairmanship." *American Journal of Psychiatry Supplement* (June, 1966), 13–14.

Rome, Howard P., "Psychiatry and Foreign Affairs." *American Journal of Psychiatry,* 125 (December, 1968), 726.

Roper, Elmo, "American Attitudes on World Organization." *Public Opinion Quarterly,* 17 (1953–54), 405–42.

Rosenberg, Leon A., and Trader, Harriet P., "Treatment of the Deprived Child in a Community Health Center." *American Journal of Orthopsychiatry,* 37 (January, 1967), 87–92.

Rosenberg, Mervin; Glueck, Bernard C., Jr.; and Stroebel, Charles F., "The Computer and the Clinical Decision Process." *American Journal of Psychiatry,* 124 (November, 1967), 595–99.

Rosenthal, David, "Changes in Some Moral Values Following Psychotherapy." *Journal of Consultative Psychology,* 19 (1955), 431–37.

Rubins, Jack L., "The Changing Role of Psychoanalysis: Beyond Action for Mental Health." *American Journal of Psychoanalysis,* 27 (1967), 156.

Sager, Clifford J., "The Treatment of Married Couples," in Silvano Arieti, ed., *American Handbook of Psychiatry,* III. New York, Basic Books, 1966.

Salzman, Leon, "Report of Long Range Planning Committee." *Newsletter of the American Academy of Psychoanalysis,* 11 (October, 1967), 14.

Sanford, Nevitt, "Personality: Its Place in Psychology," in Sigmund Koch, ed., *Psychology: A Study of a Science,* 5. New York, McGraw-Hill, 1963.

Schorer, C. E., *et al.*, "Improvement Without Treatment." *Diseases of the Nervous System,* 29 (February, 1968), 100–4.

Schuberg, H. C., cited in "Private Practice of Psychiatry: A Symposium," by Mas Rinkel. *American Journal of Psychiatry,* 123 (June, 1966), 1374.

Sharaf, Myron R., and Levinson, Daniel J., "The Quest for Omnipotence in Professional Training." *Psychiatry,* 27 (May, 1964), 135–49.

Sharaf, Myron R.; Schneider, Patricia; and Kantor, David, "Psychiatric Interest and Its Correlates Among Medical Students." *Psychiatry,* 31 (May, 1968), 157.

Spitzer, Robert L., and Endicott, Jean, "Diagno II: Further Development in a Computer Program for Psychiatric Diagnosis." *Computers in Psychiatry, Supplement to the American Journal of Psychiatry,* 125 (January, 1969), 20.

Steiner, George, "Books Behind the Barricades." London *Sunday Times* (July 28, 1968).

———, Review of *Thomas Woodrow Wilson,* by Sigmund Frèud and William Bullitt. *The New Yorker* (January 21, 1967), 111–14.

Stickney, Stonewall B., "Schools Are Our Community Mental Health Centers." *American Journal of Psychiatry,* 124 (April, 1968), 1407–14.

Stillman, Richard; Roth, Wolton T.; Colby, Kenneth Mark; and Rosenbaum, C. Peter, "An On-Line Computer System for Initial Psychiatric Inventory." *Computers in Psychiatry, Supplement to the American Journal of Psychiatry,* 125 (January, 1969), 8–11.

Stouffer, Samuel A., "Indices of Psychological Illness," in Paul F. Lazarsfeld and Morris Rosenberg, eds., *The Language of Social Research.* New York, Free Press of Glencoe, 1955.

Sypher, Wylie, Review of *Leonardo Da Vinci: Aspects of the Renaissance Genius,* by Morris Philipson. *Book Week* (September 25, 1966), 5.

Szalita, Alberta B., "Reanalysis." *Contemporary Psychotherapy,* 4 (Spring, 1968), 83–102.

Szasz, Thomas S., "Mental Illness Is a Myth." *New York Times Magazine* (June 12, 1966), 92.

———, Review of *Thomas Woodrow Wilson,* by Sigmund Freud and William Bullitt. *National Review* (March 21, 1967), 307–8.

Thompson, Clara, "A Study of the Emotional Climate of Psychoanalytic Institutes." *Psychiatry,* 21 (February, 1958), 45–51.

Tiffany, William J., Jr., "The Mental Health of Army Troops in Viet Nam." *American Journal of Psychiatry,* 123 (June, 1967), 1585–86.

Toffler, A., "The Woman Behind Barry Goldwater." *Good Housekeeping* (May, 1964), 38.

Tooley, Kay, "A Developmental Problem of Late Adolescence: A Case Report." *Psychiatry,* 32 (February, 1968), 69–83.

Torrey, E. Fuller, "The Case for the Indigenous Therapist." *Archives of General Psychiatry,* 20 (March, 1969), 365–73.

Tuchman, Barbara, Review of *Thomas Woodrow Wilson,* by Sigmund Freud and William Bullitt. *Atlantic Monthly* (February, 1967), 39–44.

Tyson, Florence, "Therapeutic Elements in Out-Patient Music Therapy." *Psychiatric Quarterly,* 39 (April, 1965), 315–27.

Wagner, Philip S., "Psychiatry for Everyman." *Psychiatry,* 30 (February, 1967), 79–90.

Wedge, Bryant, "Psychiatry and International Affairs." *Science,* 157 (July 21, 1967), 284–85.

———, "Training for a Psychiatry of International Relations." *American Journal of Psychiatry,* 125 (December, 1968), 731.

Wertham, Fredric, "The Road to Rapallo: A Psychiatric Study." *American Journal of Psychotherapy,* 3 (October, 1949), 595.

Westby, David L., and Braungart, Richard G., "Class and Politics in the Family Backgrounds of Student Political Activists." *American Sociological Review,* 31 (October, 1966), 690–92.

Wheelis, Allen, "To Be a God." *Commentary* (August, 1963), 125–34.

Winick, Charles, "The Psychiatrist in Fiction." *Journal of Nervous and Mental Disease,* 136 (January, 1963), 43–57.

Woods, Joan, and Frazier, Servert H., "Basic Psychiatric Literature." *American Journal of Psychiatry,* 124 (August, 1967), 217–24.

Yamamoto, Joe, "Racial Factors in Patient Selection." *American Journal of Psychiatry,* 124 (November, 1967), 636.

Ziferstein, Isidore, "Psychological Habituation to War: A Sociopsychological Case Study." *American Journal of Orthopsychiatry,* 37 (April, 1967), 457–68.

Zwerling, Israel, *The Mental Health Potential of Urban Life for Children and Youth.* Quoted in Celia S. Deschin, "The Future Direction of Social Work." *American Journal of Psychiatry,* 38 (January, 1968), 9–17.

UNPUBLISHED SOURCES

Lally, John J., "Interrelationships of Statuses in Status-Sets: The Case of Catholic Psychiatrists." Unpublished Ph.D. dissertation, Columbia University, Department of Sociology, 1968.

Peterson, Osler L., Department of Preventive Medicine, Harvard University Medical School (private communication).

Verden, Paul, and Michael, Archer L., "Cultural Unorthodoxy Among a Group of American Psychotherapists." Paper read before the California Psychological Association, December 15, 1962.

NEWSPAPERS AND MAGAZINES CONSULTED

American Imago
American Journal of Orthopsychiatry
American Journal of Psychiatry
American Journal of Psychoanalysis
Archives of General Psychiatry
British Journal of Medical Psychology
British Journal of Psychiatry
Digest of Neurology and Psychiatry (Institute of Living)
Imago
International Journal of Psychiatry
International Journal of Psycho-Analysis
Journal of Abnormal and Social Psychology
Journal of Nervous and Mental Disease
Journal of the American Psychoanalytic Association
McCall's
Medical Economics
Medical Opinion and Review
Medical Tribune
Menninger Quarterly
New York Review of Books
New York *Times*
Psychiatric News
Psychiatric Quarterly
Psychiatric Reporter (Smith, Kline & French)
Psychiatry
Psychiatry Digest
Psychiatry and Social Science Review
Psychoanalysis and the Psychoanalytic Review
Psychoanalytic Quarterly
Psychoanalytic Review
Psychology Today

Public Opinion Quarterly
San Francisco *Chronicle*
Science
Scientific American
The Economist
Transcultural Psychiatric Research
Trends in Psychiatry (Merck, Sharp and Dohme)
Wall Street Journal

Index